Light, chemical change and life:
a source book in photochemistry

edited by J.D. Coyle, R.R. Hill and D.R. Roberts

The Open University Press

Course Team for the Source Book

Academic editors
John Coyle
Roger Hill
David Roberts

Authors

Godfrey Beddard	Ralph Jacobson	David Phillips
Howard Carless	Trevor Laird	Sir George Porter
Alan Cox	Mike Ledger	Antony Rest
Robert Cundall	Anthony Ledwith	F. Sherwood Rowland
Graham Fleming	John Mellor	M. Sharif Salim
John Griffiths	Gerry Pattenden	Richard Wayne
Bill Horspool	Laurence Peter	

Production
Mike Bullivant (course manager)
Patrick Holligan (The Open University Press)
Laurie Melton (liaison librarian)
Jane Nelson (staff tutor)
Ian Nuttall (editor)
Fran Page (designer)
Dick Sharp (editor)
Jerry Siddall (graphic artist)

The Open University Press, Walton Hall, Milton Keynes, MK7 6AA.

First published 1982.
Copyright © 1982 The Open University.

Designed by the Graphic Design Group of the Open University.

Typeset by Santype International Limited, Salisbury, Wilts
Printed in Great Britain by Archway Press Limited, Poole, Dorset
Colour work by The Curwen Press Limited, London E13

ISBN 0 335 16100 6

Further information on Open University courses may be obtained from the Admissions Office, The Open University, P.O. Box 48, Walton Hall, Milton Keynes, MK7 6AB.

1.1

Preface

On a cosmic or planetary scale, chemical changes brought about by light are as influential on the development of matter as those brought about by heat. In the case of living matter, light is not only essential for its continued existence, but has almost certainly played a major part in its origin and evolution. Although the technological uses of photochemical change are, to date, far more limited than those of thermal chemistry, where they do occur (for example, in printing, microelectronics and polymer technology), the effects on society are profound and far-reaching. With applications of laser radiation in their infancy, and with the continuing expansion of other aspects of photochemical research, further important technological developments based on photochemistry seem assured. The most exciting possibility is undoubtedly the large-scale production of fuel directly from the energy in sunlight, rather than indirectly, as at present, via the green plant.

From this point of view, the general absence in undergraduate curricula of a broadly based study of light-induced change may seem surprising. The reasons are not difficult to appreciate, however, and are to do with the way the subject is traditionally dispersed among several disciplines in science and technology, and the relative weakness of the resulting fragments when competing with other subject matter for inclusion in individual courses.

Such considerations led an Open University Course Team, in collaboration with photochemists from the Royal Institution and the University of Southampton, to prepare a substantial undergraduate course which, although based on fundamental photophysics and photochemistry, devotes more than half of its content to related areas and particularly to biological and technological applications of photochemistry. This source book is a major component of the course, and allows, through its multiple authorship, a wide variety of topics to be treated in the most authoritative manner. It is not a text book, but a collection of short articles specially written for undergraduates to complement the basic elements of photochemistry presented elsewhere, and to help set the latter in a more meaningful context.

The choice of topics and the order of presentation were determined by the structure of the course as a whole, which is divided into six parts. Each of the six corresponding parts of this book is preceded by a short commentary outlining the relevance of the topics that follow and how they relate to each other. Briefly, the two chapters in Part 1 support a scene-setting introduction and appropriately are concerned with photochemistry on a global scale. Parts 2 and 3 include chapters on lasers and colour, both of which are suitable subjects for applying the concepts used to understand light absorption. 'Luminescence instrumentation' and 'Applications of energy transfer to macromolecules' in Part 4 are highly relevant to a study of the physical properties of excited states. The rest of the chapters in this part, however, are designed to support an in-depth study of photochemistry in the atmosphere.

Part 5 is by far the largest in the book, and extends in many directions the chemistry of organic molecules in their excited states. A wide variety of applications of organic photochemistry is presented, providing the reader with interesting opportunities to examine relationships between understanding at a basic level and technological advance. Part 6 is wholly in support of another special topic: photochemical solar energy conversion.

Inevitably, for reasons of space (and the student's time!), it has not been possible to cover all topics to which photochemistry is relevant. Silver halide photography, for example, is given very little space considering its technological impact. Photobiological triggering has been omitted entirely because, with the possible exception of vertebrate vision, knowledge of the mechanisms of such processes at the molecular level is, at best, rudimentary.*

With 20 contributors, an internal review procedure, and an immovable deadline for publication, the production of this volume has been remarkably trouble-free, and our sincere thanks are due to all concerned. First we thank our contributors, not only for their promptness and their forbearance with numerous queries and comments, but also for the dispatch with which they corrected proofs. Secondly, thanks go to our Course Manager, Mike Bullivant, who orchestrated the production, and to Jane Nelson, Fran Page, Dick Sharp and Jerry Siddall, for comment, design and editorial work. We are also grateful to the team of Open University tutors who evaluated the material in this book for use by students within the course, and to John Newton for preparing the index.

Other components of the course are:

(a) A student-active text covering the fundamental aspects of photochemistry: 1, The breadth of photochemistry; 2, Light absorption and electronic structure; 3, Colour; 4, Physical properties of excited states; 5, Chemical properties of excited states. Also three special topics are introduced: Atmospheric photochemistry (Part 4), Applications of photochemistry (Part 5); Photochemical solar energy conversion (Part 6).

(b) Twelve 25 minute television programmes: 1, Introducing photochemistry; 2, Spectroscopy in a flash; 3, Colour; 4, Excited states: spectra and lifetimes; 5, Photochemistry and the troposphere; 6, Vision; 7, Photochemical pathways; 8, Light the destroyer; 9, Light the recorder; 10, Photosynthesis—the first events; 11, Modelling photosynthesis; 12, Stratospheric ozone: Earth's vital shield.

(c) Eight 60 minute cassettes for audiovision that include the following topics: Electronic structure and light absorption; Colour and function; Introduction to chemical kinetics; Design of an energy-transfer experiment; Photochemistry of the polluted troposphere; Stratospheric ozone—controversy and uncertainty; Radical reactions; Chemical light; Vitamin D; Large-scale photochemical synthesis; Solar energy conversion, (i) background and criteria, (ii) prospects.

* Vision is the subject of one of the television programmes (see above).

Contents

Contents

Contents

part ONE

Photochemistry occurs naturally on a grand scale. It provides life with both energy and protection: energy through the conversion of *visible* solar radiation into 'food' (photosynthesis), and protection through synthesis of the ozone in the stratosphere that prevents lethal *ultraviolet* radiation from reaching the Earth's surface. The two processes are interdependent. Oxygen produced as a by product of photosynthesis is the starting material for ozone formation, and the present-day organisms that carry out photosynthesis could not survive in the absence of stratospheric ozone.

It follows that any introduction to modern photochemistry should include some reference to photosynthesis and to atmospheric photochemistry, especially in view of their importance to the topical problems of renewable sources of energy and the effect of human activity on the Earth's atmosphere. The first two chapters of the book sketch the background to both problems and provide the context for discussion of appropriate photochemistry later on.

In 'Solar energy', natural photosynthesis is related to mankind's past and present sources of energy and to options for the future. The conversion and storage of solar energy by photochemical means have particular attractions, and a detailed examination of some possible systems forms the subject of a case-study at the end of the book.

An overview of photochemistry in the atmosphere is taken in the second chapter, where processes relevant to the ozone in the stratosphere are distinguished from those affecting that part of the atmosphere in direct contact with biological matter (the troposphere). Like 'Solar energy', the chapter is both introductory to photochemistry as a whole and a prelude to a photochemical case-study examined in later chapters.

1

1·1 Solar energy

by Sir George Porter (The Royal Institution, London)

1 Introduction

Without its regular income of energy from the Sun, our Earth would rapidly become a lifeless planet, and we should first ask ourselves why this input of energy is necessary. One reason is that the Earth, being warmer than its surroundings (other than the Sun), is continually radiating heat into space, and this has to be replaced if the temperature is to be maintained approximately constant. But, even if we were able to insulate the Earth from space, life and most other forms of change on the Earth's surface would soon cease. Yet the first law of thermodynamics, the law of conservation of energy, tells us that energy in a closed system such as this can be neither created nor destroyed. So why is there this requirement for a continued input of energy?

The answer to this question is given by the second law of thermodynamics which makes the distinction between energy that is 'ordered' and energy that is 'disordered'. An example of the former would be the kinetic energy of a falling stone, in which all the atoms are moving in the same direction; an example of the latter, disordered energy, would be the random thermal motion of the atoms in the stone. In principle, all of the former can be used to do useful work, and it is therefore called 'free energy'. The second law tells us that the latter, random thermal energy, can never be completely converted into useful work.

In all natural processes the amount of disorder increases so that high-grade ordered energy is continually being converted into the low-grade disordered energy known as heat and, once this heat has reached the temperature of its surroundings, it is useless. For the Earth to sustain life, therefore, it is not sufficient merely to replace the energy lost by radiation with an input of radiation at the same temperature, it is necessary to provide a supply of free energy which can be used to replace the order that is lost by natural degradation. With only a few minor exceptions (nuclear reactions, gravitational energy of tides, and geothermal energy) the free energy income of the Earth is derived from the high-temperature radiation of the Sun. Most importantly, the Sun is the light source for those photochemical reactions occurring in the green leaves of the living plant (photosynthesis), which manufacture all our food and which were responsible in the geological past for the present deposits of coal, oil and natural gas that are the principal sources of energy, and of organic raw materials, in today's technological world.

2

2   Photosynthesis and world energy needs

Until about half a million years ago human beings, like all other organisms, obtained their energy from photosynthesis via food. Man's discovery of fire, however, provided him with a second route to the energy of photosynthesised materials and, although the process of burning is chemically crude compared with the sophisticated processes of digestion and metabolism of food in the body, it provided heat and light when the Sun did not and it led eventually, via the steam engine, to the industrial revolution.

The explosive growth of the industrial revolution was made possible by replacing the renewable photosynthetic fuel, wood, by the fossilised photosynthetic fuel, coal. This had been accumulating ever since land plants appeared on Earth, about 400 million years ago. As Figure 1 (which refers to the USA) shows, it was not until 1890 that coal overtook wood as the principal fuel used in the industrialised countries and not until 1950 that oil and natural gas together became predominant over all other energy sources. It should be noted that Figure 1 gives the *proportions* of each fuel used; the *total* fuel consumption by the industrialised countries over the past century has increased twenty-fold. The rapid changes of the past century were unpredictable, but that further rapid changes must take place over the next century

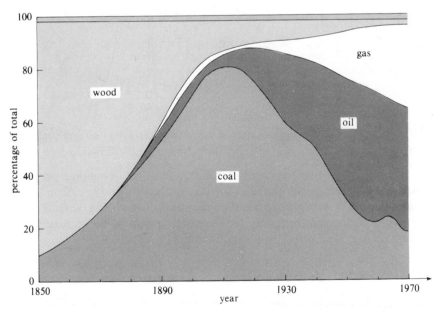

FIGURE 1   Proportional use of principal fuels since 1850. The narrow section at the top represents other energy sources, such as hydroelectric and nuclear.

is quite predictable. We know that supplies of oil, natural gas and even coal are finite and that the fuels that we find most useful and that form the predominant energy source of our civilisation today will be the first to become depleted. Figure 2 illustrates that we live in interesting times and that we have an immediate problem of immense proportions—the principal source of energy that we use today will not be adequate even for the lifetime of many of the people who are alive today. Projections of this kind must of course make assumptions about future populations and life-styles. In estimating the effects of the latter we must consider the needs and aspirations of developing countries. The world population must inevitably increase for some time but there are indications of a decrease in birth rate and possibly a stabilisation in population at about 10 billion people, that is 2.5 times the present one. If the *average* energy consumption per capita remains the same as at present, the world energy requirement would be about 50% greater by the year 2000 and 2.5 times the present by about 2200.

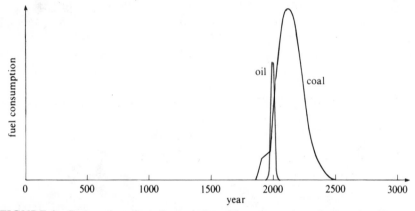

FIGURE 2   Past and projected rates of world consumption of oil and coal on an extended time scale.

If, however, the average energy consumption of the developing peoples is increased to that of the developed countries, a further increase in world energy supply by a factor of 4 becomes necessary. Together these factors lead to a ten-fold increase in energy requirements, assuming no increase in per capita energy consumption in the industrialised countries.

3   Energy sources and forms of use

We need energy for different purposes and in correspondingly different forms; the three principal forms in which it is supplied are (i) low-temperature heat for water and space heating, (ii) electricity, and (iii) storable chemical fuels. Of course, the energy may ultimately be used in other forms, particularly as mechanical energy, but it is rarely distributed in this form.

Because one form of energy may be used to produce another, it might be argued that the above distinction between these three requirements is not necessary or useful. The distinction is important however for two reasons. First, as already mentioned, it is not possible to convert heat into electrical or chemical free energy without losses, and the efficiency with which this can be done is given by the second law of thermodynamics as

$$\text{efficiency (\%)} = \frac{\text{free energy or work out}}{\text{heat in}} = \frac{T_2 - T_1}{T_2} \, (\times \, 100)$$

where T_2 is the temperature, in kelvins, of the heat source (e.g. the furnace or the Sun) and T_1 is the temperature to which this heat is degraded (e.g. of the Earth or of the water in a condenser). Whereas low-temperature heat, at say 70 °C (343 K), may serve our purpose completely efficiently if that purpose is to heat water to 70 °C, the generation of electrical energy from this heat could never be more than 15% efficient, taking T_1 as 20 °C (293 K). Thus for low-temperature heating, low-temperature heat energy should always be used in preference to high-temperature heat, electricity or chemical potential.

The second important difference between these three forms of energy is in the possibility of storage. Electrical energy cannot be stored in any significant amount and heat energy can be stored for only limited periods, in insulated water tanks for example. The potential energy from which electricity is generated in a hydroelectric plant can be stored in the form of elevated water reservoirs but, once generated, the electrical energy must be instantly used and it is therefore also fortunate that the transport of electrical power is almost instantaneous. The only form of energy that can be stored indefinitely in transportable form is the chemical energy of a fuel, and it is for this reason that these fuels have become so necessary for transport and all purposes where a primary source of energy is required on site, for example for domestic heating. Nuclear energy is also stored almost indefinitely in the nuclear fuel, but the means of converting the nuclear energy into heat or electricity is not readily transportable except in large sea-going vessels.

Let us now turn from the forms in which energy is used to consider the forms in which it is received. The energy sources available to us are partly terrestrial and partly extra-terrestrial. Terrestrial sources are (i) fossil fuels accumulated in the past from extra-terrestrial solar energy, (ii) nuclear fuels potential able to be degraded to elements of lower energy, and (iii) geothermal energy contained in the interior of the Earth which, in certain favourable places, is accessible near the Earth's surface.

Extra-terrestrial sources of energy are almost all derived from the Sun's radiation, the only exception being the tides, whose energy is derived from the kinetic energy of the Earth's rotation via the gravitational attraction between the Moon (and to a lesser extent the Sun) and the Earth. The radiation of the Sun not only heats and lights the Earth, not only provides the source of light for photosynthesis of food, fuels and raw materials, but the differences of temperature that it creates at different points on the Earth result in the winds and waves and the thermal gradients of the oceans, all of which are potential secondary sources of solar energy.

Apart from tidal and geothermal energy, which are unlikely to make more than a relatively small contribution, we therefore have only two primary sources of energy which, in the long term when fossil fuels are exhausted, have the possibility of meeting our energy requirements: solar energy in all its forms and nuclear energy. In fact, because the Sun is a nuclear thermal reactor, we might say that we have a choice only between two forms of nuclear energy—one of them 93 million miles away and the other on Earth. There are today (1981) some 350 nuclear fission reactors of the non-breeder type supplying electrical power of about 150 gigawatts and, although there are still doubts and difficulties to be overcome, nuclear power is an established technology which may provide a major part of our energy requirements in the near future. However, the fissile materials, such as uranium or thorium, that fuel these reactors are themselves neither renewable nor available in unlimited amounts. Indeed, proven resources, at present economically recoverable levels, have an energy content less than that of our proven coal resources. Breeder reactors, if they can be developed to an acceptable safety standard, would extend the supply of fissile materials by a factor of about 80, and there is a longer term hope (probably at least 50 years) that it may be possible to develop reactors based on nuclear fusion and so provide a virtually inexhaustible supply of power.

The arguments for proceeding with the development of solar as well as nuclear energy are three-fold. First, to rely for such an essential commodity as energy on only one technology, even if that technology had been long established and its consequences seemed predictable, would be unwise. Second, it is almost certain that solar technologies will be economically preferable to nuclear ones for some purposes. Third, whilst nuclear energy may provide a solution to our electricity needs, it is unable, in itself, to solve the most immediate problem that we face, the rapidly dwindling supply of liquid chemical fuels.

4 Potentialities of solar energy

It is easy to be euphoric about the potential of solar energy, so large is the energy input to the Earth compared with our needs. The energy falling on the

Earth's surface, after absorption and scattering by the atmosphere, is 3 × 10^{24} joules per year, corresponding to an average power of 10^{17} watts. The present consumption of primary energy in all forms by mankind is 2 × 10^{20} joules per year, corresponding to an average consumption per person of 2000 watts. Thus the input of solar energy exceeds present use by a factor of more than 10^4. We have seen that reasonable projected needs of mankind are about ten times the present use and, if we were able to collect and use solar energy with an efficiency of 10%, the available solar energy would still exceed future requirements by a factor of 150. There is more than enough. Furthermore, solar energy has other advantages in being non-polluting and renewable and it is widely, if not equally, distributed to all peoples.

There must be snags, and there are. Principally the difficulty is that the large amounts of energy referred to in the last paragraph fall over a correspondingly large area of the Earth and so the energy is expensive to collect. A second difficulty is that the energy arrives intermittently at any point and there is least of it when we need it most—at night and in the winter. These difficulties lead immediately to two conclusions: the collectors must cover large areas and therefore will be very expensive and second, in order to spread the usefulness of the collected energy, it should preferably be stored.

It is already possible to convert solar energy directly into each of the three principal forms of distribution as follows.

4.1 Low-temperature heat

Any absorbing surface becomes warm if placed in sunlight and, because the Sun's temperature is much higher than that required for domestic heating, there are virtually no thermodynamic restrictions on the efficiency of collection in this form. If energy loss by conduction and convection is reduced by glass covers over a 'black' plate, the absorbed energy can be transferred to water flowing in or beneath the plate up to a temperature of 50 °C with an efficiency of about 40%. The glass cover also introduces the 'greenhouse effect': the glass is transparent to visible radiation and hence to most of the Sun's radiation, but opaque to infrared and therefore to most of the radiation from the hot plate, which is at a much lower temperature than the Sun. A further improvement can be made by coating the 'black' plate with selective absorbers which are good absorbers in the visible region but poor absorbers (and hence poor emitters) in the infrared. By these methods and without the use of mirror concentrators, temperatures exceeding 100 °C can be produced in bright sunshine. Solar heaters are already economically useful in some countries; in Israel for example some 30% of households heat their water in this way for much of the year.

4.2 Electrical power

The conversion of solar radiation into electricity by means of the photovoltaic cell is at present the most sophisticated technical development in solar energy devices. The silicon cell, which was developed for powering space vehicles and satellites, is still the most efficient and reliable. A thin slice of very pure crystalline silicon is impregnated with a small amount (a few parts per million) of an 'impurity' such as phosphorus, whose atoms fit into the silicon lattice but, having one more outer-shell electron than silicon (five instead of four) tend to lose this electron and so acquire a positive charge. Now a very thin section of the crystal near the surface is impregnated with a different impurity, such as boron, which has only three outer-shell electrons and so tends to acquire an electron. We thus have a bulk material that is positively charged and a surface layer that is negatively charged.

Silicon absorbs light throughout the visible region into the infrared and, when it is irradiated, electrons are released from a localised situation, such as a covalent bond (the valence band) into a delocalised situation, as in a metal (the conduction band). Being free to move, the electrons in the conduction band flow towards the positively charged bulk crystal from the surface layer and, if the circuit is completed through metal contacts on the two surfaces of the crystal, an electrical current will continue to flow as long as the crystal is irradiated. Efficiencies as high as 17% for conversion of the total incident energy of the Sun into electrical power can be achieved in this way, and efficiencies of about 10% are now commonplace.

Unfortunately, the manufacture of pure silicon crystals is very expensive, and electrical power from silicon photovoltaic cells costs about a hundred times more than conventional electrical power. This is still economical for some special purposes, such as supplying electrical power to remote areas, and future developments, such as the use of amorphous silicon, may reduce costs considerably. Nevertheless, storage adds further to the cost and it is by no means certain that power generation on a large scale, rather than for special applications, will ever be economical from photovoltaic cells.

4.3 Chemical fuels

The conversion of solar energy into a gaseous or liquid fuel on a renewable basis and in an economic manner would be of immense importance in overcoming our immediate as well as our long-term energy problems.

A photobiological approach to solar energy utilisation, by 'energy farming', is already possible and long established. Here the energy stored in biological materials is made available either for direct use in combustion or as other fuels via fermentation. Unfortunately, the efficiency of such processes of energy conversion in the field is much less than that of conversion into low-temperature heat or into electricity and rarely exceeds 1%, even under the best conditions. Furthermore, to obtain even these efficiencies requires energy expenditures in the form of fertiliser, irrigation, and harvesting followed by processing, because the agricultural product is usually not in a form suitable for direct use as a fuel. Nevertheless there is an increasing interest in replacing oil by renewable fuels: in Brazil for example, petroleum for motor cars is being augmented by the addition of 20% ethanol obtained by fermentation of sugar.

The low efficiencies of natural photosynthesis, and the other disadvantages mentioned above, are a result, at least in part, of the fact that the plant did not evolve to provide man with a motor fuel. The question must then be asked: cannot a photosynthetic process for production of fuels using the Sun as light source be evolved on purely photochemical lines, but one which is simpler than the biological process and which produces directly the product required—ethanol for example, or hydrogen to replace liquid and gaseous fuels? This is a great challenge, certainly the greatest of all challenges to photochemistry and perhaps to the whole of chemistry at the present time.

1·2 Photochemistry in the atmosphere

by David Phillips (*The Royal Institution, London*)

1 Introduction and definitions

Of the many possible views that can be taken of the atmosphere, the one most appropriate to this text is that it is a large-scale dynamic photochemical reactor. Although the atmospheric 'skin' to the planet represents only 1% of the Earth's diameter, nonetheless the atmosphere extends out from the surface some hundreds of kilometres into space. Compared with a laboratory-scale experiment, path lengths over which absorption of radiation can occur are long, and thus even weakly absorbing chemical species can undergo photochemical reactions. Because the only light source for the reactor is the Sun, it is necessary to consider the spectral distribution and intensity of the sunlight reaching the Earth's surface.

The outside temperature of the Sun is approximately 5 900 K, and Figure 1 shows that the intensity distribution of a black-body radiator at this tem-

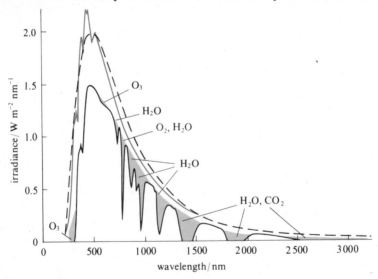

FIGURE 1   The variation of the intensity of solar radiation (irradiance, H_λ) with wavelength. The values for H_λ are obtained by measuring the total energy in a wavelength interval of one nanometre. The red line is the curve for solar radiation outside the atmosphere, and the dashed line is the curve for a black-body radiator at 5 900 K. The continuous black line is the curve for solar radiation at sea level. The shaded areas show which wavelengths are partially absorbed by chemical species in the atmosphere. Note particularly the absorption by ozone at short wavelengths. (source: *Handbook of Geophysics and Space Environments*, by Air Force Cambridge Research Laboratories, edited by Shea L. Valley, McGraw-Hill Book Company, 1965)

perature reproduces rather well the curve for solar radiation outside the atmosphere. However, it also shows that the intensity is greatly attenuated by atmospheric constituents, because the intensity distribution at the surface of the Earth shows very strong absorption regions corresponding to absorption by recognisable molecular species, some of which are identified in Figure 1. Some of these have special significance and it is particularly noteworthy that at sea level, the short-wavelength cut-off is at about 320 nm, whereas the distribution outside the atmosphere extends to wavelengths less than 200 nm. Ultraviolet light is conveniently categorised into three regions: UV-A, between 320 and 400 nm; UV-B, between 280 and 320 nm; and UV-C, below 280 nm. UV-A is largely unattenuated by the atmosphere, whereas UV-B and UV-C are reduced in intensity to small fractions of their intensity outside the atmosphere. This is of critical importance for biological systems on the surface of the planet, because light of these short wavelengths is extremely harmful to living organisms, being energetic enough to cause molecular changes in proteins and other important macromolecules, such as DNA. The removal of the UV-B from sunlight is achieved largely by a single absorbing species, ozone, which is the subject of extensive discussion in later chapters.

Although the intensity distribution of solar radiation reaches a peak at around 500 nm, it is important to recognise that there is still copious energy for photochemical reactions in the far ultraviolet region. The total amount of radiation received per unit area, normal to the direction of the Sun, outside the Earth's atmosphere is termed the solar constant, H_0, and has a value close to 1400 W m^{-2}. The amounts of incident light in various wavelength

Table 1 The amounts of incident solar radiation, $H_{\Delta\lambda}$, in various wavelength regions, expressed as percentages of the total amount, H_0 (source: McEwan and Phillips, 1975).

Wavelength region, $\Delta\lambda$/nm	$H_{\Delta\lambda}/H_0$ (%)	Wavelength region, $\Delta\lambda$/nm	$H_{\Delta\lambda}/H_0$ (%)
0.1–0.8	$< 10^{-11}$*	121.6–180	2.3×10^{-3}
0.8–4.0	1.4×10^{-7}**	180–225	6.5×10^{-2}
4.0–10.0	1.1×10^{-5}***	225–300	1.3
10.0–30.4	1.35×10^{-4}	300–400	7.9
30.4–46.0	1.1×10^{-5}	400–500	14.4
46.0–121.6	4.13×10^{-4}		

* Increased by a factor of 10 for disturbed Sun and 10 for Class 3 solar flare.

** Increased by a factor of 50 for disturbed Sun.

*** Increased by a factor of about 7 for disturbed Sun.

regions $\Delta\lambda$ are shown in Table 1, as percentages of the total. The total fraction of output in the region below 200 nm is only about one tenth of one per cent, and with strongly absorbing chemical species and long path lengths, almost total absorption of these wavelengths occurs in the upper atmosphere. A wavelength of 120 nm is equivalent to an energy of 996 kJ mol^{-1}, sufficient to photo-ionise many molecules, and it is thus not surprising to find that the upper atmosphere contains a reasonably high concentration of positive ions and electrons. This is the basis for terrestrial long-distance telecommunications systems.

The present atmosphere of the Earth can be thought of as consisting of a number of layers. These are shown schematically in Figure 2, in which the different regions are denoted on the basis of the variation of temperature with altitude. Near the surface the temperature decreases with increasing altitude, and this region up to around 10 km is turbulent and well mixed, and is referred to as the *troposphere*. The temperature passes through a minimum at the *tropopause*, above which it rises with increasing altitude up to a maximum at the *stratopause*. The region between the tropopause and the stratopause is the *stratosphere*. Because these are the only regions of interest to us, we will not confuse the issue by naming the regions above the stratopause. However, it should be noted that other terminologies are used to identify

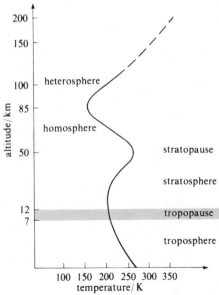

FIGURE 2   The variation of temperature with altitude in the atmosphere. Note that the altitude scale is not linear (source: McEwan and Phillips, 1975)

regions of the atmosphere with specific properties. Thus, the region that contains large concentrations of positive ions and electrons, referred to earlier, is termed the *ionosphere* and lies between 50 and 900 km; it is subdivided into the D, E and F layers, corresponding to electron densities of 10^4, 10^5 and 10^6 electrons cm^{-3}, respectively. Clearly the chemical composition of the ionosphere differs markedly from that of the regions below it, where concentrations of ions are low.

A division of great chemical significance can be made between the region below about 85 km, termed the *homosphere*, that has an approximately constant chemical composition similar to that at sea level, and the region above, the *heterosphere*, where composition varies with altitude. An important difference between these two regions is that in the homosphere diffusion is relatively slow, and thus the composition of the air is governed by mixing through turbulence, wind, etc. By contrast, diffusion is of great importance in the heterosphere. The concentrations of major and minor constituents of the homosphere at sea level are given in Table 2.

We should also note that the study of the troposphere is a branch of *meteorology*, whereas that of the upper atmosphere is referred to as *aeronomy*, although to the chemist such distinctions are quite arbitrary.

Table 2 Constituents of the homosphere at sea level (source: McEwan and Phillips, 1975)

Species	Typical concentration*/molecules cm^{-3}	Typical mole fraction
N_2	2.1×10^{19}	0.78
O_2	5.6×10^{18}	0.21
Ar	2.5×10^{17}	9.3×10^{-3}
CO_2	8.9×10^{15}	3.3×10^{-4}
H_2O	2.7×10^{14}–2.7×10^{17}	10^{-5}–10^{-2}
Ne	4.9×10^{14}	1.8×10^{-5}
CH_4	4×10^{13}	1.5×10^{-6}
Kr	3.1×10^{13}	1.15×10^{-6}
H_2	1.35×10^{13}	5×10^{-7}
N_2O	5.4×10^{12}	2×10^{-7}
O_3	5.4×10^{12}	2×10^{-7}
CO	1.62×10^{12}–5.4×10^{12}	6×10^{-8}–2×10^{-7}
Xe	2.3×10^{12}	8.7×10^{-8}
$NO + NO_2$	1.35×10^{10}–5.4×10^{11}	5×10^{-10}–2×10^{-8}

* At standard temperature and pressure.

What has been defined thus far is the atmosphere at present experienced on Earth. It has been suggested that photochemical processes play an important role in maintaining the compositions of the different atmospheric regions. We shall now outline briefly some of the questions discussed in later chapters, in which the role of photochemistry is explored in more detail.

2 Evolution of the atmosphere

Table 3 shows the cosmic abundance of the principal elements, such as would be found in primitive celestial bodies, for example in the gas cloud regions of interstellar space.

Table 3   Cosmic abundance of the principal elements

Element	Relative abundance	Element	Relative abundance
hydrogen	10^5	neon	10
helium	10^4	silicon	2
oxygen	50	magnesium	2
carbon	20	iron	2
nitrogen	10	sulphur	1

Because of the abundance of hydrogen, the elements are likely to exist as hydrides. All simple hydrides, except CH_4, NH_3, H_2S, and PH_3, react with water, and thus these gases, together with molecular hydrogen and water vapour, might be expected to constitute primitive gas clouds. A comparison of the composition of the planet Jupiter with that of the Sun shows that Jupiter is composed of the same material from which our solar system was originally formed (Table 4). Jupiter is a non-evolved 'primitive' body, as are all of the outer planets, with an atmosphere comprising principally molecular hydrogen, methane and ammonia. This composition is, of course, drastically different from that which we experience in the gaseous atmosphere on Earth

Table 4   Relative abundance of elements in the Sun and Jupiter (source: McEwan and Phillips, 1975)

Atom ratio	Sun	Jupiter	Cosmic
H/He	11	9	10
H/C	2.9×10^3	3.0×10^3	5×10^3
H/N	1.2×10^4	1.6×10^4	10^4

at present, and also from those of the atmospheres of our nearest neighbours, Venus and Mars, and thus all three bodies can be said to have 'evolved' atmospheres. That the Earth's atmosphere has evolved in a unique way is evident from the fact that we alone enjoy a high concentration of oxygen. Most investigators agree that this is the result of the development of life on this planet, with the subsequent evolution of green plants to the stage at which photosynthesis became a dominant food provider, and, as a consequence, a source of gaseous molecular oxygen. In Chapter 4·3 we discuss briefly the role of photochemistry in prebiotic chemistry in producing from 'primitive' constituents those complex molecules required as precursors to life.

3   The stratospheric ozone filter

It is implicit in any model for the evolution of proliferate life on this planet that the surface of the Earth is screened from the effects of harmful UV-B and UV-C radiation, principally by a single atmospheric constituent, ozone. Ozone is found mainly in the stratosphere, and present concentrations of ozone are a result of a long evolutionary process. Enormous attention has been focused on the ozone layer in the past decade with the growing awareness that the global large-scale activities of mankind might conceivably introduce into the atmosphere chemical species that would reduce the steady state concentration of ozone, with potentially catastrophic results for biological organisms. The ensuing strenuous debate has been widely reported in the media. The alarm bells were first sounded at the end of the 1960s, when it was feared that large fleets of supersonic transport aircraft would inject sufficient amounts of nitric oxide into the stratosphere to reduce the ozone concentration through the so-called NO_x catalytic cycle. This will be discussed fully later, but for the moment it can be represented cryptically (but incompletely) by reactions (1) and (2).

$$O_3 + NO \longrightarrow NO_2 + O_2 \tag{1}$$

$$NO_2 + O \longrightarrow NO + O_2 \tag{2}$$

The fears of the consequences of such reactions spurred intense and useful research in aeronomy, and by the end of the 1970s it had been generally accepted that fears concerning NO_x emissions in the stratosphere at current levels were groundless. A second, more mundane, and seemingly innocuous 'pollutant' was first highlighted in 1974, however, and by contrast with the case of oxides of nitrogen, the assessment of potential risk relating to chlorofluorocarbons has grown rather than diminished as experimentation has mushroomed. The fear is that release into the troposphere of chloro-

15

fluorocarbons, typified by dichlorodifluoromethane, CCl_2F_2, is followed by transport to the upper atmosphere where photolysis through reaction (3) produces chlorine atoms:

$$CCl_2F_2 + hv \longrightarrow \cdot CClF_2 + Cl \cdot \qquad (3)$$

These catalytically destroy ozone through reactions (4) and (5), the so-called ClO_x cycle.

$$Cl \cdot + O_3 \longrightarrow ClO \cdot + O_2 \qquad (4)$$

$$ClO \cdot + O \longrightarrow Cl \cdot + O_2 \qquad (5)$$

In order to understand the effects of such reactions, an understanding of the 'unpolluted' stratosphere is required, and this will be considered in later chapters.

4 Tropospheric photochemistry

By one of those interesting paradoxes, the same atmospheric constituent, ozone, to which we owe our continued existence because of its presence in the stratosphere, represents a dangerous pollutant when present even in very small concentrations in the troposphere. The production of ozone photochemically in urban environments through the action of sunlight on exhaust gases from the internal combustion engines of automobiles is a well documented phenomenon but a seemingly insoluble problem. The photochemical processes and subsequent oxidative chain reactions leading to secondary pollutants in urban atmospheres are discussed in a later chapter.

Other tropospheric potochemical reactions occur which are worth mentioning, notably the photo-oxidation of sulphur dioxide to sulphur trioxide and hence sulphuric acid. Although injections of man-made sulphur into the atmosphere, at some 6.8×10^{10} kg yr^{-1}, amount to only half that produced naturally by volcanic action $(1.3 \times 10^{11}$ kg yr$^{-1})$, local concentrations can be very high, particularly downwind of electricity-generating stations that burn fossil fuels. Thus a large power station can produce as much as 25 tonnes of SO_2 per hour, which is photochemically oxidised to SO_3 up to 70 km downwind of the smoke-stack. The subsequent effect on the environment is highlighted in Scandinavia, which seems to act as a sink for European atmospheric discharges during the winter months. During spring, when the snows melt, the pH of virgin rivers and lakes drops to 4 because of the sulphuric acid present, with devastating effects on, for example, breeding fish. Hence the photochemical oxidation of sulphur dioxide is of more than academic interest.

5 Important problems for the atmospheric photochemist

An understanding of the chemistry of the atmosphere can be gained only if the chemist can begin to tackle some of the following problems.

1 *Photochemical reactions* What are the absorbing chemical species and their concentrations, the intensity of solar radiation, and hence the overall rate of light absorption (recognising that this shows seasonal and diurnal variations)? What are the products and extent of photochemical reactions, the wavelength dependence, and hence the overall rate of product formation? What are the effects of competitive absorption by other chemical species, the temperature dependence of photochemical reactions, and the back reactions?

2 *Non-photochemical reactions* What are the rates (from laboratory studies) of non-photochemical reactions, their temperature dependence, and the effects of competitive reactions? Recognition that scores of reactions may compete leads to an understanding of why computer modelling of atmospheric reactions is essential.

3 *Non-chemical problems* What are the rates of vertical and horizontal transport of material within atmospheric boundaries, and across atmospheric boundaries, e.g. from troposphere to stratosphere? What is the role of diffusion, and what are the temperatures of different atmospheric regions? What 'natural' physical and chemical sinks exist for 'man-made' atmospheric constituents? How reliably can concentrations of natural and man-made chemical species be monitored in order to assess the effects of pollutants?

Later chapters attempt to answer some of these questions.

part TWO

Any course in photochemistry needs to consider at an early stage the primary event, namely absorption of a photon by an atom or molecule to give an electronic excited state. Accordingly the following three chapters deal with various aspects of the relationship between light absorption and electronic structure.

The first essential in the experimental investigation of electronic excited states is a light source. There is no doubt that such studies have been revolutionised by the advent of lasers. Chapter 2·1 deals with the mode of action, properties and uses of these remarkable sources of radiation. The unique properties of laser radiation (e.g. extreme spectral purity, possibility of very short pulses, high intensity) have found an amazing variety of applications, but they have been exploited particularly in photochemical studies. The wide application of lasers in contemporary photochemical research will become even more apparent in several of the later chapters in this text.

The other two chapters in Part 2 examine the relationship between light absorption and electronic structure for substances of biological or industrial importance. Chapter 2·2 deals with linearly conjugated systems (found in the naturally occurring carotenes and the synthetic cyanine dyes); Chapter 2·3 covers systems containing the porphin nucleus (as found in the naturally occurring chlorophyll and the synthetic phthalocyanine pigments). These absorb radiation in the visible region of the spectrum, and so appear coloured. In each case the text describes the spectra of a selection of typical molecules before going on to look at the way in which some simple theoretical models are used to explain and interpret the main features of the spectra.

2·1 Lasers

by Graham Fleming (University of Chicago)

Lasers are unique sources of light. Many recent advances in science have depended on the application of their uniqueness to specific problems. Lasers can produce the most spectrally pure light available, enabling atomic and molecular energy levels to be studied in greater detail than ever before. Certain types of laser can give rise to the shortest pulses of light available from any light source, allowing measurement of some of the fastest processes in nature.

In this chapter we try to show the underlying reasons for the special properties of lasers, to outline how lasers are constructed, and to give some indications of how lasers are modified to be of use in photochemical studies. There are many types of laser, just as there are many types of application, but all lasers work in essentially the same way and depend for their function on the absorption and emission of light associated with transitions between atomic or molecular energy levels.

1 Principles of lasers

If an atom (or molecule) is in an excited state (state 2 in Figure 1) with energy E_2, it can lose energy by emitting light of energy $E_2 - E_1$. There are two ways in which such direct emission of light can occur; one is by *spontaneous emission* and the other is by *stimulated emission*.

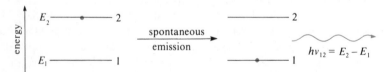

FIGURE 1   Spontaneous emission from an excited atom (or molecule).

1.1 Spontaneous emission

Spontaneous emission occurs when an excited atom emits a photon without the influence of any other atoms or photons† (Figure 1). Because individual

---

† Described in this way, spontaneous emission appears a very mysterious process. Physical systems change their state by interactions with other systems (e.g. other molecules, fields of force). Just as in the quantum theory of molecular vibrations where 'vibrationless' molecules still retain half a quantum of vibration (the zero-point energy), in the absence of photons 'empty' space still retains zero-point electromagnetic fields because the electromagnetic field is also quantised. It is the interaction of the excited atoms with these zero-point fields that gives rise to spontaneous emission.

atoms do not influence each other, from a collection of atoms the light is emitted at random times and in all directions. This means that the many light waves emerging from the excited atoms are out of phase with each other in both space and time. Light from such a source is therefore called *incoherent light*. We will denote the probability per unit time that an atom will emit a photon spontaneously as A_{21}.

1.2 Stimulated emission

Stimulated emission can occur when a photon of frequency v_{12} (where $hv_{12} = E_2 - E_1$) interacts with an excited atom. The excited atom can be induced to emit another photon of frequency v_{12}, as depicted in Figure 2.

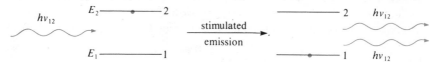

FIGURE 2   Stimulated emission. The incoming photon (at the left) stimulates the excited atom (or molecule) to emit an identical photon.

Photons emitted by stimulated emission are in phase with the stimulating photons and travel in the same direction. Stimulated emission is thus called a source of *coherent light*, because the light waves are in step with each other in both space and time. The probability for this process is denoted by B_{21}, and the rate of stimulated emission is proportional to the number of photons of the correct frequency present per unit volume, denoted by U_{12}. The total probability per unit time (P_{21}) to go from state 2 to state 1 with emission of photons of frequency v_{12} is the sum of the spontaneous and stimulated emission probabilities:

$$P_{21} = A_{21} + U_{12}B_{21}$$

1.3 Absorption

Excitation from state 1 to state 2 requires photons: spontaneous absorption does not occur (Figure 3). The probability of absorption is denoted by B_{12}, so the total probability per unit time (P_{12}) of absorption is

$$P_{12} = U_{12}B_{12}$$

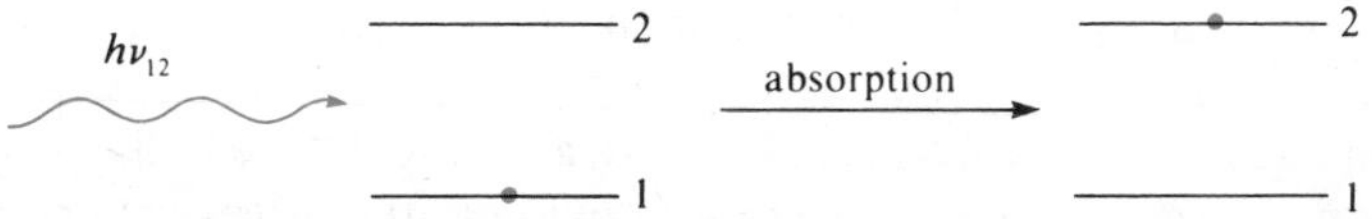

FIGURE 3   Absorption of a photon by a ground state atom (or molecule).

Einstein derived the relationship between the A and B probabilities (which are now known as the *Einstein coefficients*). For an atom (or molecule) in which states 1 and 2 are not degenerate:

$$B_{12} = B_{21}$$

$$A_{21} = \frac{8\pi h v_{12}^3}{c^3} B_{21}$$

where c is the velocity of light.

1.4 Amplification of light

Now let us consider a large set of atoms, with N_1 of them in state 1 and N_2 of them in state 2, and what happens when a collimated beam of photons, of frequency v_{12} and number per unit volume U_{12}, passes through the atoms (Figure 4). Some photons will be absorbed (causing a transition from

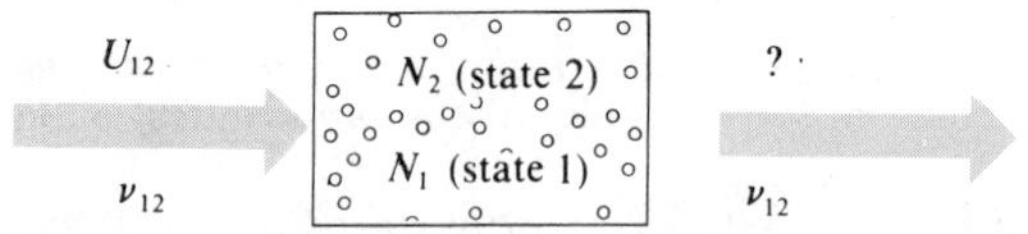

FIGURE 4 The amplification of a light beam by stimulated emission.

state 1 to state 2; other photons will stimulate emission (causing a transition from state 2 to state 1). The number of transitions per second, from state 2 to state 1, is given by

$$A_{21}N_2 + U_{12}B_{21}N_2$$

The number of transitions per second, from state 1 to state 2, is given by

$$U_{12}B_{12}N_1 \quad (= U_{12}B_{21}N_1, \text{ because } B_{12} = B_{21})$$

We can ignore the contribution to the emerging beam of the spontaneously emitted photons ($A_{21}N_2$) because they are emitted in all directions. So whenever N_2 is less than N_1 the beam will have a net loss of $(N_1 - N_2)U_{12}B_{21}$ photons per second. However, if we can make N_2 larger than N_1—in other words, create a *population inversion*—the number of downward transitions will exceed the number of upward transitions. The incident beam will then be *amplified* by stimulated emission on passing through the system. A *laser* is a device that amplifies or generates radiation by stimulated emission. 'Laser' is an acronym for *l*ight *a*mplification by *s*timulated *e*mission of *r*adiation. A laser does not need an external source of photons because spontaneous emission from the excited atoms can 'seed' the stimulated emission process, and will operate providing the necessary population inversion can be created.

The first device of this type used microwave radiation with a wavelength of 1.25 cm, rather than visible light. This was the ammonia maser (*microwave amplification*...) built by Charles Townes at Columbia University (USA) in 1954. The first optical maser or laser was the ruby laser made by Theodore Maiman at the Hughes Research Laboratory (USA) in 1960. In 1964 Townes, and Basov and Prokhorov in the USSR, received the Nobel Prize for Physics for the work that led to the discovery of the laser.

2 Specific lasers

The construction of almost all types of laser involves placing the amplifying medium between two mirrors. Such an arrangement is called a *laser cavity* and is shown schematically in Figure 5. The two mirrors allow only photons travelling in one direction—back and forth between the two mirrors—to make many passes through the amplifying medium. This means that the

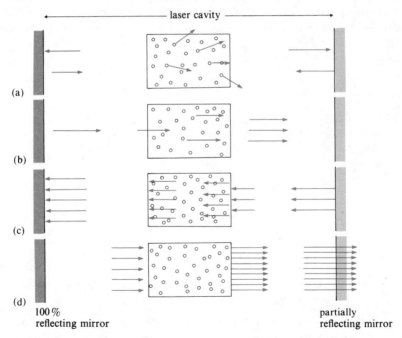

FIGURE 5   A laser cavity. The sequence shows the build-up of laser action following the spontaneous emission of a photon along the axis of the cavity (a). This photon stimulates another atom to emit a photon. The amplification process continues very rapidly (b and c) until there is no longer a population inversion. The result is an intense burst of light emerging from the partially reflecting mirror (d). (from Schawlow, A. L., 'Optical Masers' in *Scientific American*. Copyright © 1961 by Scientific American Inc. All rights reserved.)

23

laser light is emitted as a narrow parallel beam. One of the two mirrors is made partially reflecting so that a portion of the laser light is allowed to leave the laser cavity.

Methods of achieving the required population inversion and hence amplification vary from laser to laser. In order for the laser to operate, a certain critical value for the population inversion must be reached: this is called the *threshold condition*. In the helium–neon laser, for example, the threshold occurs when the population difference between state 2 and state 1 $(N_2 - N_1)$ is about 10^9 atoms cm^{-3} under typical operating conditions. Some specific lasers are now described, to illustrate the above ideas.

2.1 The ruby laser

Ruby consists of Al_2O_3, containing about 0.05% by weight of chromium ions as Cr_2O_3. It is the Cr^{3+} ions that give ruby its pink colour. Ruby is made to amplify by a process known as *optical pumping*. A xenon flash-lamp, coiled around a rod of ruby typically 15 cm long and 1–1.5 cm in diameter, is made to flash by the discharge of a previously charged capacitor. This flash lasts for about a millisecond. The rod is placed between two mirrors, one of 100% reflectivity, and one of about 50% reflectivity (Figure 6).

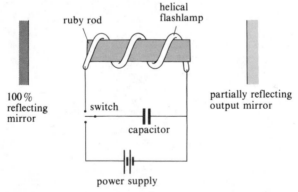

FIGURE 6   A schematic representation of a ruby laser.

The flash excites the Cr^{3+} ions to one or the other of the sets of states labelled 3 in Figure 7, which decay rapidly to the state 2 by a non-radiative process known as intersystem crossing. State 2 has a relatively long lifetime (about 3 ms) and so its population builds up. When the population of state 2 becomes greater than that of the ground state the ruby becomes amplifying in a narrow region around 694 nm—the region of emission between state 2 and state 1. When the threshold condition is exceeded an intense pulse of light of this wavelength emerges from the partially reflecting mirror.

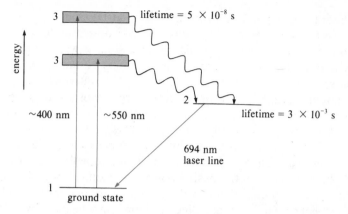

FIGURE 7 The Cr^{3+} energy levels and transitions important in the ruby laser.

Although the ruby laser was the first to be made, it is rather unusual in that the stimulated emission terminates in the ground state. This means that to achieve population inversion at least half of the ground state atoms must be excited. The ruby laser is called a *three-level laser*. It would be more efficient if the lower laser level was not the ground state, and so normally had a very low population. This can be achieved in *four-level lasers*, of which the neodymium laser is an important example.

2.2 The neodymium laser

The energy levels of neodymium (Nd^{3+}) are shown in Figure 8. As with ruby, neodymium lasers are excited with a flash of white light from a xenon flashlamp, and again the laser light is emitted as a short pulse. However,

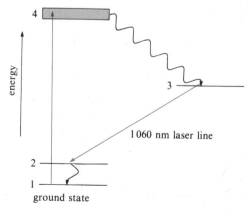

FIGURE 8 The Nd^{3+} energy levels and transitions important in the neodymium laser.

in this laser the emission is in the near infrared at 1 060 nm. The lower laser level, 2, has a population of only about 5×10^{-5} of that of the ground state at room temperature, and so population inversion between levels 3 and 2 is fairly easy to achieve. Neodymium can be incorporated into very large glass rods and extremely intense pulses (up to 10^{15} watts) can be generated from neodymium lasers. Neodymium lasers are one of several kinds being used in the development of laser-initiated nuclear fusion.

In both the ruby and neodymium lasers the light is emitted as pulses rather than as a continuous beam, but some applications of lasers require a continuous beam. In fact it's not easy to make three-level lasers such as the ruby laser operate continuously because the required population inversion can be readily obtained only with the high fluxes of light available from pulsed flashlamps. To illustrate a different pumping scheme we will describe two gas lasers.

2.3 The helium–neon and argon ion lasers

In the helium–neon laser an electric discharge is put through a gas mixture typically consisting of 1 mmHg of helium and 0.1 mmHg of neon. The electrons in the discharge excite the helium atoms into a variety of excited states. The states labelled 2^1S and 2^3S in Figure 9 are long-lived and their population builds up. These two helium states have very similar energies to

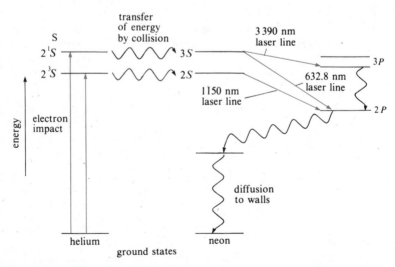

FIGURE 9   The helium and neon energy levels and transitions important in the He–Ne laser.

the 3*S* and 2*S* states of neon, and efficient transfer of excitation energy can take place by collision between the excited helium atoms and the ground state neon atoms, giving a significant population in the 3*S* and 2*S* neon levels. As shown in Figure 9, a number of laser transitions are possible in this system. The red laser transition (wavelength 632.8 nm) usually produces 0.5–2 mW and is probably the best known and most widely used source of laser light. It is used extensively in optical alignment and surveying, and is beginning to enter everyday life in product scanners at supermarket check-outs and in video disc readers for home entertainment.

A second important gas laser is the continuous argon ion laser which can give rise to a number of lines in the visible and ultraviolet regions. Very high powers (up to 40 watts of continuous power) have been obtained from these lasers. A photograph of a commercial argon ion laser of 18 watts continuous power is shown in Plate 1.

The output of the argon ion laser (and its close relative the krypton ion laser) is sufficient to enable it to be used as an optical pumping source for many other continuous lasers. A notable example is the organic dye laser.

2.4 The organic dye laser

Transitions between energy levels in atoms have a very narrow spread of energy. In contrast, transitions between states of large molecules, particularly in solution, are often very broad (roughly 1000 cm^{-1} wide as compared with less than 1 cm^{-1} wide for the argon ion laser). Consequently organic dye lasers, of which the rhodamine 6G laser is the most common example, can be tuned over a range of wavelengths (570–620 nm in the case of rhodamine 6G) by insertion of a variable-wavelength filter into the laser cavity, which inhibits the build-up of laser action except in the selected narrow range of wavelengths.

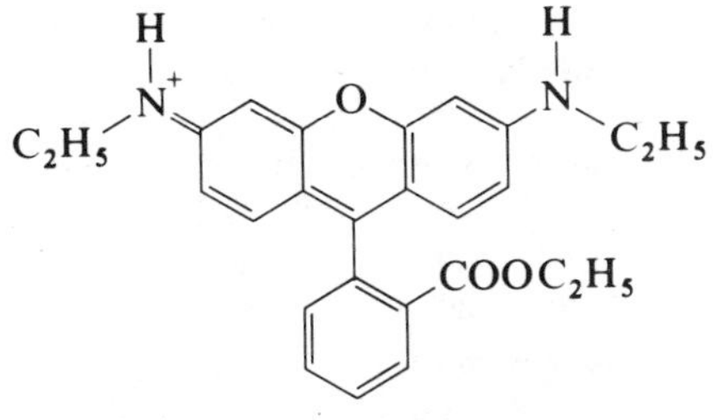

rhodamine 6G

3 Properties of laser light

The light generated by lasers has several general properties that distinguish it from light generated by conventional sources. Laser light is much more intense, directional, monochromatic and coherent than 'ordinary' light. The thin beam of parallel light arises from the geometry of a laser cavity (see Figure 5). The coherence and spectral purity, as well as the intensity, come about because of the co-operative nature of the stimulated emission process.

In an ordinary incandescent lamp, the atoms emit independently and the resulting light waves are out of step (spatially incoherent) and have various wavelengths (temporally incoherent) (Figure 10a). Spatial incoherence arises because waves, even of the same wavelength, emitted in different directions will be out of phase with each other. Temporal incoherence arises because waves of different wavelengths, even if initially in phase, will soon get out of step. A pinhole can be used to obtain spatially coherent light, but with great loss of intensity (Figure 10b). A filter or monochromater can give temporally coherent light, again with loss of intensity (Figure 10c). A combination of pinhole and filter gives light that is coherent both spatially and temporally, but the resulting beam is very weak (Figure 10d). In contrast, laser light is both spatially and temporally coherent because the waves are emitted in step, in the same direction, and with the same wavelength (Figure 10e).

The applications of high intensity, monochromaticity, directionality, and coherence are legion. Table 1 lists representative examples of applications of these properties. As an example, consider spatial coherence. All the light across the section of the laser beam is in phase and this means that all the

Table 1 Some applications of laser light

Property	Typical applications
intensity	laser machining (cutting and welding, surgery); non-linear optics (e.g. frequency doubling for generation of u.v. light); laser-initiated nuclear fusion
coherence	holography (information storage, non-destructive testing, entertainment)
short pulse duration	communications (e.g. fibre optic telephone systems); study of very fast processes (photochemistry, photobiology, ballistics)
monochromaticity	high resolution spectroscopy; isotope separation; analytical chemistry
well collimated beam	alignment (optics, surveying, building industry); remote sensing (e.g. of oil spills at sea and of emissions from tall industrial chimneys)

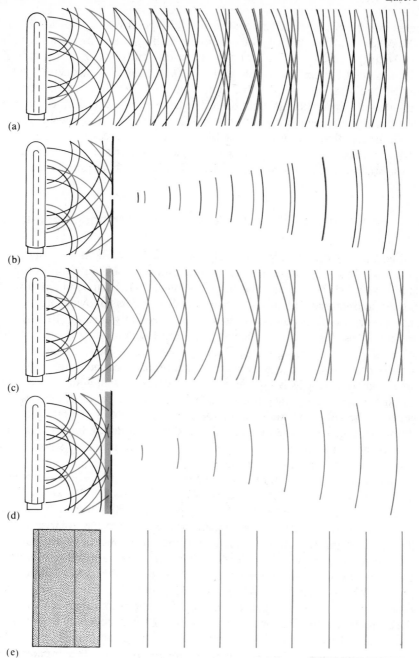

FIGURE 10   A comparison of ordinary light and laser light. See text for explanation. (From Schawlow, A. L., 'Laser Light', in *Scientific American*. Copyright ©
1968 by Scientific American Inc. All rights reserved.)

beam can be concentrated into a very small spot by means of a lens. A 500 W carbon dioxide laser for example (which operates at a wavelength of 10.6 μm) focused to a 100 μm spot can readily cut through 3 or 4 mm of stainless steel—a feat impossible with a 500 W source of incoherent light. In fact, the total output of visible light from most continuous lasers is less than that of a typical 100 W light bulb. The laser light is, however, contained in a narrow wavelength region and thus its power per unit wavelength is much greater than the power available from other sources.

There are a number of properties of laser light that are of special value in the study of photochemistry and we will now briefly consider these.

4 Properties of lasers important in photochemistry

Pulsed lasers can produce extremely short flashes of light—the shortest pulse produced to date (1981) had a duration of 90 femtoseconds ($1 \text{ fs} = 10^{-15}$ s). This means that photochemical events can be initiated very rapidly and subsequent physical and chemical events followed in time as they occur. Lasers producing pulses of nanosecond duration (10^{-9} s) are commonly used in photochemical studies, and lasers producing picosecond (10^{-12} s) pulses are being increasingly applied to the study of many fundamental processes in photochemistry. Intense nanosecond pulses can be produced by a relatively simple technique called Q-switching. If we take the ruby laser cavity shown in Figure 6 and put a shutter or optical switch between the ruby rod and one of the mirrors, lasing is inhibited. If the shutter is suddenly opened the excitation is dumped in one huge burst. For ruby or neodymium lasers pulses of several hundred megawatts lasting for about 10 ns are typically produced.

One common type of shutter is the electro-optic shutter. Here the switching is done electronically by means of a device called a Pockels cell. A Pockels cell is a crystal of, for example, potassium dihydrogen phosphate which, when an electric field is applied to it, can rotate the polarisation of light passing through it. A typical arrangement is shown in Figure 11.

Production of pulses of shorter duration than a few nanoseconds requires a different technique from the one described above. Picosecond pulses are produced by a technique called *mode-locking*, in which a switch or shutter inside the laser cavity is opened and closed at the round-trip frequency of the cavity (equal to $c/2L$ for a cavity of length L). The details of this process are beyond the scope of this chapter; however, the result of such a periodic loss is to produce a train of pulses separated by $2L/c$. The broader the laser line the shorter the pulse produced, and both neodymium and dye lasers are used in many laboratories to produce pulses of about 1 picosecond.

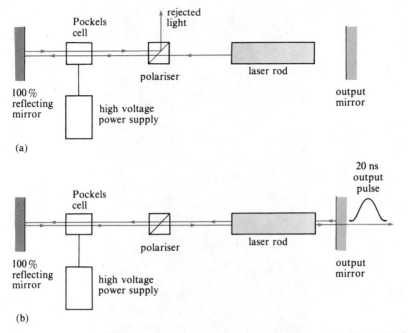

(a)

(b)

FIGURE 11   A schematic representation of a Pockels cell Q-switched laser. In (a) a high voltage is applied to the Pockels cell which, in a double pass, rotates the polarisation of light at the laser wavelength by 90°. The light is rejected from the laser cavity by the polariser and the laser does not lase. If the voltage is suddenly removed from the Pockels cell (b) it has no influence on the polarisation of light in the cavity and laser action builds up very rapidly until there is no longer a population inversion. This results in an intense pulse of typically 20 ns duration emerging from the laser cavity.

Pulses such as the one shown in Figure 12 are being used in the study of a wide range of fundamental processes some of which are described elsewhere in this book.

The high intensity available from lasers that produce short pulses enables *non-linear optical processes* to be observed and exploited. 'Non-linear' simply means that the process, rather than being simply proportional to the light intensity, depends on the square (or higher power) of the light intensity. Perhaps the most important non-linear optical process for photochemistry is *frequency doubling* (or *second harmonic generation*) a process whereby certain crystals are able to convert a proportion of an input laser beam with frequency v_L to frequency $2v_L$. This technique provides an important method for the generation of ultraviolet laser light. For example, ruby light of wavelength 694 nm is readily converted (with about 10% efficiency) into light of wavelength 347 nm in crystals of ammonium dihydrogen phosphate (see Plate 2).

31

FIGURE 12 A photograph of a single pulse of light from a mode-locked neodymium glass laser. The pulse is travelling through a glass cuvette filled with milky water which scatters some of the light towards the camera. The scale on the cuvette is in millimetres. A very fast shutter based on a rapid molecular relaxation process was used to take this 'stop-action' picture of the pulse. The pulse has a duration of about 10 ps. The finite aperture of the shutter makes the pulse appear slightly elongated, because the pulse has moved slightly during the time the shutter was open. (source: Giordmaine and Duguay, 1971.)

A final aspect of lasers that we want to mention is their ability to produce light with an extremely small spread of frequency. Some dye lasers can produce linewidths as narrow as 10^{-5} cm^{-1}, compared with a limiting value of about 10^{-2} cm^{-1} for the lines in atomic emission spectra. Such highly monochromatic light enables the electronic states of atoms and molecules to be studied with greatly improved precision, and because single isotopic species of a single chemical substance can be excited, also holds much promise for the efficient separation of isotopes by photochemical means. This latter application is taken up in some detail in Chapter 5·14.

2·2 Polyenes and linearly conjugated dyes

by Antony Rest (University of Southampton)

1 Introduction

Linearly conjugated π-electron systems have been the subject of renewed experimental and theoretical interest in recent years. This is because such systems constitute the *chromophores*, or colour-bearing parts, of naturally occurring carotenoid pigments (e.g. **1** and **2**) and visual pigments (e.g. **3**, **4** and **5**) and also of synthetic dyes (e.g. cyanines **6**). An understanding of the energy levels, and transitions between them, in such systems is part of the general understanding of the colour and constitution of molecules.

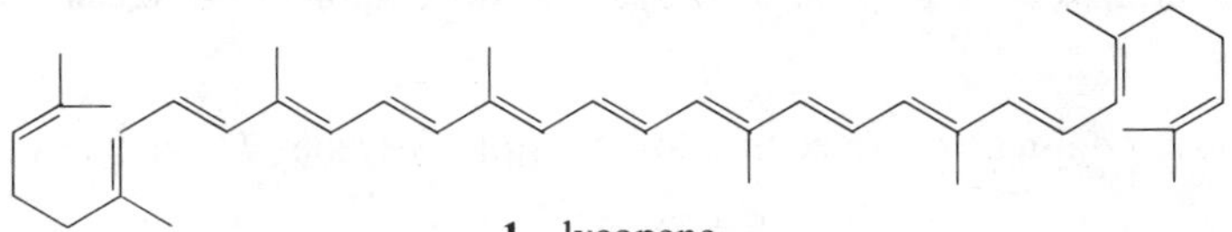

1 lycopene

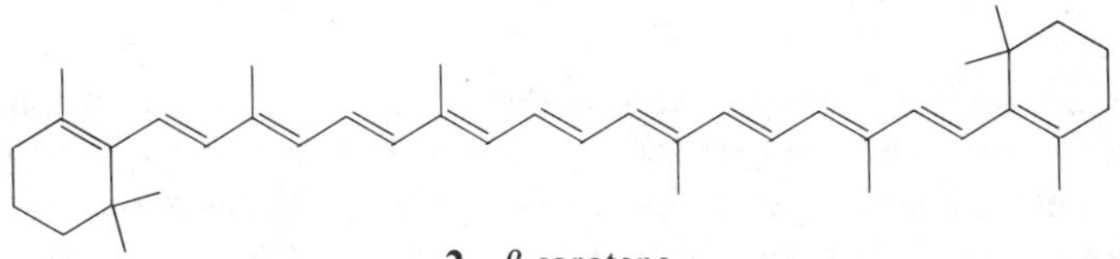

2 β-carotene

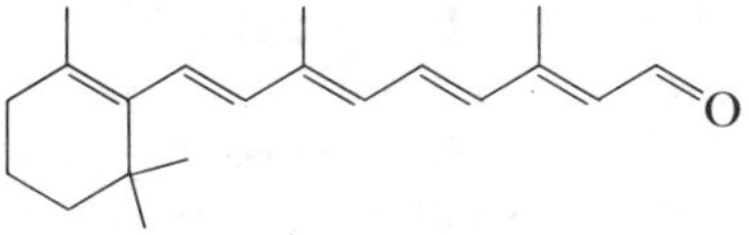

3 retinal₁

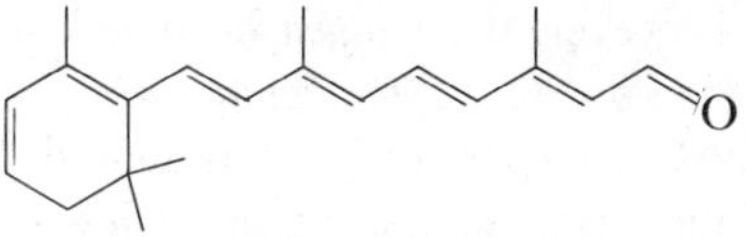

4 retinal₂

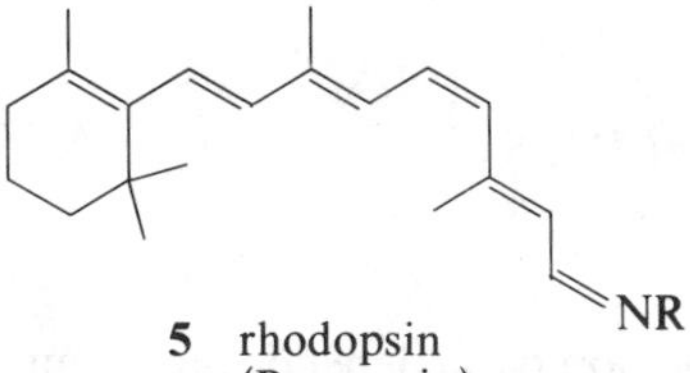

5 rhodopsin
(R = opsin)

$$R_2\overset{+}{N}=CH\text{---}(CH=CH)_{\overline{n}}NR'_2$$

6

Small polyatomic molecules in general have filled σ-bonding, π-bonding and non-bonding (n) orbitals. The longest wavelength (i.e. lowest energy) absorption band often corresponds to an $n \to \pi^*$ transition with the more intense $\pi \to \pi^*$ and $\sigma \to \sigma^*$ absorptions occurring at shorter wavelengths (Figure 1a).

33

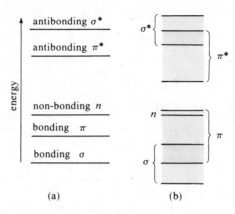

FIGURE 1 The relative energies of the bonding, antibonding, and non-bonding orbitals in (a) a simple and (b) a complex unsaturated molecule.

In linearly conjugated molecules, for example polyenes **7** and cyanine dyes

$$R\text{+}CH\text{=}CH\text{)}_n R'$$

7

6, there are as many π-type levels as there are conjugated atoms, and the orbitals of both the π and π^* sets are spread over a range of energies (as are those of the σ and σ^* sets; Figure 1b). Neither polyenes nor cyanine dyes have non-bonding pairs of electrons to give $n \to \pi^*$ transitions, so that the lowest energy bands correspond to $\pi \to \pi^*$ transitions. In some situations, however, the *highest occupied molecular orbital* (HOMO) happens to be a *non-bonding π-molecular orbital* (NBMO) rather than a bonding π orbital. As the number of conjugated atoms in a linearly conjugated molecule increases, so the π and π^* levels are spread over a greater range of energy and the position of the lowest energy absorption band moves to longer wavelength. For example, Figure 2 shows the absorption spectra of a series of cyanine dyes **8**.

$$\langle\ \rangle \overset{+}{N}\text{=}CH\text{+}CH\text{=}CH\text{)}_n N \langle\ \rangle$$

8

The position of the lowest energy absorption band depends on the number of conjugated atoms, the nature and position of heteroatoms and substituents, and the solvent in which the molecules are dissolved. Two theoretical approaches, the simpler resonance or valence bond theory and the more rigorous molecular orbital theory, can be used to understand these effects These two approaches are presented and critically evaluated.

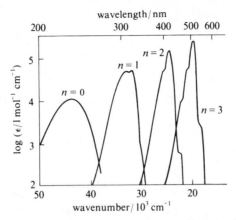

FIGURE 2 The absorption spectra of the α,ω-di(N-piperidinyl)polymethine cyanines (**8**; n = 0–3) in ethanol at 100 K. (source: Scheibe, 1966)

2 Valence bond theory

Acyclic polyenes (**7**) can be represented as a sequence of alternate single and double bonds (**9**). Although there is delocalisation in polyenes so that

9

such a classical picture of fixed double and single bonds is not completely adequate, the fact that experimentally there are differing bond lengths shows that there is a significant degree of bond alternation. Note that these polyenes have an even number of conjugated carbon atoms. However, for chains with an odd number of carbon atoms (obtained by adding a CH_2^- group to the end of the polyene chain, so that the p orbital of the new carbon overlaps efficiently with the p orbitals of the chain), then there is little or no bond alternation. For example, when the additional carbon atom provides not one but two electrons a carbanion is formed, which can be represented by resonance forms **10a** and **10b** and also by many other forms with the negative charge on intermediate atoms; that is, the set of resonance structures leads to extensive delocalisation of the additional pair of electrons. Several other types of compound, for example true cyanines (**11**), oxonol anions (**12**) and merocyanines (**13**), are isoelectronic with **10** and are described as cyanine-type systems.

For cyanine-type systems, the ability to write classical valence bond resonance forms (**11a** ↔ **11b**, **12a** ↔ **12b**, **13a** ↔ **13b**) provides a basis for explaining solvent effects. For example, the $\pi \to \pi^*$ band of the merocyanine **14** undergoes a very large shift to shorter wavelengths from toluene

35

$$CH_2=CH(CH=CH)_nCH_2^- \longleftrightarrow {}^-CH_2(CH=CH)_nCH=CH_2$$

10a   **10b**

$$R_2N(CH=CH)_nCH=\overset{+}{N}R'_2 \longleftrightarrow R_2\overset{+}{N}=CH(CH=CH)_nNR'_2$$

11a   **11b**

$$^-O(CH=CH)_nCH=O \longleftrightarrow O=CH(CH=CH)_nO^-$$

12a   **12b**

$$R_2N(CH=CH)_nCH=O \longleftrightarrow R_2\overset{+}{N}=CH(CH=CH)_nO^-$$

13a   **13b**

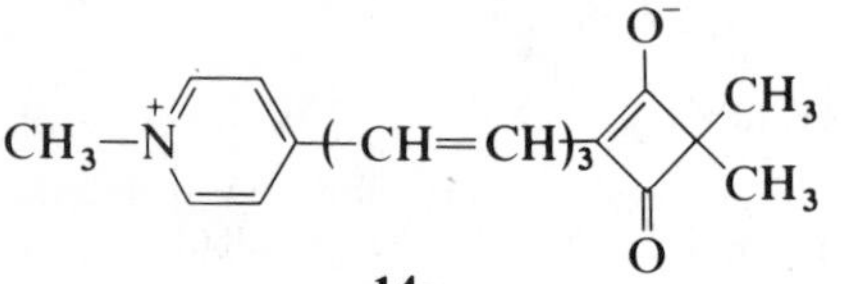

14a

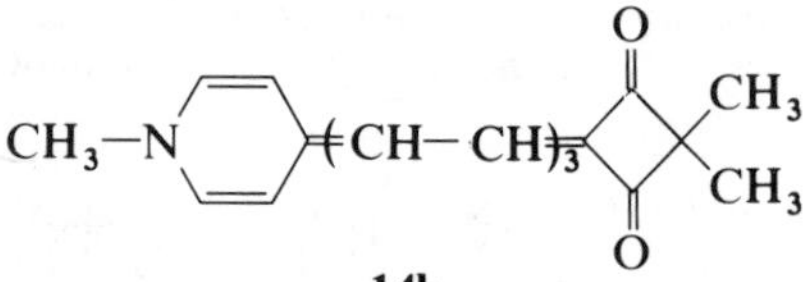

14b

($\lambda_{max} = 732$ nm) to water ($\lambda_{max} = 458$ nm) because the zwitterionic form (**14a**) is the more stable in water and makes the major contribution to the ground state of the dye. If the two forms of **14** are described by wavefunctions ψ_a and ψ_b, respectively, then in the simple valence bond treatment the wavefunction for the ground state, Ψ, is given by the symmetric combination of ψ_a and ψ_b (equation 1) whereas that for the excited state, Ψ^*, is given by the corresponding antisymmetric combination (equation 2):

$$\Psi = a\psi_a + b\psi_b \tag{1}$$

$$\Psi^* = b\psi_a - a\psi_b \tag{2}$$

$$\text{where} \quad a^2 + b^2 = 1$$

If the resonance structures are equal in energy, then $a = b$ (Figure 3a). In the case shown in Figure 3b, ψ_a makes the larger contribution to Ψ and a is greater than b. In the case of the merocyanine **14** the stability of the zwitterionic form, which arises from the aromaticity of the pyridine ring, is further enhanced in the polar solvent, water, and hence a *hypsochromic shift* occurs, i.e. a blue shift corresponding to an increase in ΔE and the band shifting to shorter wavelengths. In contrast, the absorption band of phenol blue (**15**) undergoes a red or *bathochromic shift* from 552 nm in cyclohexane to 688 nm in water, indicating that the non-polar structure (**15a**) has the lower energy and makes the major contribution to the ground state in non-polar solvents. The energy of the zwitterionic form (**15b**) is

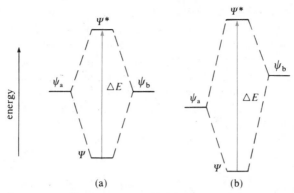

FIGURE 3   The interaction between two classical resonance structures when they are (a) of equal energy, and (b) of unequal energy. Note, however, that in general the difference in energy between ψ_a and Ψ (and between ψ_b and Ψ^*) is greater in (a) than in (b). (source: Griffiths, 1976)

lower in a polar solvent and the contributions of the two structures to the hybrid states of phenol blue become more nearly equal (Figure 3a), producing the red shift corresponding to a decrease in ΔE.

15a   **15b**

Although the valence bond approach provides a satisfactory qualitative account of the colour of cyanine dyes and of *solvatochromism* (i.e. colour changes between polar and non-polar solvents), the method becomes increasingly complex when quantitative calculations are attempted. This is because the contributions of an enormous number of resonance structures must be considered and it becomes difficult to describe the excited states.

3   Molecular orbital theory

There are a number of ways in which molecular orbital theory can be applied to polyenes. Perhaps the simplest of these is the so-called 'free-electron model'. This assumes that the electrons are free to move within a conjugated π-electron system (**9**). It can then be shown that the energy of the lowest energy $\pi \rightarrow \pi^*$ transition is given by the expression:

$$\Delta E_1 = \frac{h^2}{8md^2} \frac{1}{(n+1)} \tag{3}$$

where h is Planck's constant, m is the mass of the electron, d is the average bond length and n is the number of atoms in the chain. Figure 4 shows that there is a reasonable agreement between calculated and experimental band positions for cyanines, whereas there is a poor correlation for polyenes (Figure 5). The poor agreement between theory and experiment for polyenes can be attributed primarily to the breakdown in the assumption, made in deriving equation (3), that the bond lengths are all equal. It is significant that there is better agreement for the cyanines where there is a higher degree of delocalisation, via the many resonance structures, and hence greater uniformity of bond lengths.

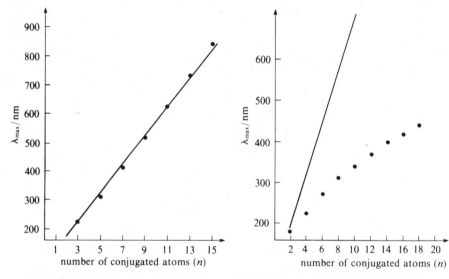

FIGURE 4 The relationship between the λ_{max} value of the first absorption band of the cyanines (11) and the number of conjugated atoms (n). The points are experimental results, and the line is calculated.

FIGURE 5 The relationship between the λ_{max} value of the first absorption band of a polyene and the number of conjugated atoms (n). The points are experimental results, and the line is calculated.

Molecules containing an even number of conjugated atoms, such as 9, are described as *even-alternant* molecules. An alternant molecule is one in which alternate conjugated atoms can be labelled with stars (cf. 16) without any two starred atoms being adjacent, as is the case for conjugated molecules with odd-membered rings. Even-alternant molecules, which have an equal number of starred and unstarred positions in the chain (16), have an even number of π levels, half of them bonding and half of them antibonding (Figure 1). Molecules containing an odd number of conjugated atoms are described as *odd-alternant* molecules. These molecules (e.g. carbanions 10 and compounds 11–13) have an odd number of π levels and an unequal number of starred and unstarred positions (17) (the starred positions are always chosen so that there is one more starred position than unstarred). It turns out that in even-alternant molecules the π and π^* orbitals are paired.† For odd-alternant molecules, after pairing of the π and π^* orbitals, the remaining

$$\overset{\star}{C}H_2=CH-\overset{\star}{C}H=CH-\overset{\star}{C}H=CH_2 \qquad \overset{\star}{C}H_2=CH-\overset{\star}{C}H=CH-\overset{\star}{C}H_2^-$$

16   **17**

level will lie at the centre of the energy-level system and will effectively be an NBMO. The energy required to promote electrons from this level to the lowest π^* level will obviously be less than that for the corresponding even-alternant molecule. This is borne out, for example, by the fact that the even-alternant molecule $CH_3-(CH=CH)_8-CH_3$ has an absorption band at 396 nm, whereas $(CH_3)_2N-(CH=CH)_6-CH=\overset{+}{N}(CH_3)_2$, an odd-alternant species with one conjugated atom fewer, absorbs at 850 nm.

The effect on the first absorption (lowest energy) band of introducing a heteroatom or a substituent into a polyene or cyanine dye can be explained as follows. The lowest energy band corresponds to a transition between the highest energy occupied bonding orbital and the lowest energy unoccupied antibonding orbital. For an even-alternant hydrocarbon, these two orbitals form a pair and it turns out that such paired orbitals have identical charge distributions at each carbon atom. Thus the charge distribution in the ground and excited states should be the same. Hence the energies of the two states should be affected equally by the presence of a substituent or heteroatom in the chain, and there should be a minimal effect on the position of the first absorption band. For example, the diaza compound **18** ($\lambda_{max}= 280$ nm) and the isoelectronic alkene **19** ($\lambda_{max}= 299$ nm) absorb at similar wavelengths.

$$CH_3-CH=CH-CH=N-N=CH-CH=CH-CH_3 \qquad CH_3-(CH=CH)_4-CH_3$$

18   **19**

For an odd-alternant system such as **6**, however, there is a marked effect. In such systems, the first absorption corresponds to a transition from the NBMO to the lowest energy antibonding orbital. Now, it can be shown that the electrons in the NBMO have zero electron density at unstarred atoms but a greater electron density at the starred atoms than for the other orbitals. So if the electron density at an unstarred atom is increased, for example by the introduction of a nitrogen atom or an electron-donating

---

† This is strictly true only for alternant *hydrocarbons*, but can be used as an approximation for systems such as the cyanines.

substituent, then the energy of the π^* orbital will be lowered relative to that of the NBMO. The net result is a decrease in the energy separation and a bathochromic shift of the first absorption band. By contrast, if the electron density at a starred atom is increased, the energy of the NBMO will be lowered relative to that of the π^* orbital, the energy separation will increase and a hypsochromic shift will be observed. The various possibilities are summarised in Figure 6. A specific example is given by the cyanines **20** and **21**, where an increase in the electronegativity at the central carbon

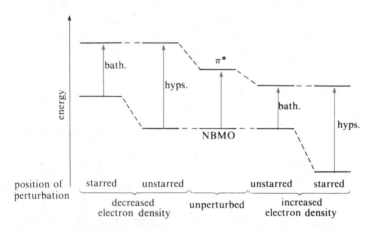

20 X = H (λ_{max} = 708 nm)
21 X = NO$_2$ (λ_{max} = 580 nm)

atom produces a large hypsochromic shift. A similar effect could have been produced by placing the substituent at any other starred position.

FIGURE 6   The effect of changing the electron density in an odd-alternant molecule on the energies of the orbitals and the energy of the first electronic transition (bath. = bathochromic and hyps. = hypsochromic shift). Decreased electron density can be caused by an electron-withdrawing substituent e.g. NO$_2$; increased electron density can be brought about by the substitution of a heteroatom, e.g. N or O, or by an electron-donating substituent e.g. CH$_3$. (based on Griffiths, 1976)

The effect of the solvent can be similarly explained as arising from a change in the energy of the ground or excited state depending on solvent polarity (Figure 7). The solvent molecules arrange themselves around the solute molecules so as to minimise the energy of the system. If the excited state is less polar than the ground state, the ground state will be stabilised by a polar solvent more than the excited state. Thus a polar solvent produces a blue shift with respect to the idealised absorption spectrum produced in the vapour phase or in a non-polar solvent. Conversely, stabilisation of the excited state, i.e. when the excited state is more polar than the ground state (Figure 7c) leads to a red shift.

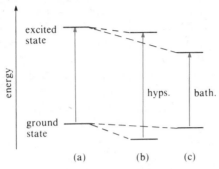

FIGURE 7 The effect of a polar solvent on the transition energy of a molecule; (a) the situation in the vapour phase, or in non-polar solvents; (b) ground state more polar than excited state; (c) ground state less polar than excited state (bath. = bathochromic and hyps. = hypsochromic). (based on Griffiths, 1976)

The absorption of dyes on to solid substrates can be regarded as a special case of solvent–solute interaction, and has important consequences for the dyeing of textiles and the staining of tissues, and also for biological systems. For example, it appears that the red, green and blue colour receptors in the retina are produced by a single pigment, retinal, which has its spectrum modified by bonding to one of three proteins.

4 Vibrational progressions

Any vibrational fine structure observed in an absorption band must be due to vibrational modes active in the electronic excited state (Figure 8). The promotion of an electron from a π to a π^* orbital involves a decrease in π-bonding and hence an increase in the average bond length. This will lead to an overall increase in the size of the molecule. The length of the vibrational progression (i.e. the bandwidth) depends on the extent of the change in the configuration of the atomic nuclei that is induced by the excitation (Figure 8). If there is little or no change in the molecular size or shape, the minimum of the potential energy curve for the excited state will be more or less directly above that for the ground state, so the intensity will be concentrated in the 0–0 band. With increasing change of nuclear configuration (i.e. as the minimum of the excited state is displaced further from that of the ground state), the 0–0 band becomes weaker and the band intensity is spread over

41

higher members of the progression. In the even-alternant polyenes **7** and **9**, electronic excitation results in a reversal of the alternation of single and double bonds so that progressions with maxima separated by the frequency of the C=C vibration in the excited state are observed. In the series of related cyanines **8** (Figure 2), the $\pi \to \pi^*$ band shifts to longer wavelengths with increasing values of n, and the larger molecules have generally narrower bands bacause there is a decreasing net change in bond length per conjugated bond as n increases. The width of the $\pi \to \pi^*$ absorption band of a dye determines the colour characteristics of the dye: for example, a narrow band produces a bright colour whereas a broad band gives a dull colour. Thus the colours of the natural carotenoid pigments such as lycopene **(1)**, and β-carotene **(2)**, and of the visual pigments retinal$_1$ **(3)** and retinal$_2$ **(4)** and rhodopsin **(5)**, are typically dull, whereas those of the cyanine dyes are bright.

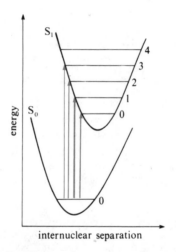

FIGURE 8 The potential energy curves of the ground state, S_0, and the first excited electronic state, S_1, and the relative intensities, denoted by the relative breadths of the vertical arrows, of the vibrational bands in the $S_0 \to S_1$ electronic band system. (For a polyatomic molecule, the internuclear separation refers to some hypothetical composite change of bond lengths and bond angles, i.e. of nuclear configuration). (source: Mason, 1970)

2·3 Porphyrins and phthalocyanines
by Antony Rest (University of Southampton)

1 Introduction

The porphyrins are probably the most important class of compounds in biological systems because of their central role in photosynthesis, biological oxidation and reduction, and oxygen transport. The basic porphyrin skeleton (1) comprises four pyrrole rings (2), conjugated together through four extra

1 porphyrin skeleton   2 pyrrole

carbon atoms. If at each position 1–8 and α–δ in **1** there is a single hydrogen atom, and if there are two hydrogen atoms in the centre, then the compound is called a *free-base porphin*. The outer hydrogen atoms can be substituted and the molecules so derived are referred to as *porphins*. Such systems can accept two protons to form dipositive cations or donate two protons and become dinegative anions. It is in the latter form that porphins bond to metal ions to form *metalloporphins*, in which the metal sits in the hole at the centre of the rigid planar conjugated system.

Metalloporphins are highly coloured compounds, and it is these compounds that constitute the active sites involved in some key biological processes. For example, chlorophyll *a* (**3a**) and chlorophyll *b* (**3b**), which contain magnesium, are the green pigments that absorb light in plants; the role of the chlorophylls in photosynthesis is discussed at some length in Chapter 6·3. The haem proteins, which contain iron, e.g. iron(II) proto-porphin (**4**), are associated with the transport (haemoglobin) and storage (myoglobin) of oxygen in blood. A second series of porphyrins (no longer called porphins) arises from the reduction (i.e. hydrogenation) of the outer double bonds. Compounds with one hydrogenated outer double bond are called *chlorins* (hence the name chlorophyll), and those with two reduced double bonds are called *tetrahydroporphins*. A third series of porphyrins

43

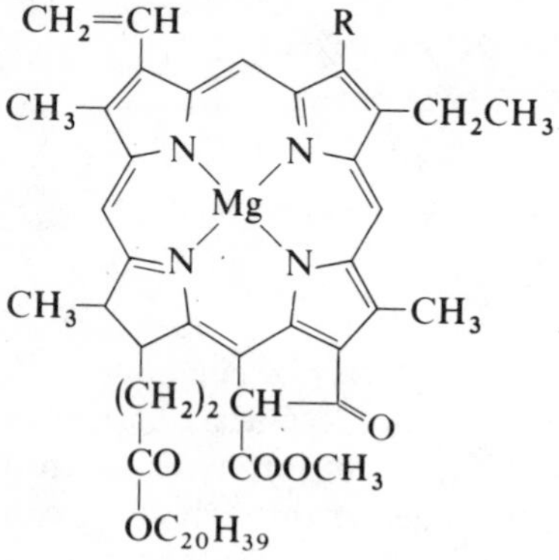

3a R = CH$_3$: chlorophyll *a*
3b R = CHO: chlorophyll *b*

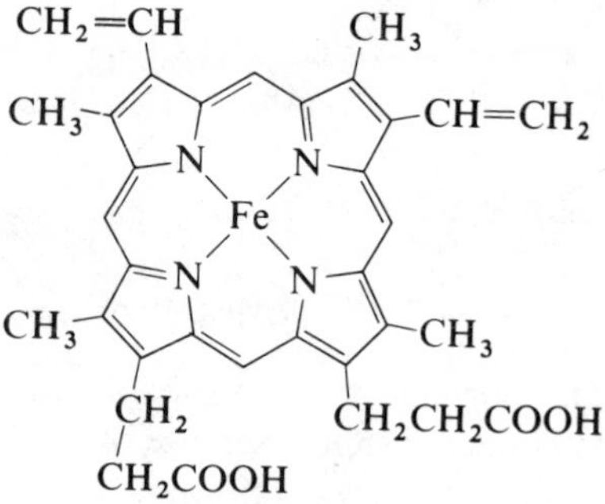

4 iron(II) protoporphin

arises by fusing benzene rings across the outer double bond positions and these compounds are called *benzporphins*. The most important benzporphins are the *tetrazatetrabenzporphins*, which are more usually called *phthalocyanines*; compound **5** is the free-base form. In addition to serving as model compounds for metalloporphins, *metallophthalocyanines* (**6**) are also important in their own right as dyes and pigments that have high thermal and chemical stability, partly as a result of interactions between adjacent parallel sheets (**7**), in which a nitrogen of one molecule can bond to the metal of another molecule.

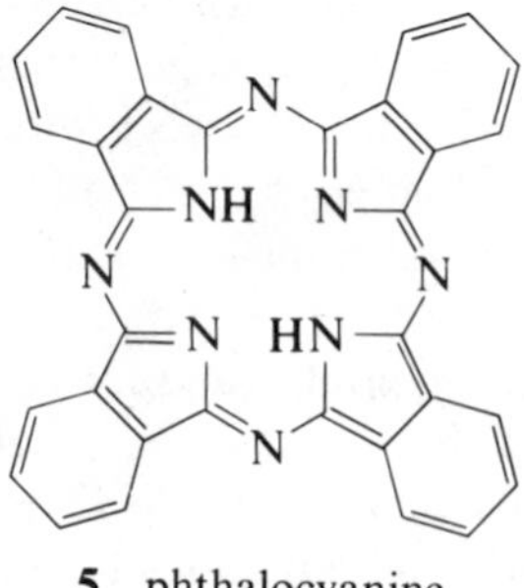

5 phthalocyanine

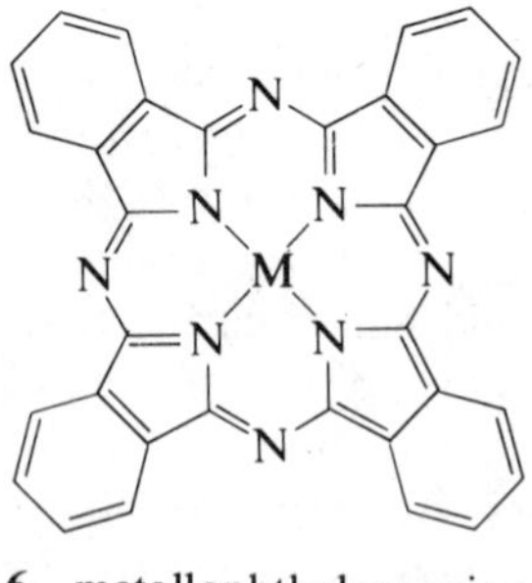

6 metallophthalocyanine

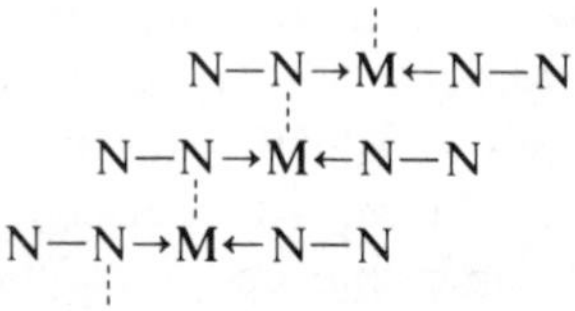

2 Spectra

In contrast to linearly conjugated molecules, porphins and metalloporphins show two principal absorptions in the visible region, one a series of bands of moderate intensity (ϵ about $10^4 \ 1 \ mol^{-1} \ cm^{-1}$) at approximately 550 nm and the other a band of higher intensity (ϵ about $10^5 \ 1 \ mol^{-1} \ cm^{-1}$) near 400 nm. These are referred to as the Q bands and B band, respectively. Figure 1(a) shows a typical spectrum of a free-base porphin, $\alpha,\beta,\gamma,\delta$-tetra-phenylporphin (see **1**). All free-base porphins show a similar four-banded

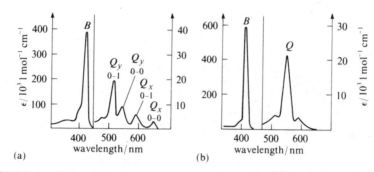

FIGURE 1   Absorption spectra of tetraphenylporphin: (a) free-base, and (b) zinc salt. (Note that the absorption coefficients for the Q and B bands refer to different scales.) (source: Gouterman, 1961)

absorption in the 400–700 nm region, although the relative intensities of the four bands vary from compound to compound.

A striking change occurs when a free-base porphin is converted into a metalloporhin. The spectrum of zinc tetraphenylporphin, given in Figure 1(b), shows the general effect, i.e. the four-banded Q absorption collapses and the B band increases in intensity. Haemoglobin appears red (Figure 2) because the molecules absorb the blue and green components of the visible spectrum but the red component (600–700 nm) is reflected. If the metal is changed in a given porphin skeleton, changes in the intensity of the Q band may occur and the whole spectrum may shift.

The effect of hydrogenating one of the outer double bonds in the porphin skeleton (**1**) is to produce a large change in the relative intensities of the Q and B bands, as shown in the spectra of free-base and zinc tetraphenylchlorin (Figure 3), compared with those of tetraphenylporphin (Figure 1), but the positions of the bands are relatively unaffected. The chlorophylls (**3**), which are chlorins, appear green (Figure 4) because the molecules absorb the blue and red components of the visible spectrum but the green component (500–600 nm) is reflected. Substitution of an aza nitrogen ($=N-$) for a methine ($=CH-$) bridge, as in the phthalocyanines, causes the whole

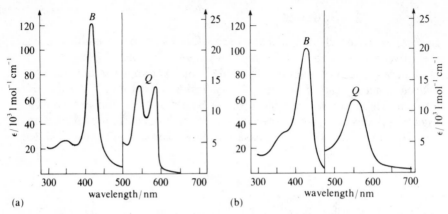

(a) wavelength/nm   (b) wavelength/nm

FIGURE 2 Absorption spectra of haemoglobin: (a) oxyhaemoglobin and (b) deoxyhaemoglobin. (Note that the absorption coefficients for the Q and B bands refer to different scales.) (source: Weissbluth, 1967)

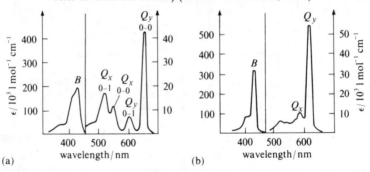

(a) wavelength/nm   (b) wavelength/nm

FIGURE 3 Absorption spectra of tetraphenylchlorin: (a) free-base and (b) zinc salt. (Note that the absorption coefficients for the Q and B bands refer to different scales.) (source: Gouterman, 1961)

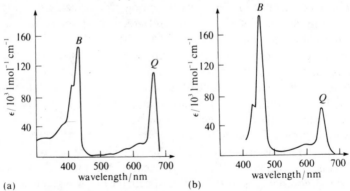

(a) wavelength/nm   (b) wavelength/nm

FIGURE 4 Absorption spectra of chlorophylls in ether: (a) chlorophyll a and (b) chlorophyll b. (source: Goedheer, 1966)

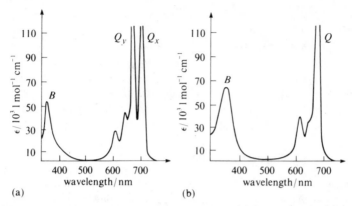

FIGURE 5   Absorption spectra of phthalocyanine: (a) free-base and (b) zinc salt. (source: Gouterman, 1961)

spectrum to move to longer wavelengths, and the Q band to become more intense than the B band. This is illustrated by comparison of Figure 5, which shows the spectra of free-base and zinc phthalocyanine with Figure 1.

The constancy of the energy separation of some of the Q bands allows them to be assigned to different vibrational components of the same electronic transition, for example $Q_y(0\text{–}0)$ and $Q_y(0\text{–}1)$. The label Q_x or Q_y signifies an electronic transition in which the transition dipole lies along the x or y axis of the molecule, respectively (see **8** and **9**). These assignments

arise following the results of an experiment in which the extent and direction of the polarisation of the fluorescence emission were measured when the molecules were excited with polarised light. In the free-base porphin (**8**) the transition dipole moments in the x and y directions are different, whereas in the metalloporphin (**9**) the dipole moments are identical (because the x and y directions are equivalent), so that in the latter the Q_x and Q_y

47

transitions have the same energy and hence overlap (Figure 1b). The introduction of other elements of asymmetry, for example by hydrogenating one of the outer double bonds, as in the chlorins, will increase the differences in the energies of the Q_x and Q_y transitions (compare Figures 3a and 1a). In the metallochlorins there is still a difference between the transition moments in the x and y directions so Q_x and Q_y progressions are observed (compare Figures 3b and 1b). Note that for both free-base porphin and free-base chlorin the Q_y transition has the greater intensity.

3 Electronic structure

If the formal double and single bonds in **1** are ignored and each conjugated atom is regarded as a source of a p orbital available for π overlap, then several closed conjugated paths can be drawn. For example, if the 1–2 and 5–6 double bonds and the two NH groups in **1** are ignored, an 18-atom pathway can be traced (**10**). Exclusion of the outer 1–2, 3–4, 5–6, and 7–8 double bonds produces a 16-atom pathway (**11**). The pathway of greatest conjugation will show the highest degree of bond length equalisation. In fact, X-ray crystallographic data and theoretical calculations point to an 18-atom pathway for the free-base porphins (**10**) and a 16-atom pathway for metallo-

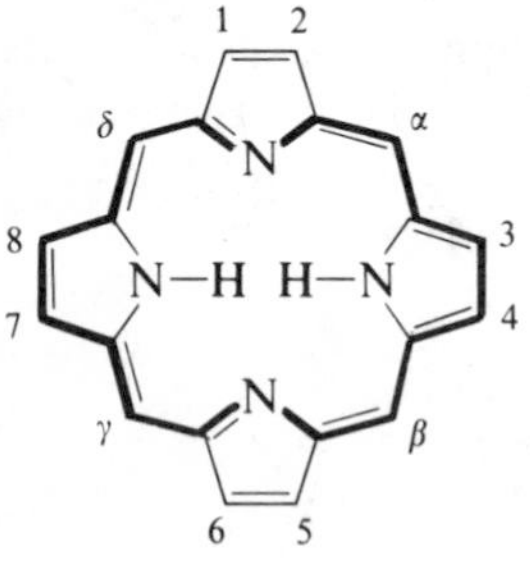

| **10** | **11** | **12** |

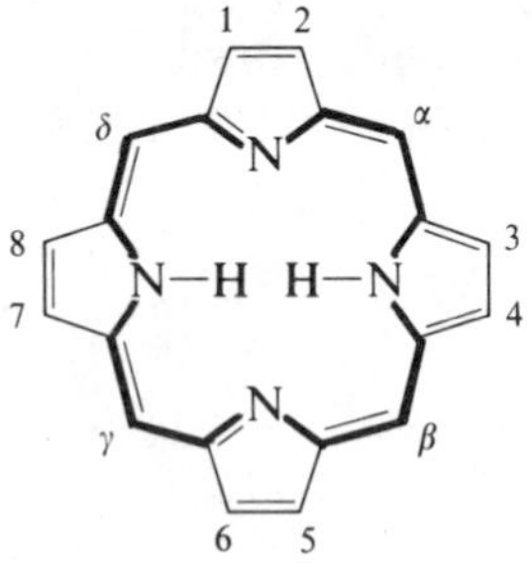

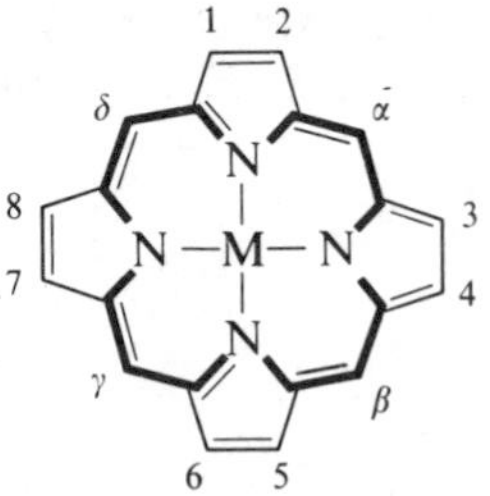

porphins (**12**). One contributing factor in the case of the free-base porphin is the steric effect of the hydrogen atoms attached to the central nitrogen atoms, which forces them out of the plane, with the result that conjugation involving the non-bonding pairs on these nitrogen atoms is hindered, and the less symmetric 18-atom pathway is favoured. For such a pathway Q_x and Q_y are not equivalent (**8**), whereas for the 16-atom pathway Q_x and Q_y are equivalent (**9**). For either pathway, however, some of the outer double bonds are not involved, which explains why the hydrogenation of outer double bonds, as in the chlorins, despite the apparent reduction in overall conjugation, need not have a large effect on the positions of the absorption bands (Figures 1 and 3). The asymmetry resulting from the protons in free-base porphin or the hydrogenated double bond in chlorin causes the Q_y transition to be the more intense in both cases. A comparison of the spectra of free-base phthalocyanines (13) with those of metallophthalocyanines (14) shows a

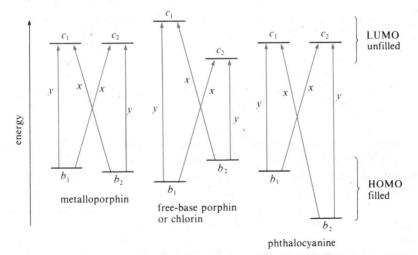

13   **14**

simplification of the Q band for the metallophthalocyanines (Figure 5) analogous to that described earlier for the porphins, again because the metallo compounds have higher symmetry.

A more detailed explanation of the spectra can be satisfactorily deduced by considering the two highest occupied molecular orbitals (HOMO) and the two lowest unoccupied molecular orbitals (LUMO). The relative energies of these for the four cases that primarily concern us (metalloporphin, free base porphin, chlorin and phthalocyanine) are shown in Figure 6.

FIGURE 6   Schematic diagrams showing the relative energies of the two highest occupied molecular orbitals (HOMO) and the two lowest unoccupied molecular orbitals (LUMO) with the various possible transitions. (based on Gouterman, 1961)

49

For the highly symmetric metalloporphin the degeneracy of the two un-
filled orbitals and the approximate degeneracy of the two filled orbitals
leads to four configurations of almost identical energies (a situation familiar
from the electronic structure of benzene). Unlike in the benzene case, however, inclusion of electron repulsion in calculating the energies of the transi-
tions $b_1 \rightarrow c_1$ and $b_2 \rightarrow c_2$ compared with $b_1 \rightarrow c_2$ and $b_2 \rightarrow c_1$ does not
remove the degeneracy. Consequently, when configuration interaction (CI)
is taken into account, this gives rise to two allowed states (from the reinforce-
ment of the transition dipoles of the transitions before CI is taken into

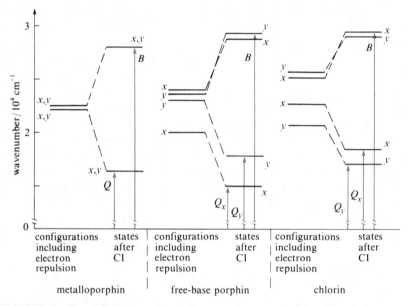

FIGURE 7 Simplified energy level diagram showing the energies of the excited
states of various porphyrins in the single-configuration approximation and after
configuration interaction is included.

account) and two forbidden states (from cancellation of the transition
dipoles) as shown in Figure 7. Because the orbitals b_1 and b_2 are not exactly
degenerate, the cancellation is not exact as in benzene and the 'forbidden'
transitions are stronger than otherwise might be expected.

In the case of the less symmetric free-base porphin, the two HOMOs
and the two LUMOs are not degenerate (Figure 6). The result, very approximately, is observation of a pair of x transitions of about the same energy
that are very similar to the metalloporphin case (i.e. one 'allowed', one
'forbidden') and a pair of y transitions that are slightly different in energy.
This leads to a more intense low energy band because the y transition

dipoles now cancel one another less effectively. When electron repulsion and CI are taken into account the result shown in Figure 7 is obtained. Thus the stronger y-polarised Q_y band is at *higher* energy than the Q_x band. For chlorin a similar picture is obtained, except that the detailed calculations give slightly different results in that when CI is taken into account the Q_x and Q_y bands are reversed in energy. This provides the reason why haemoglobin is red and chlorophyll is green: the Q bands in haemoglobin are at higher energy than in chlorophyll where the strongest Q band (Q_y) is at a very low energy.

The effect of the four extra nitrogens in the phthalocyanines is shown in Figure 6. The bands correspond much more closely to transitions between single-configuration states and accordingly the Q band is very much more intense.

part THREE

The predominantly green colour evident in many parts of the world manifests the first event in photosynthesis. The first event in *any* photochemical reaction is absorption of light, and if the wavelengths absorbed are from the visible part of the spectrum, the substance will appear coloured. It follows that only coloured substances can undergo photochemistry with visible light. But colour does not lead necessarily to photochemistry. First, light absorption can occur without consequent photochemical change; second, selective absorption of visible light is but one of several mechanisms leading to the appearance of colour; and third, colour itself is a sensation we experience, so its perceived quality is only partly a physical property of the substance under observation.

The following three chapters are all concerned with that aspect of colour relevant to what happens before light enters the eye; that is, with the ways particular visible wavelengths are selected.

'Classes of colour producers' is an outline of the variety of ways in which colour is produced. The second chapter, 'Natural pigments', shows how molecular structure is related to light absorption by the main classes of coloured substances found in nature. These are to be contrasted with the kinds of molecule that we have synthesised to brighten our surroundings, and which are surveyed in the third chapter, 'Man-made colour'.

In combination, the three chapters use an everyday experience to illustrate the molecular factors that influence light absorption, while at the same time allowing photochemistry with visible light to be seen in the broad context of the interaction of visible light with matter as a whole.

3·1 Classes of colour producers

by John Mellor (University of Southampton)

1 Introduction

Many phenomena can cause the perception of colour by the human eye. In all cases the colour perceived may inaccurately represent the combination of wavelengths produced. In contrast, spectrometers can accurately record the complete spectral information. At low light intensities, such as on a dark night, the human eye fails to perceive colour, but a colour photograph of adequate exposure shows a coloured scene. An extreme example of the inaccurate physiological response of the eye to spectral information is provided by a figure known as Benham's disk (Figure 1). Rotation of the

FIGURE 1   Benham's disk.

disk at, say, 120 r.p.m. in daylight leads the human eye to perceive colour, where in reality the only pigments present are black and white. The outer arc might appear yellow and the inner arcs blue–green and black. Here colour perception and absence of colour production are related by a failing of the human eye.

2 Mechanisms of colour production

Notwithstanding such failures of perception by the human eye, the following four mechanisms of colour production can be distinguished:

1   Colour production by interference and diffraction phenomena

2   Colour production by scattering and dispersion phenomena

3   Colour production by emission processes

4   Colour production by selective absorption of particular wavelengths in white light.

Table 1 Familiar colour producers

Object	Colour	Origin of colour
grass	green	preferential absorption of red light
blood	red	preferential absorption of green light
indigo blue of jeans	blue	preferential absorption of orange light
an orange	orange	preferential absorption of blue light
sky	blue	observation of scattered blue light
sunset	red	subtraction of blue light by preferential scattering by dust particles and gas molecules
rainbow	varied	dispersion; angle of refraction in raindrops varies with wavelength
soap bubbles	varied	interference produced by thin film
oil film on water	varied	interference produced by thin film
blue eyes	blue	preferential light scattering by iris tissue above highly absorbing dark membranes
iridescence in pea fowl, pheasants and some beetles	varied	interference produced by minute scales
iridescence of human hair	varied	interference produced by hair tissue
mother of pearl	varied	interference by layers of shell
firefly	varied	light emission
colour television	varied	light emission

Examples are given in Table 1 of familiar coloured objects and natural phenomena and the mechanism of colour production involved in each case. Selective absorption has the greatest importance for the photochemist and will be discussed the most fully. However, other classes of colour production have great biological significance. In combination with selective absorption they can dramatically modify one's perception of the colour of an object.

Wherever white light is reflected from a very thin, layered surface, iridescence or interference colours may be produced. Similarly, transmitted light is subject to interference and anomalous colours can be produced. The colour perceived depends on the thickness of the layers, on the space between the surfaces giving rise to the colours, and on the angle of vision of the viewer.

In birds' feathers the colour perceived is a combination of the colours produced by interference and by light scattering, superimposed on that caused by feather pigmentation. Thus, if a green feather is soaked in a suitable solvent to remove the yellow organic pigment, then after drying the feather will be blue. This blue colour derives from preferential scattering of the light with shorter wavelengths. An alternative way of demonstrating the colour production by complementary phenomena is to remove the light-scattering component. This can be achieved by wetting the feather, when the green feather described would change colour as a result of reduced light scattering.

Newton recognised the phenomena of interference. When a convex lens is placed on a plane piece of glass the reflected light is viewed as a series of coloured rings (Newton's rings) produced by interference. The intensity of light from interference at thin plates is proportional to λ^{-2}. In contrast, the intensity of light scattered from particles with a diameter of the same (or smaller) magnitude as the wavelength of the light is proportional to λ^{-4}. Lord Rayleigh showed experimentally that the intensity of skylight did vary with λ^{-4}, and hence concluded that the origin of the colour of the sky is a light-scattering phenomenon. At sea level the observed blue colour of the sky comes from the preferential light scattering by the atmosphere of the shorter wavelength light from the Sun. From a high-flying aeroplane, a darker blue colour is perceived because of reduced light scattering. Outside the atmosphere there is no light scattering and hence, in directions remote from the Sun, blackness. A similar light scattering by the atmosphere removes the shorter wavelength light from the setting Sun, and hence the observed transmitted light is red. As the Sun descends to the horizon, where the path length and the density of dust and gas are greatest, the colour becomes more red because of increased light scattering.

Bioluminescence, as in fireflies or in deepwater fishes, has important biological functions when light intensity is low. In normal daylight the biological function would be ineffective because the intensity of the biological signal would be very low in comparison with the ambient light levels. A related limitation applies to colour television. A picture is obtained by emission from substances (known as phosphors) that give out light when struck by electrons. On a bright sunny day, adequate viewing may be possible only in a darkened room. If colour television could be based on selective absorption rather than emission, then higher levels of incident light would lead to brighter pictures because the reflected intensity would be greater.

We come now to the fourth, and from the point of view of photochemists, the most important class of colour producers: those that act by selective absorption of visible light. If part of the visible region of the electromagnetic spectrum (see Plate 4) is absorbed, the remaining wavelengths will normally be perceived as colour. The most important electronic transitions leading to colour are (i) transitions in isolated molecules, (ii) transitions in inter-molecular complexes, and (iii) transitions in macromolecular assemblies.

In the simplest cases of colour production there is a single absorption band in the visible region and the colour is determined by the wavelength of maximum absorption (λ_{max}) and by the intensity and width of the absorption band. For example, a narrow absorption in the blue region (say λ_{max} 400 nm) will leave the object yellow, whereas similar absorption in the red (λ_{max} 700 nm) will give the object a green appearance. In more complicated cases, colour is determined by several bands in the visible region. An example of a spectrum having two absorption maxima in the visible region is shown in Figure 2 (*black line*). The two bands will give a combined appearance of olive-green as if the absorption were centred at about 570 nm (*red line*).

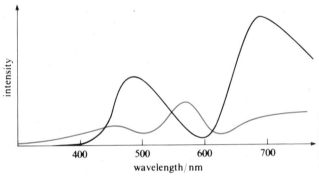

FIGURE 2 These two spectra will both be perceived as the same olive-green colour.

It is unusual to find a coloured organic compound that does not have several multiple bonds in conjugation. Some exceptions are given in Table 2. Examples of more typical chromophores giving rise to colour are shown in Table 3. If a compound absorbs strongly in the ultraviolet region close to the visible (i.e. about 300 nm) then the tail of the absorption band may extend sufficiently into the visible region to produce a yellow colour by subtraction of blue–violet. Yellowing associated with photo-oxidative pro-

Table 2 Spectral characteristics of some simple coloured organic groups

Class of compounds	Group	Colour	λ_{max}/nm	ϵ/l mol^{-1} cm^{-1}
aliphatic azo	$R-N=N-R'$	yellow	345	12
nitroso	$R-N=O$	blue	665	20
nitrite	$R-O-N=O$	yellow	313–384	20–40
thione	$R_2C=S$	red	492	13

Table 3 Spectral characteristics of chromophores giving rise to colour

Class of compounds	Example	Colour	λ_{max}/nm	ϵ/l mol^{-1} cm^{-1}
polyene	β-carotene (**1**)	red	$\sim$450	$\sim$100 000
quinone	anthraquinone (**2**)	yellow	405	$\sim$100
conjugated aromatic	*p*-nitroaniline (**3**)	yellow	375	$\sim$15 000
porphin	octaethylporphin (**4**)	blue	620	$\sim$6 000

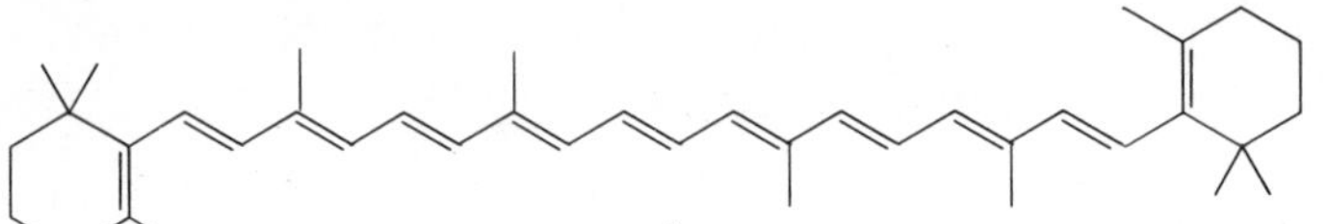

cesses is caused by absorption in this region, often by $\alpha\beta$-unsaturated ketones, and can be masked by optical brighteners, which fluoresce in this spectral region, thereby effectively replacing the blue light absorbed.

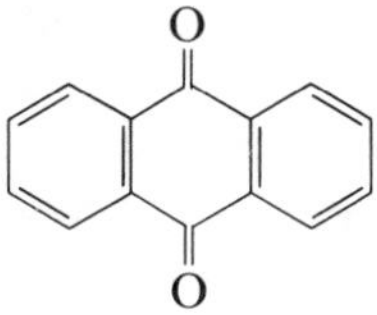

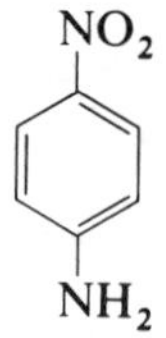

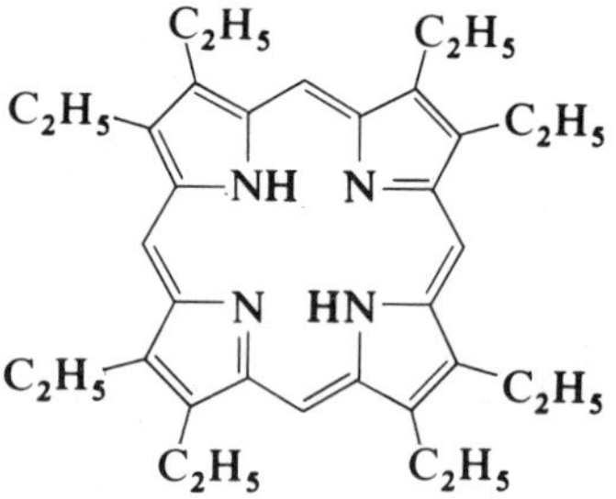

The data in Tables 2 and 3 relate to molecules that are effectively isolated and are not markedly affected by solvent interactions. Highly polarisable molecules whose electron distribution responds readily to external influences can show marked colour changes according to their environment. For example, iodine is purple in the gaseous state as it is in carbon tetrachloride, where interaction with the solvent is weak; in benzene, however, a pink colour is observed, because a charge-transfer complex is formed with benzene as the electron donor and iodine as the acceptor. The position of the charge-transfer maximum of absorption is determined by the ionisation potential of the donor and by the electron affinity of the acceptor. For iodine in benzene this maximum is at 292 nm; for iodine in hexamethylbenzene, which is a better electron donor than benzene, it is red-shifted to 375 nm. The spectral characteristics of some common donor–acceptor systems are given in Table 4.

Table 4 Spectral characteristics of intermolecular charge-transfer complexes

Donor	Acceptor	Solvent	λ_{max}/nm
benzene	1,3,5-trinitrobenzene	$CHCl_3$	284
p-xylene	1,3,5-trinitrobenzene	$CHCl_3$	312
anthracene	1,3,5-trinitrobenzene	$CHCl_3$	461
benzene	DDQ (5)	CH_2Cl_2	406
p-xylene	DDQ (5)	CH_2Cl_2	510
anthracene	DDQ (5)	CH_2ClCH_2Cl	826
benzene	TCNE (6)	CH_2Cl_2	387
p-xylene	TCNE (6)	$CHCl_3$	467
anthracene	TCNE (6)	CCl_4	741

5 dichlorodicyano-
benzoquinone (DDQ)

6 tetracyanoethylene
(TCNE)

The colours of salts of transition elements arise typically from a combination of charge-transfer effects and transitions between d orbitals. Such d–d transitions normally cause only weak absorption but account, for example, for the blue colour of aqueous copper(II) sulphate solution and the violet colour of chromium(III) sulphate. In contrast, charge-transfer absorption is usually intense and often masks the weaker d–d absorption. Charge transfer can be either from the metal ion to the complexing group (ligand) or the reverse, from ligand to metal ion. Some examples are given in Table 5.

Finally, selective absorption of visible light to give colour can occur by a variety of phenomena in the solid state. Metals are characterised by 'loosely bound' valence electrons, leading to absorption throughout the visible region. Of course, the appearance of metals is modified by the polished surface, which increases the reflection of light. The 'loosely bound' electron state is also available in many other inorganic solids, but as an excited state rather than as a ground state. In such compounds (semiconductors) the energy or band gap between the ground state (valence band) and the excited state (conduction band) often corresponds to light in the visible region. The band gap determines the colour, as shown in Figure 3. Because

59

Table 5   The origin of the colour in some salts of transition elements

Compound	Metal ion	Ligand	Colour	Origin of colour
copper(II) sulphate	Cu^{2+}	H_2O	blue	d–d transition
chromium(III) sulphate	Cr^{3+}	H_2O	violet	d–d transition
cobalt(II) sulphate	Co^{2+}	H_2O	pink	d–d transition
iron(III) thiocyanate	Fe^{3+}	SCN^-	red	charge transfer towards cation
Prussian blue	Fe^{3+}	$Fe(CN)_6{}^{4-}$	blue	charge transfer in mixed valence complex
copper(I) cuproine complex	Cu^+	2,2′-biquinoline	purple	charge transfer towards ligand
nickel(II) oxime complex	Ni^{2+}	anion of dimethylglyoxime	red	charge transfer towards ligand

the band gap is very sensitive to impurities, the colour of semiconductors is variable. In a related manner, defect sites and dislocations in the microscopic structure of solids can lead to the development of colour centres. For example, if solid potassium chloride is exposed to potassium vapour at a high temperature so that, on cooling, incorporation of excess potassium into the salt is of the order of 1 part in 10^4, a blue crystal is obtained. The colours of many common minerals, galena and pyrites for example, arise in this way. The colours of sulphur, copper and gold are all attributed to band gap absorption.

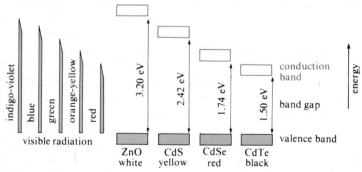

FIGURE 3   The behaviour of semiconducting materials towards visible radiation. (source: Orna, 1978)

3·2 Natural pigments

by John Mellor (University of Southampton)

Natural selection has ensured that coloration of biological tissue almost always has a function. Coloration, whether in animals, fish, birds, insects, algae, flowers or other vegetable matter, is mainly produced by natural pigments. We will discuss in some detail the distribution of three major classes of pigments: carotenoids, quinones, and various heterocyclic compounds. Typical examples are shown in Table 1. However, natural colours can originate from other phenomena such as light scattering, interference, and bioluminescence.

Table 1 The distribution of pigments in nature

Structure, name, and class	Distribution
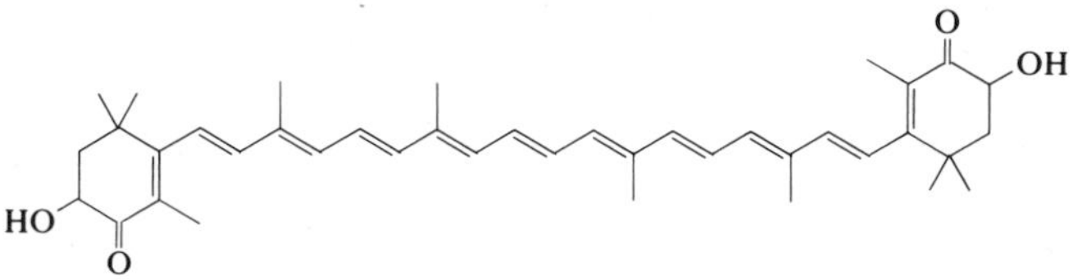 O OH HO O astaxanthin (class: carotenoid)	carotenoids are normally found in vegetable matter but astaxanthin is found in lobsters
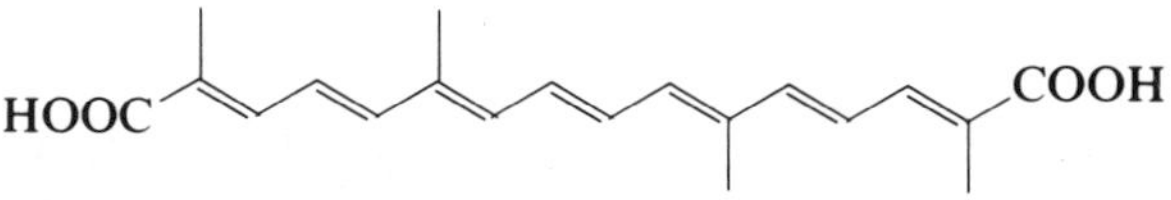 HOOC COOH crocetin (class: carotenoid)	vegetable matter, e.g. saffron
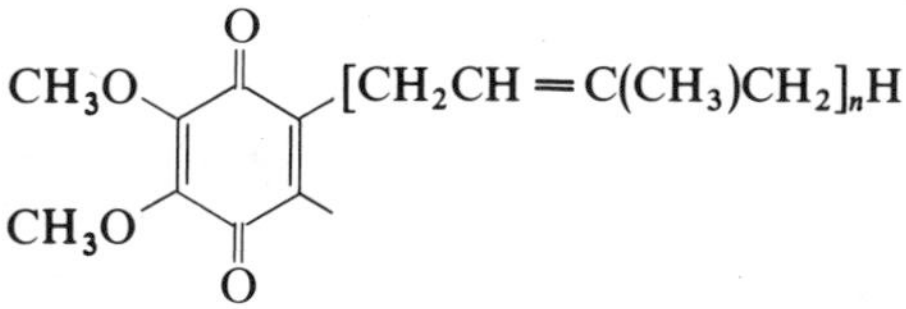 O CH_3O $[CH_2CH=C(CH_3)CH_2]_nH$ CH_3O O ubiquinone (class: quinone)	yeasts

(*continued*)

Table 1 (*continued*)

Structure, name, and class	Distribution

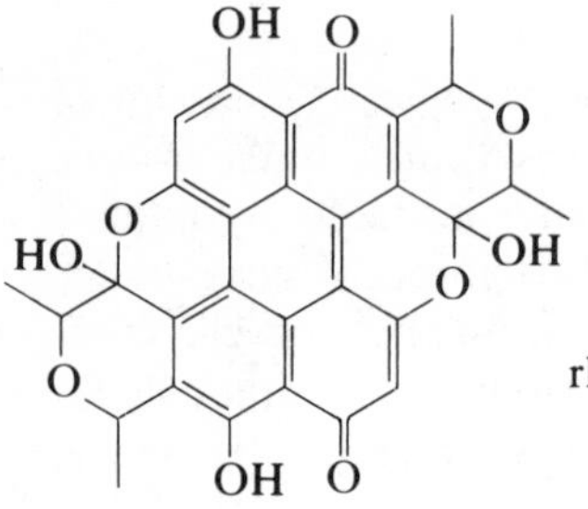

rhodaphin-*be* (class: quinone)

aphid pigment

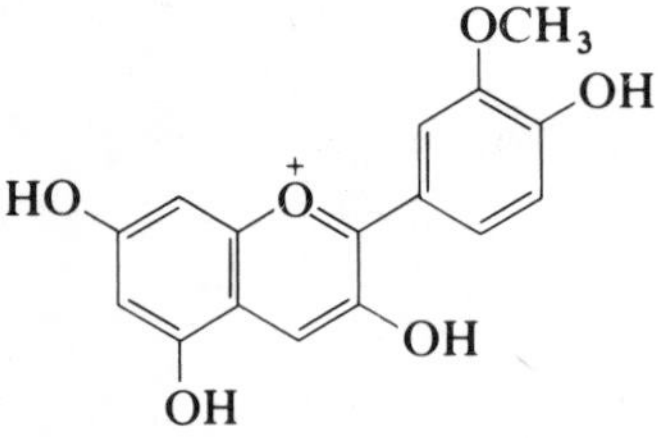

peonidin (class: anthocyanin heterocyclic)

flowers and fruits, e.g. bilberry

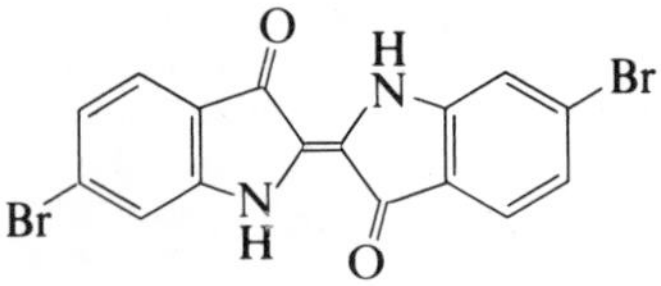

Tyrian purple (class: indole heterocyclic)

pigment of the purple snail *Murex brandaris*

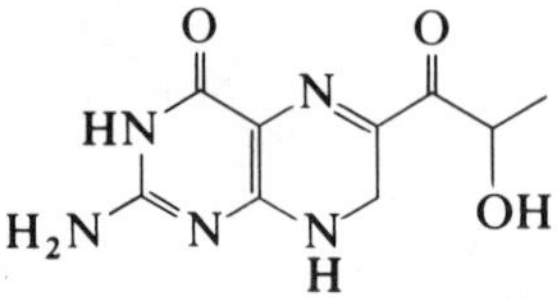

sepiapterin (class: pteridine heterocyclic)

fruit fly pigment

In many cases pigments are secondary metabolites, or in a sense, metabolic waste products that do not play a part in growth. Adaptation of different pigments to perform various functions illustrates how natural evolution can be based on widely distributed substances. Typical functions of pigments are concealment, for example in the eggs of cuckoos, or attraction, for example in the coloration of the bee orchid.

1 Carotenoids

Biosynthesis of carotenoids is limited to plants, algae and photosynthetic bacteria. Carotenoids isolated from animal tissue normally have a plant origin, and fall into two categories: (i) the hydrocarbons, which are soluble in lipids, and (ii) those containing oxygen, called xanthophylls, which are more soluble in aqueous media.

The origins and spectral characteristics of the more important carotenoids are given in Table 2. In the solid state the pure pigments range in colour from red through purple to blue-black, but in dilute solution the appearance is deep orange or red. The Table shows a number of interesting trends associated with the $\pi \rightarrow \pi^*$ transition. As conjugation increases through the series phytoene, ζ-carotene, and ε-carotene (three, seven and nine conjugated double bonds respectively) the λ_{max} shifts to longer wavelength. Extension of conjugation through a carbonyl group leads to a similar bathochromic shift (compare β-carotene, echinenone, and canthaxanthin). Comparison of β-carotene and lycopene reveals an interesting case of steric effects (in β-carotene) preventing full conjugation. Full conjugation requires all the

Table 2 Spectra of carotenoids

Structure, name, and origin	λ_{max}/nm
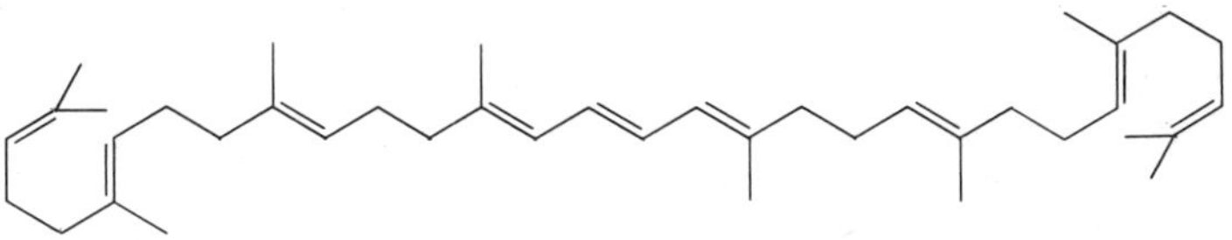 phytoene (traces in plant tissue)	298, 286, 276
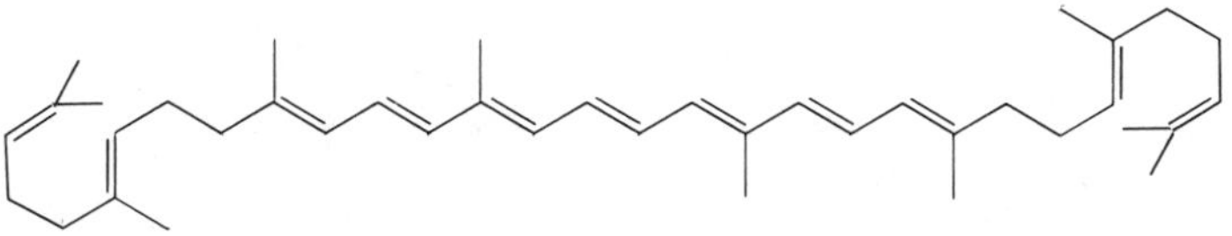 ζ-carotene (traces in plant tissue)	366, 347, 331
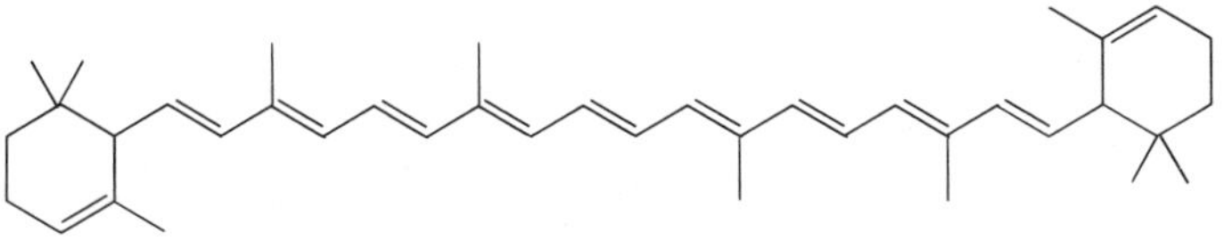 ε-carotene (traces in plant tissue)	471, 440, 418

(*continued*)

Table 2 (*continued*)

Structure, name, and origin	λ_{max}/nm

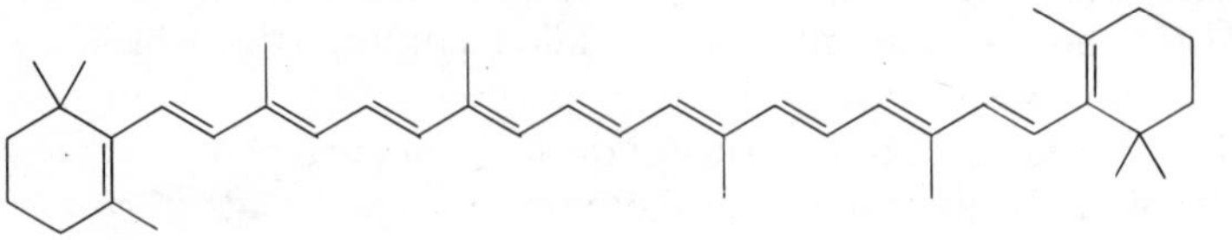

β-carotene (carrots)

477,
466,
450,
425

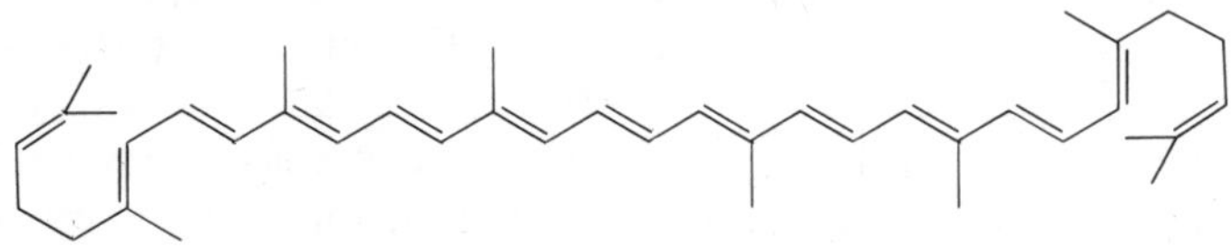

lycopene (tomatoes)

504,
473,
448

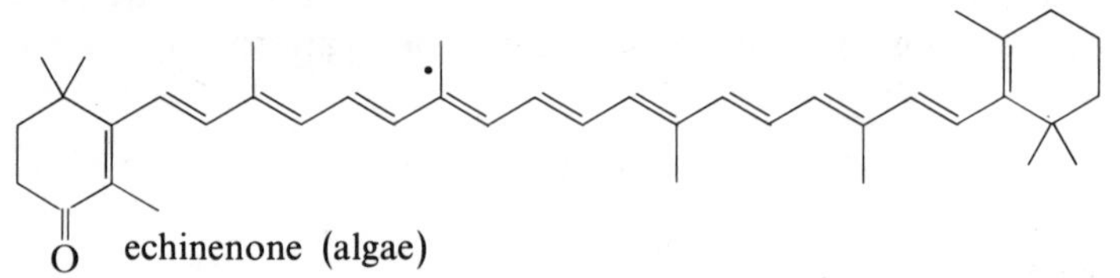

echinenone (algae)

480

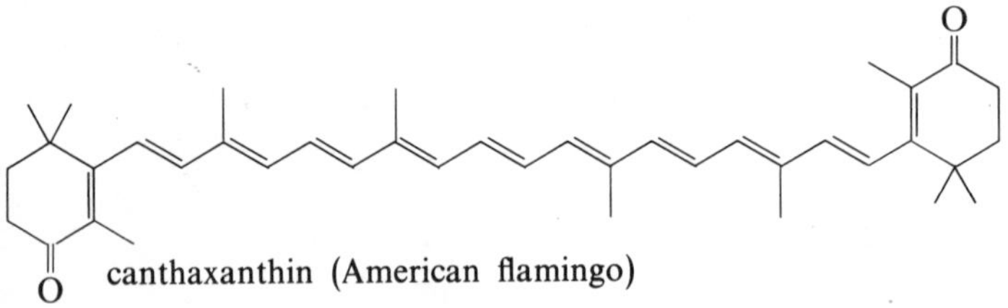

canthaxanthin (American flamingo)

486.5

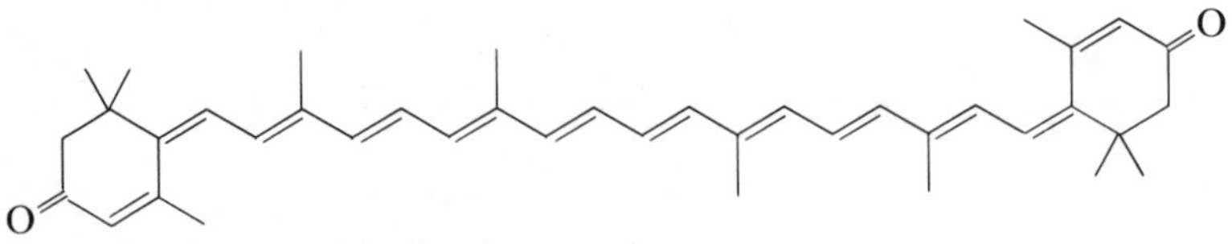

rhodoxanthin (yew)

510

conjugating double bonds to be coplanar. In the acyclic lycopene this is possible, but β-carotene contains two six-membered rings, which cause the molecular skeleton to twist in an attempt to relieve steric congestion. Hence, although β-carotene has the same number of double bonds in sequence as lycopene, those in the rings are not conjugated with the rest of the chain. The degree of conjugation is revealed in the λ_{max} values. In contrast, in the cyclic rhodoxanthin a double bond attached directly to the rings from out-side prevents analogous twisting and hence rhodoxanthin absorbs at longer wavelengths than β-carotene.

In photosynthetic organisms the function of carotenoids is to collect, or harvest light; a typical absorptivity is $150\,000\,l\,mol^{-1}\,cm^{-1}$ at $\lambda_{max} = 450$ nm. Certain carotenoids also quench singlet oxygen very rapidly, and so can protect an organism from photodegradation initiated by the singlet oxygen that is produced by energy transfer from biological dyes. Carotenoids are also readily oxidised by triplet oxygen (i.e. molecular oxygen in its ground state). Hence isolation pure from biological sources is difficult.

Carotenoids are also an important source of the structurally related vitamin A. In most animals, conversion by oxidation of carotenoids into vitamin A is efficient, but certain carnivores are unable to transform caro-tenoids efficiently. They rely on their food as a source of vitamin A.

2 · Quinones

Although they are coloured and widely distributed, most simple benzo-quinones and naphthoquinones (e.g. vitamin K) are more associated with regulation of biochemical processes than with pigmentation. One exception is a group of naphthoquinones, the echinochromes, which are important pigments in sea urchins. Examples of various pigmentary quinones are shown in Table 3.

Table 3   Spectra of quinones in ethanol

Structure and name	λ_{max}/nm	Colour	Origin
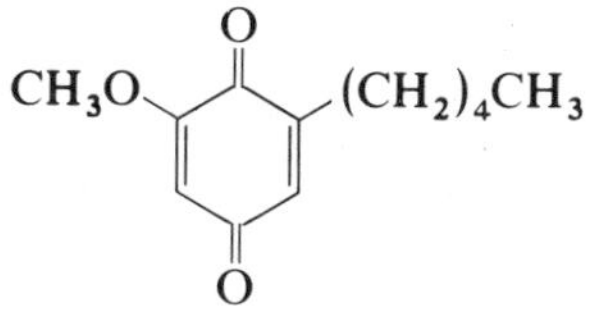 primin	267, 365	yellow	dermatitic principle of *Primula abconica*
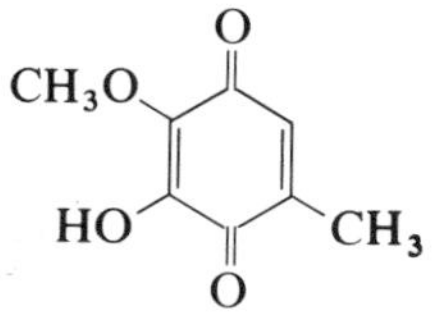 fumigatin	265, 450	maroon	fungal metabolite

(*continued*)

Table 3 (*continued*)

Structure and name	λ_{max}/nm	Colour	Origin
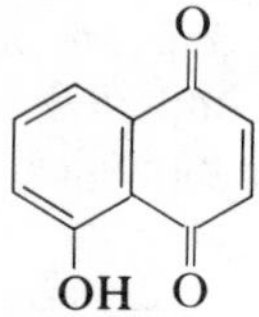 juglone	249, 345(sh)*, 422	orange	walnuts
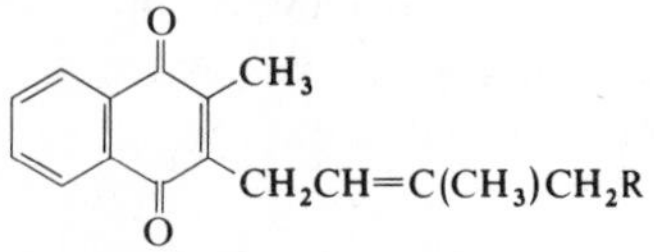 R = [CH$_2$CH$_2$CH(CH$_3$)CH$_2$]$_2$CH$_2$CH$_2$CH(CH$_3$)$_2$ vitamin K	270, 325	pale yellow	widespread in animal tissue
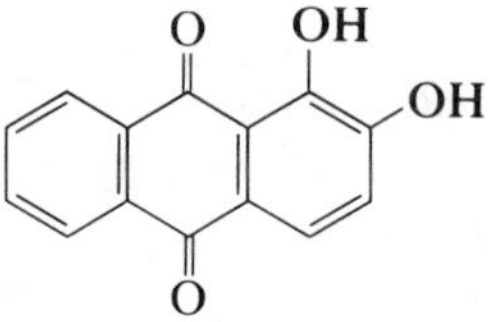 alizarin	247, 278, 330, 434	red as aluminium complex	principal colouring matter of madder used as salt of aluminium chelate as a mordant dye 'Turkey Red'
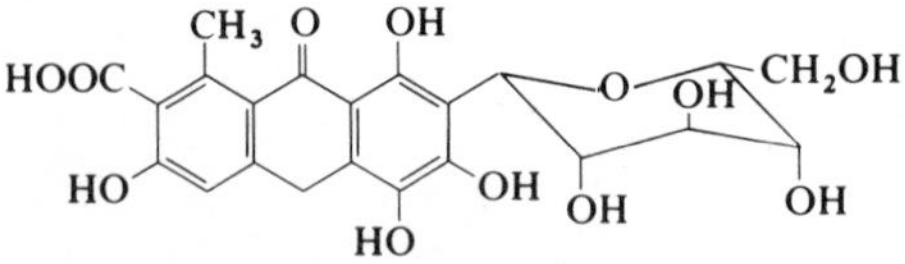 carminic acid	278, 311(sh), 491, 540(sh)	red	principle of food colorant cochineal from insects
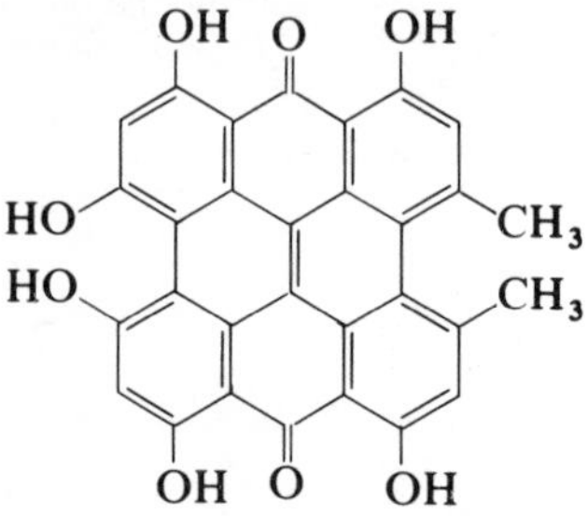 hypericin	508, 548, 590	violet	pigment in Hypericum

*sh = 'shoulder' on absorption peak

Anthraquinones are widely distributed in plants. Madder (*Rubia tinctorum*) is the source of alizarin, a dihydroxyanthraquinone that has been used as a mordant dye for centuries. Anthraquinones are also found as insect pigments. The food colorant cochineal is the potassium salt of carminic acid, isolated from the scale insect *Coccus cacti*. A polycyclic quinone, hypericin, is a constituent of the common weed St. John's wort, and other members of the Hypericum family. These plants are highly toxic to animals and in particular afford a danger to cattle and sheep. After ingestion of the plant, an inflammation of the skin results, and in extreme cases death of the animal. This hypericism, as it is known, is caused by the hypericin absorbing light at an exposed surface and thereby initiating photochemical processes injurious to the animal.

An interesting trend can be seen in Table 3. As the ring system is extended so the energy required for the $\pi \rightarrow \pi^*$ transition is reduced. Hence the colour of the polycyclic quinones stems from such transitions. In contrast, the colour in simple quinones originates in $n \rightarrow \pi^*$ transitions, which are weak.

3 Oxygen heterocyclic pigments

The purple, blue and red colours of flowers originate mainly from pigmentation by oxygen heterocyclic compounds called flavonoids. Flavonoids, which are also responsible for many of the white and yellow colours of the vegetable world, occur mainly as derivatives of sugars (glycosides). Spectral data for some important flavonoids are given in Table 4.

The colours of flavonoids can be drastically modified by a change in pH or by bonding to different metal ions. Consequently, the same anthocyanin can produce different colours in different plant species. The blue of the blue cornflower and the red of the poppy are produced by the same pigment, cyanidin, with the colour being determined by the pH of the sap. Cyanidin exists as the aromatic salt only at acidic pH. Anthocyanins are not used as dyes because they are unstable at alkaline pH.

Colour in plant tissue is critically dependent on the concentrations of many metal ions. This principle has been used for centuries in mordant dyeing, whereby complexes are formed between natural dyes and metal ions derived from minerals to produce impressive colours. Luteolin has been used since Roman times as an orange pigment, and until recently was used for dyeing silk with aluminium mordants.

Table 4 Spectra of flavonoids

Structure, name, and class	λ_{max}/nm	Colour	Origin
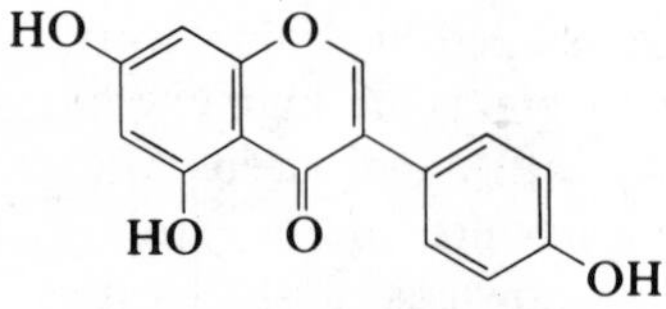 genistein (class: isoflavone)	262, 331	pale yellow	Dyer's broom *Genista tinctoria*
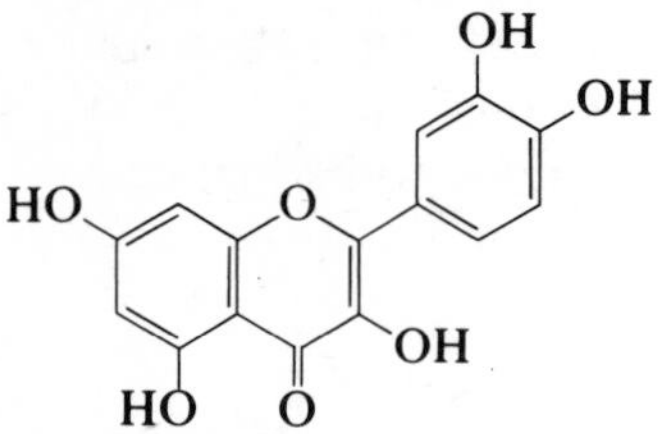 quercetin (class: flavonol)	257, 375	yellow	Dyer's oak *Quercus tinctoria*
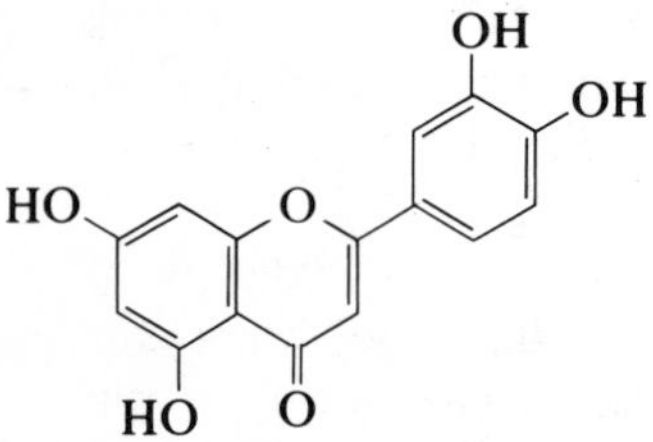 luteolin (class: flavone)	268, 350	yellow	*Chrysanthemum indicum*
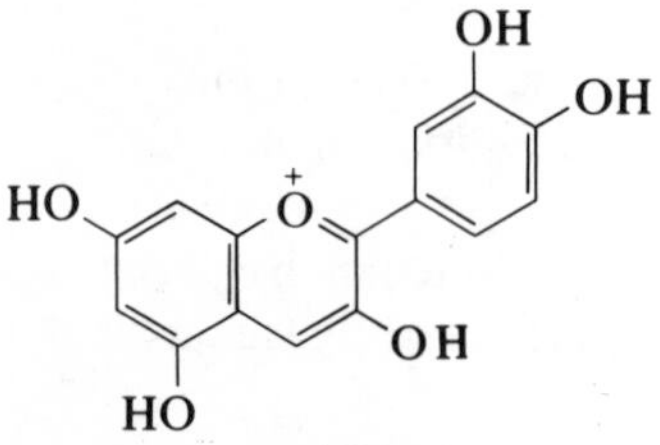 cyanidin (class: anthocyanin)	545	pH 3:red pH 8.5:violet pH 11.0:blue	common red poppy and blue cornflower (see Plate 7)

PLATE 1 (*right*)
An argon ion laser.
(source: Coherent
(UK) Ltd, Cambridge)

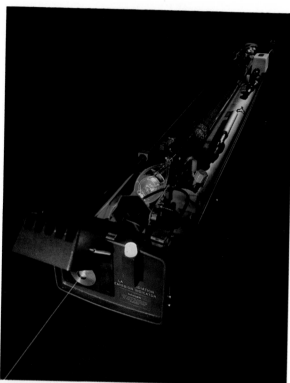

PLATE 2 (*below*)
Frequency doubling.
Ruby light (694 nm) is
converted into ultra-
violet light (347 nm)
on passing through a
crystal of ammonium
dihydrogen phos-
phate. The latter
wavelength shows up
as violet on photo-
graphic film. (source:
Scientific Research
Staff, Ford Motor
Company)

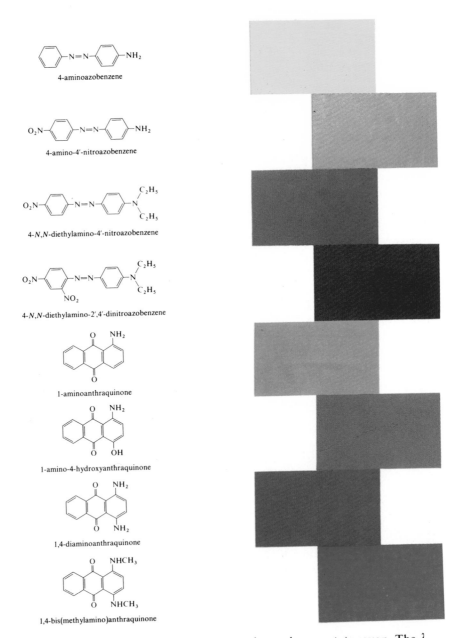

4-aminoazobenzene

4-amino-4'-nitroazobenzene

4-N,N-diethylamino-4'-nitroazobenzene

4-N,N-diethylamino-2',4'-dinitroazobenzene

1-aminoanthraquinone

1-amino-4-hydroxyanthraquinone

1,4-diaminoanthraquinone

1,4-bis(methylamino)anthraquinone

PLATE 3   Some artificial dyes commonly used on acetate rayon. The λ_{max} values of some of these compounds are listed in Table 2 of Chapter 3·3. (source: Yorkshire Chemicals Ltd, Leeds)

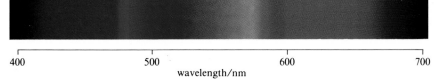

400   500   600   700

wavelength/nm

PLATE 4   Colours perceived over the range of wavelengths in the visible region of the electromagnetic spectrum.

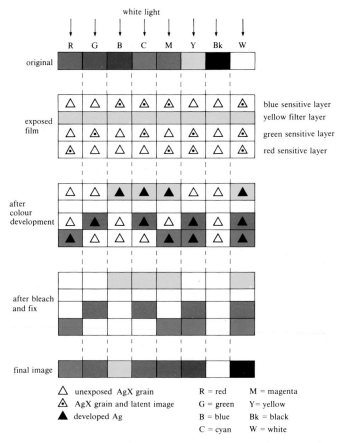

PLATE 5   The colour negative system. The subject ('original') is a composite of coloured elements through which the multilayer film is exposed to white light—as would be the case when colour-printing with an enlarger. Note that red arises from a combination of magenta and yellow, green from a combination of cyan and yellow, and blue from a combination of cyan and magenta.

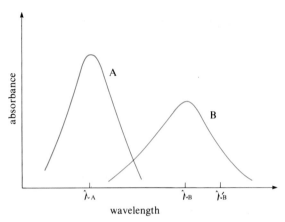

PLATE 6 The reversible colour change known as photochromism. The blue curve is the absorption spectrum of chemical species A. When A is irradiated in this region (λ_A, often in the ultraviolet) it is converted into B, which has the absorption spectrum shown by the red curve (in the visible region). The reverse reaction may be brought about by heat or by irradiation of B with light in the wavelength region λ_B. In some systems, B is stable to light of a different wavelength (λ'_B).

PLATE 7 The colours in this scene derive mainly from two pigments: chlorophyll (the foliage) and cyanidin (the flowers). Cyanidin absorption is affected by pH; the environment is acidic in the poppy and alkaline in the cornflower. The picture also shows colour associated with both visible light photo-chemistry (photo-synthesis in the foliage) and light absorption with no net chemical change. (source: Heather Angel)

4   Nitrogen heterocyclic pigments

The most important members of this class are compounds with structures based on pyrrole and indole and on the purines and pteridines.

4.1   Tetrapyrrole pigments

No other group of pigments has such a visual impact on the world of man as the tetrapyrroles, through the greens of the chlorophylls and the reds of the haems. A major structural distinction can be made between the linear assembly of four pyrrole units found in phytochromes and the bilichromes, and the large ring assembly characteristic of the chlorophylls, haemoglobin, and vitamin B_{12}. Complex biosynthetic pathways relate the linear and the macrocyclic groups. Function is very varied, and in the case of the macrocyclic assemblies depends on the presence in the molecule of the appropriate metal ion, for example magnesium in chlorophylls, cobalt in vitamin B_{12}, and iron in haemoglobin. Spectral data of some of the more important representatives of these groups are presented in Table 5 and a brief note of non-pigmentary function is given. The spectra are complex. Compounds of a given skeletal type have characteristic spectra that permit identification of unknown compounds by empirical correlation. However, whilst the influence of substituents is similar to that observed with other classes of pigments, further analysis is beyond the scope of this chapter (see Chapter 2·3).

Table 5   Spectra of tetrapyrroles

Structure and name	λ_{max}/nm	Origin and function
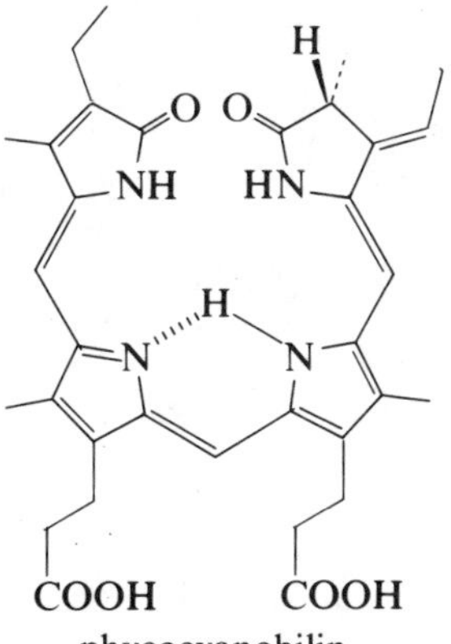 phycocyanobilin	375, 685 in 5% HCl–CH$_3$OH	chromophore of the protein-bound algal pigment phycocyanin, used in photosynthesis

(continued)

69

Table 5 (*continued*)

Structure and name	λ_{max}/nm	Origin and function
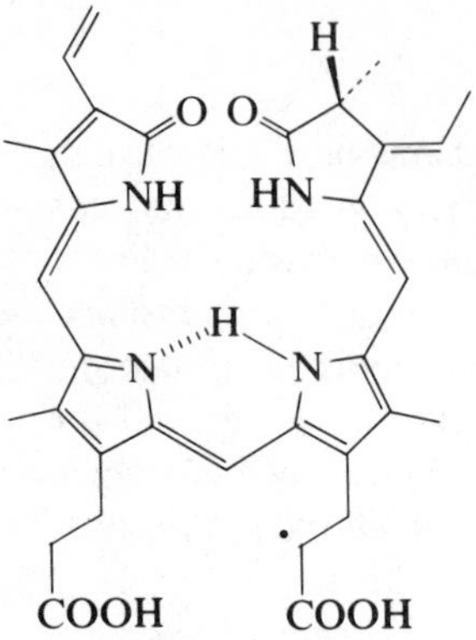 phytochromobilin	380, 690 in 5% $HCl-CH_3OH$	chromophore of the protein-bound phytochrome responsible for the influence of light on the shape and structure of higher plants
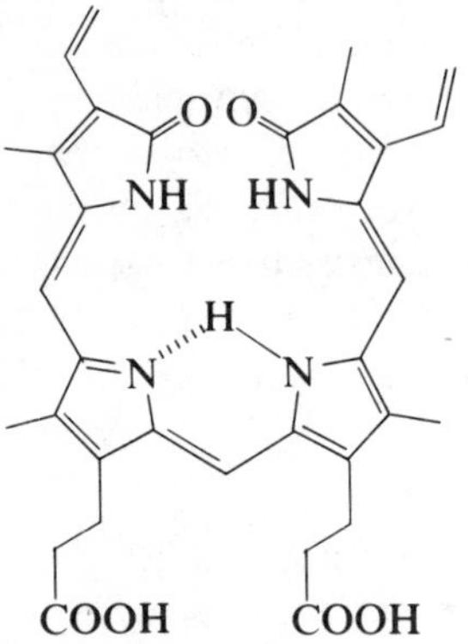 biliverdin-IXα	372, 680 in 5% $HCl-CH_3OH$	bile pigment; and a fish pigment
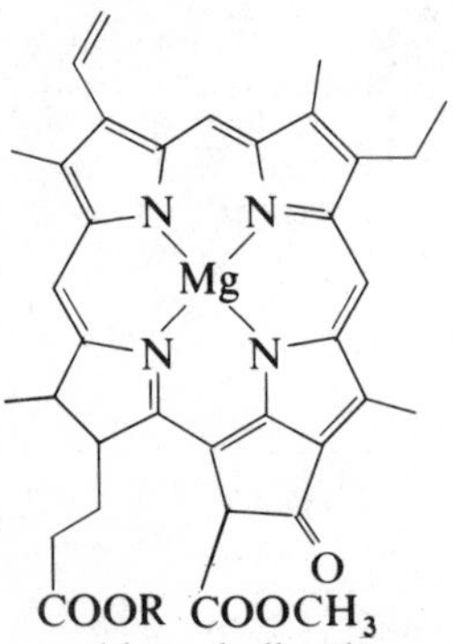 chlorophyll *a* (R = a hydrocarbon chain, $C_{20}H_{41}$)	377, 408, 660 in diethyl ether	photosynthesis in plants

4.2 Indole pigments

Melanins are brown and black pigments, obtained by biosynthetic poly-merisation of indole derivatives. Widely distributed in both animal and vegetable tissue, these pigments account for the colours of the ink of the squid and octopus, the skin of potatoes, the brown of decaying apples, and the pigmentation of human hair and skin. In fair-skinned people the lower layer of skin contains only a little melanin. Sun-tanning leads to increased melanin pigmentation.

Melanin is unique among the pigments described here in that all the others have defined chemical structures and relatively small molecules. Melanin is a polymer of variable composition produced from the amino acid tyrosine.

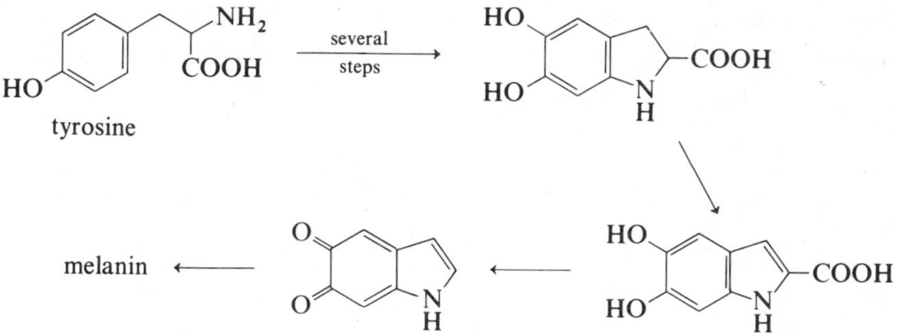

tyrosine

melanin

Indigoid dyes are based on indole substructures. Indigo is the blue dye of woad used in Ancient Britain as a body paint. Tyrian purple is the pigment used since the time of the Phoenician civilisation for obtaining the purple colours associated with royalty. Neither indigoid dye occurs naturally. Indigo is obtained from the naturally occurring glycoside indican, following hydrolysis and oxidation.

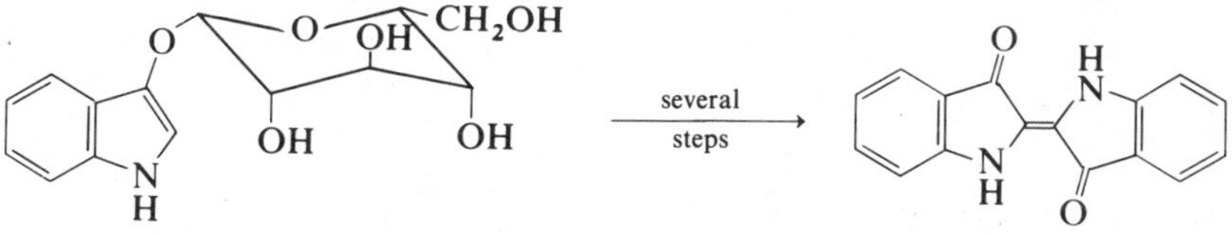

indican (colourless)

indigo (blue)

4.3 Purine and pteridine pigments

A common yellow pigment in wasps and certain butterflies is xanthopterin, a pteridine. Other pteridines account for similar pale colours in insects. Nature produces a brilliant whiteness in butterflies, flowers, shells, and

71

certain sea anemones. This is often achieved by deposits of microcrystals, which act as efficient reflectors. In the large white butterfly the colourless pteridine leucopterin is deposited. In sea anemones the colourless uric acid occurs as microcrystals.

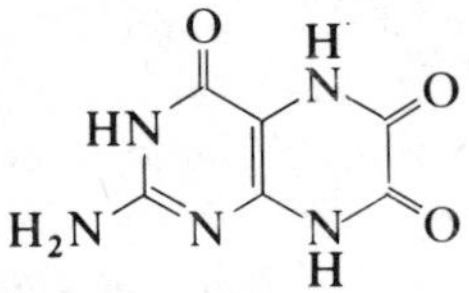

leucopterin 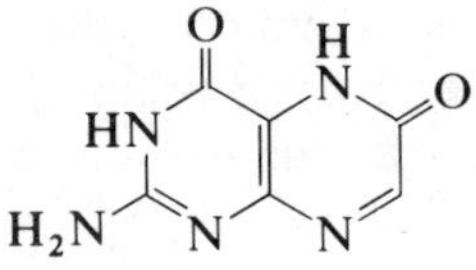   xanthopterin 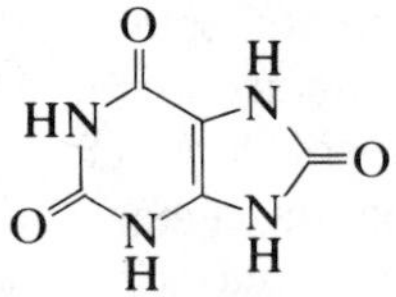   uric acid

The examples in Tables 1–5 show the diversity of chromophores developed by evolutionary processes. Although pigments of related structure may be important in the coloration of related species, similar colours in unrelated species are usually produced by pigments of very different structure.

3·3 Man-made colour

by John Griffiths (University of Leeds)

1 Introduction

From prehistoric times people have been fascinated by the colours of nature, and have attempted to duplicate these in their artefacts, usually for aesthetic, religious, or purely functional purposes. For thousands of years they could achieve the desired effects only by isolating naturally occurring colorants, such as certain minerals, or the pigments to be found in plant and animal species. It was not until the early part of the nineteenth century that synthetic colorants became available, and today vast industries have been built up around the production or utilisation of synthetic dyes and pigments.

Colour makes a formidable, though largely unrecognised, contribution to our everyday lives. Almost any product from industry benefits from artificial coloration, be it in textiles, furnishings, buildings, motor vehicles, or even food. The marketability of all finished products can be enhanced by their coloration or by their presentation in attractively coloured packaging. Even white products can be enhanced visually by the use of special blue-fluorescent 'dyes', known as optical brightening agents. The psychological impact of colour is, of course, important in areas other than marketing, most notably in communication, safety, and art.

Most artificial, and indeed natural, coloration is provided by light-absorbing substances generally referred to as dyes and pigments, and we shall consider the relationships between the molecular structure of these compounds and their colour in some detail. Dyes and pigments produce their colour by a *subtractive* process, that is they possess absorption bands in the visible region of the spectrum so that they appear coloured in white light as a result of the selective removal of certain wavelengths from the incident radiation. The observed colour is the *complementary* of the colour actually absorbed. Thus, for example, a dye that absorbs blue light (wavelengths 435—480 nm) will appear yellow, yellow and blue being complementary colours.

2 Characteristics of synthetic dyes and pigments

The terms *dye* and *pigment* are often used indiscriminately to describe any intensely coloured substance. To the colour chemist, however, these terms have specific connotations. Thus a dye is a colorant that has, or can be induced to have, a specific affinity for a polymeric substrate, and is generally applied to the substrate in monomolecular form. A pigment, on the other hand, is a colorant with no affinity for a substrate, and is consequently applied in the form of discrete crystalline particles. In general, dyes are readily soluble substances (usually in water, but sometimes in organic solvents), whereas all pigments must exhibit high insolubility in common solvents.

The colouring matters found in plants and animals are often referred to as 'pigments' (cf. Chapter 3·2), principally for historical reasons. From a modern technological point of view, however, the majority of these would be regarded as dyes.

When designing the molecular structure of a dye, the chemist has several goals to achieve before the compound is worthy of detailed testing for commercial viability. First, the structure must exhibit the correct characteristics of light absorption, in order that the desired colour and colour intensity are obtained. Second, structural features must be built into the molecule to ensure that the dye has a natural affinity for the polymer to which it will eventually be applied. This affinity, which may involve electrostatic forces of attraction between the dye and the polymer, hydrogen bonding with the polymer, or some other mechanism, ensures that when the polymer is immersed in a solution of the dye, the dye will migrate into the polymer. This same affinity prevents subsequent removal of the dye from the polymer by the action of washing, rubbing, etc. Commercial dyes must satisfy many other criteria, generally referred to as *fastness properties*. Light fastness, the resistance of the dye to photochemical fading, is particularly important. The uses to which dyes are put are particularly varied, and in addition to their principal use in textile coloration, they are also employed for the coloration of food, oils, solvents and cosmetics, and have valuable applications in histology (selective staining of biological tissue), laser technology, and liquid-crystal display devices.

Pigments are used principally in the mass coloration of plastics, and in surface coatings (e.g. paints and inks). Their permanence depends not on any specific interactive forces between the pigment molecules and the substrate, but on the general insolubility of the pigment particles. Thus the fastness properties of a pigment are more a function of crystal structure than molecular design. Two important fastness properties of pigments are light fastness and solvent resistance.

A typical modern textile dye is exemplified by structure 1 (Astrazon Red GTL). This dye can be applied to polyacrylic fibres, which contain negatively charged sulphonate or carboxylate groupings. Electrostatic forces between the positive dye molecule and the negative polymer provide the necessary affinity.

Pigments may be inorganic, for example iron oxides (yellow, orange, red and brown), or organic; Hansa Yellow G (2) is a commercially valuable example of the latter.

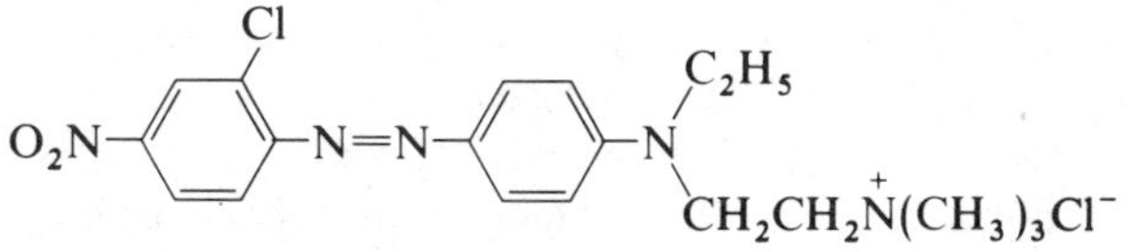

1

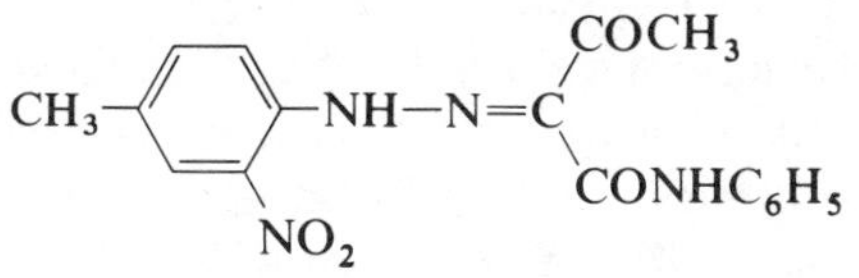

2

Here we are more concerned with the molecular design of a dye for obtaining specific colour properties, rather than for obtaining substrate affinity or particular fastness properties. Thus we shall consider the relationships between molecular structure and colour in more detail.

3 Colour–structure relationships in organic dyes

The colour properties of a dye, as determined spectrophotometrically, depend on three features of its visible absorption spectrum:

1 the wavelength position of the absorption band (generally defined by the wavelength of maximum absorption, λ_{max})

2 the width of the absorption band

3 the intensity of the absorption band (generally defined by the molar absorption coefficient at λ_{max}, i.e. ϵ_{max}).

The value of λ_{max} determines the general hue of the dye, whereas the width of the band determines the brightness of the colour. Thus narrow absorption bands are associated with bright colours. The intensity of the absorption band is a colour property of particular commercial concern, as a more intense dye can be used more economically to give a specified colour effect. Useful dyes generally have ϵ_{max} values above $15\,000\,l\,mol^{-1}\,cm^{-1}$, and values nearer $50\,000\,l\,mol^{-1}\,cm^{-1}$ are fairly common. It is this stringent requirement that eliminates so many coloured organic systems as potential sources of useful dyes, and explains why all dyes rely on $\pi \rightarrow \pi^*$ rather than $n \rightarrow \pi^*$ absorption bands for their colour. Quantitative prediction of the λ_{max} and ϵ_{max} values for a particular dye can now be achieved remarkably well by various molecular orbital calculations. However, we shall consider more qualitative approaches to the prediction of colour properties of organic dyes.

Qualitative relationships between colour and molecular structure are almost always concerned with the wavelength of the visible absorption band, and rarely with bandwidths or band intensities. As noted previously, the visible bands of dyes are invariably $\pi \rightarrow \pi^*$ in character, and thus the visible band corresponds to the excitation of an electron from the highest occupied π molecular orbital (the HOMO) to the lowest unoccupied π^* molecular orbital (the LUMO); this transition will be the one of lowest energy available to the molecule. Qualitative theory is thus concerned with those structural factors that help to bring the HOMO and the LUMO closer together in energy, i.e. that cause a bathochromic shift of the absorption band.

The term *chromophore* can be used to describe any unsaturated part of a molecule that absorbs ultraviolet or visible light, be it a simple double bond or a complex system of conjugated double bonds. The term *chromogen* is frequently used to describe an unsaturated system that absorbs in or near the visible region of the spectrum, and is conveniently used when discussing the light absorption properties of organic dyes. The basic chromogens of commercial dyes can be divided for convenience into three main types, namely *cyanine-type*, *donor–acceptor*, and *polyene* chromogens.

3.1 Cyanine-type chromogens

A cyanine-type chromogen is a positively or negatively charged system in which an odd number of atoms ('*p*-centres') contribute to the π-electron system. The molecule $(CH_3)_2 \overset{+}{N}=CH+CH=CH \overset{..}{\underset{4}{\cancel{}}} N(CH_3)_2$ is a typical example; it has eleven *p*-centres and carries a net positive charge. A characteristic feature of such chromogens is that equivalent, or nearly equivalent, resonance forms can be drawn by a simple shift of electrons, which in turn means that the charge is extensively delocalised over the chromogen, and that the bond lengths show a high degree of uniformity. In the quoted example an equivalent formulation can be obtained by displacing the non-bonding electrons of the terminal amino group towards the positive nitrogen atom, thus giving $(CH_3)_2 \overset{..}{N} + CH=CH \overset{+}{\underset{4}{\cancel{}}} CH=N(CH_3)_2$. The true structure will thus be a resonance hybrid of these two extreme forms. Several examples of this type of chromogen have been given in

Chapter 2·2. A common example of a negatively charged cyanine-type chromogen is the phenolphthalein dianion (**3**), which is magenta in colour.

3

From the coloration point of view, cyanine-type dyes are particularly interesting because of their ability to absorb at very long wavelengths for a relatively small molecular size. This phenomenon can best be understood by molecular orbital theory, as discussed in Chapter 2·2, and can be attributed to the odd number of p-centres in the chromogen. Thus cyanine-type chromogens can be regarded to a reasonable approximation as odd-alternant molecules, with an occupied π-orbital of high energy. The electronic transitions, corresponding to very long wavelengths, that occur in these chromogens involve the latter orbital. The theoretical treatment developed in Chapter 2·2 shows how this analogy to odd-alternant hydrocarbons can be used to predict the effect of structural changes on colour.

Although cyanine-type dyes absorb at particularly long wavelengths and with high intensity, and are usually bright in appearance (i.e. have narrow absorption bands), their commercial value is marred by their generally low photochemical stability. They are very important in non-textile areas, however.

3.2 Donor–acceptor chromogens

The majority of present-day commercial dyes are of a type most appropriately termed donor–acceptor chromogens, and can be represented schematically as in Figure 1 (exemplified by dye **4**), or as in Figure 2 (exemplified by dye **5**).

The donor group is a substituent with non-bonding electrons that are conjugated with the π-electron system of the molecule. The ionisation potential of the donor atom is low, thus rendering the substituent a good electron-releasing group. This means that the donor atom is usually nitrogen (as in H_2N-), oxygen (e.g. $HO-$) or sulphur (e.g. CH_3S-). The electron-donating strength can be modified by attaching inductive substituents to the heteroatom, and some examples frequently encountered in dyes are (in order of decreasing donor ability): $(C_2H_5)_2N- > (CH_3)_2N- > CH_3NH- > H_2N- > CH_3O- > HO-$.

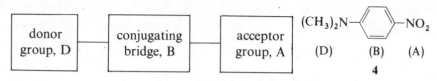

FIGURE 1   Schematic representation of a donor–simple acceptor chromogen.

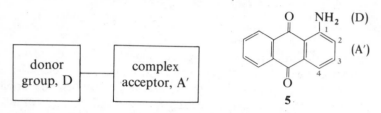

FIGURE 2   Schematic representation of a donor–complex acceptor chromogen.

The acceptor group indicated in Figure 1 is a substituent with a high electron affinity, and has heteroatomic multiple bonds that are conjugated to the π-electron system of the molecule. Such groups exert a strong electron-attracting effect, and are typified by the following (in order of decreasing acceptor ability): $-NO_2 > -C\equiv N > -COCH_3 > -SO_3H$.

In the chromogen shown in Figure 1, the donor and acceptor groups are linked together by a conjugating bridge, B, which is simply a collection of multiple bonds (including aromatic rings in many cases) that permit direct resonance interaction between D and A. In the ground state, the donor electrons will be partly polarised towards the acceptor. Thus, compound 4, for example, has a high dipole moment. When such a molecule absorbs visible light, electronic excitation results in an even greater movement of π-electron density from the donor to the acceptor. Clearly any factor that facilitates such a movement of electrons will lower the excitation energy, and thus cause the absorption band to move to longer wavelengths. This can then be achieved by increasing the donor strength and/or the acceptor strength. Bathochromic shifts can also be induced by attaching more than one donor group or acceptor group to the bridge B, but the relative positions of the substituents can have a critical effect. Some examples of bathochromic shifts resulting from such structural changes are given in Table 1.

Many important dyes cannot be divided neatly into the form shown in Figure 1, and it is found that the electron acceptor part of the chromogen is compounded inextricably with the bridge B. Thus it is convenient to regard the electron-accepting bridge as a 'complex acceptor', as indicated in Figure 2. 1-Aminoanthraquinone (5) is a typical example, in which the amino donor group is attached to the anthraquinone complex acceptor.

Table 1 Examples of donor–simple acceptor chromogens showing the effect of structural changes on the wavelength of maximum absorption

Compound	λ_{max}/nm (in ethanol)	Colour
2-nitroaniline	402	yellow

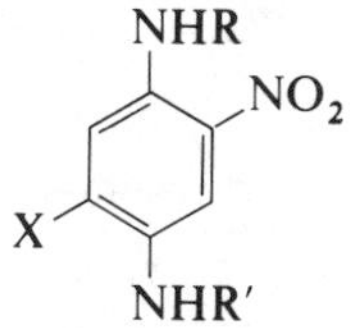		
(a) R = R′ = X = H	473	orange
(b) R = CH$_3$; R′ = X = H	498	red
(c) R = R′ = CH$_3$; X = H	520	purple
(d) R = R′ = CH$_3$; X = NO$_2$	624	blue

Although the carbonyl groups of the quinone system are the principal electron-withdrawing groups, it can be shown from molecular orbital calculations that other atoms in the anthraquinone system also play a significant role in accepting electrons when the molecule is electronically excited. As with chromogens containing a simple acceptor, bathochromic shifts can be effected by increasing the strength of the donor group, by increasing the number of donor groups, or by attaching additional simple acceptor groups to the complex acceptor.

From the commercial point of view, by far the most important classes of dyes containing a complex acceptor are the anthraquinones, such as **5**, and the azobenzenes, generalised as structure **6**. Examples of both classes, illustrating how the colour can be varied between wide limits by simple structural

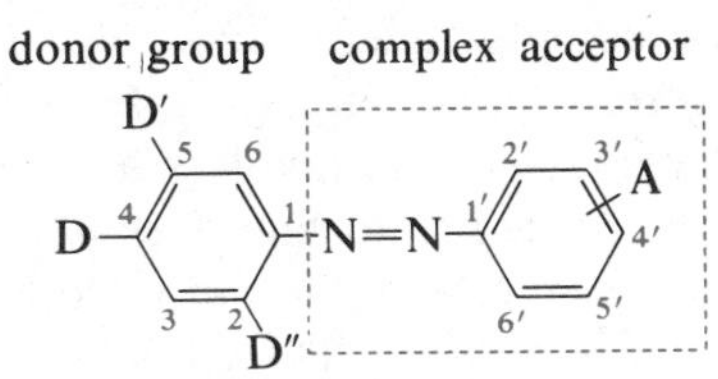

6

changes, are given in Table 2. In general, it is easier to produce violet and blue anthraquinones than it is to produce similarly coloured azo dyes, and thus commercially the two classes tend to complement each other, azo dyes giving yellows, oranges and reds, and anthraquinones the violets, blues and greens.

Table 2   Examples of donor–complex acceptor chromogens (see also Plate 3)

Compound	λ_{max}/nm	Colour
1-aminoanthraquinone **(5)**	457*	orange
1-methylaminoanthraquinone	495*	red
1-methylamino-4-methoxyanthraquinone	514*	purple
1,4-bis(methylamino)anthraquinone	650†	blue
4-aminoazobenzene	385‡	yellow
2,4-diaminoazobenzene	411‡	yellow
4-*N*,*N*-diethylaminoazobenzene	415‡	yellow
4-*N*,*N*-diethylamino-4′-nitroazobenzene	490‡	red
4-*N*,*N*-diethylamino-2′,4′,6′-tricyanoazobenzene	562‡	violet

* In dichloromethane.   † In benzene.   ‡ In ethanol.

Many other useful dyes belong to the donor–acceptor class, and it is interesting to note that the dyes used in colour photography to provide the three subtractive primary colours, yellow, magenta, and cyan, are of this type.

3.3   Polyene chromogens

The classification 'polyene chromogen' is a convenient, if imprecise, means of grouping together various coloured systems that do not fall into the cyanine-type or donor–acceptor definitions. A polyene chromogen may be regarded as a molecule possessing several conjugated double bonds (C=C, C=N, C=O, N=N) and/or aromatic rings (carbocyclic or heterocyclic) such that the degree of conjugation is high enough to give an absorption band in the visible region of the spectrum. The chromogen contains no obvious electron donor–acceptor interactions and, unlike the cyanine-type chromogens, has no formal non-bonding molecular orbital. The visible transition is $\pi \rightarrow \pi^*$ in character, and involves a generalised redistribution of electron density in the excited state, and does not involve a pronounced polarisation of electrons from one region of the molecule to another.

The polyenes themselves, R_2C=CH$\left(\text{CH=CH}\right)_n$CH=CR$_2$, are the simplest examples, and their light absorption properties are discussed in Chapter 2·2. The carotenoids are naturally occurring yellow to red colorants of this type, and are used commercially as food dyes. The porphins and phthalocyanines, dealt with in Chapter 2·3, are further examples of polyene chromogens, albeit of a complex nature. Copper phthalocyanine is the most important synthetic blue pigment in use today.

Useful textile dyes in this class are the *vat dyes* for cellulose polymers such as cotton. Most of these are extensively conjugated quinones, which do *not* contain electron donor groups. A typical example is the yellow dye dibenzpyrenequinone (7).

7

4   Fluorescent dyes and pigments

So far we have considered dyes and pigments as subtractive colorants, that is to say they are coloured because of their ability to absorb specific bands of wavelengths from white light. In a small number of cases, however, a chromogen can absorb and re-emit visible light, and can thus give rise to the impression of colour simultaneously in two different ways. The subtractive colour will correspond to the complementary of the colour absorbed. The fluorescence colour will differ, however, and will correspond to that of the emitted wavelengths. The sodium salt of the dye fluorescein, for example, is red by absorption but has a green fluorescence.

Light absorption involves excitation of the ground-state molecule to the first excited singlet state, and in all commercial fluorescent and non-fluorescent dyes the transition ($\pi \rightarrow \pi^*$ in character) is quantum mechanically allowed, and the absorption band has a high intensity. The process of fluorescence, the decay of the first excited singlet state back to the singlet ground state, is also allowed and may also be of high intensity. Loss of energy by fluorescence is favoured if the molecule has a planar, rigid structure. Molecules that do not fluoresce lose their excess energy as heat to the surrounding medium, or by taking part in a photochemical reaction.

When a molecule is promoted to the first excited state, it will in most cases have an excess of vibrational as well as electronic energy. Rapid loss of vibrational energy to the surroundings will occur, so that when the molecule fluoresces it will emit slightly less energy than was absorbed. Thus a fluorescent dye will emit light at longer wavelengths than those absorbed. This important characteristic of fluorescence is exploited commercially in the case of *optical brighteners* (fluorescent brightening agents). These substances are used to enhance the whiteness of textiles, paper, plastics, and other materials. Most white polymers in an untreated state contain traces of yellow impurities which impart a dull appearance to their surface. An optical brightener on the substrate will absorb ultraviolet light from incident daylight by virtue of its absorption band just outside the visible region (λ_{max} about 320–380 nm). The brightener has no absorption in the visible region, and thus is colourless in the subtractive sense. The brightener will fluoresce at longer wavelengths, just inside the visible region (λ_{max} about 400–450 nm), and will thus show an emission colour of violet or blue. The violet or blue cast thus imparted not only neutralises the yellow colour of the substrate, but also makes the surface brighter in appearance, because more visible light is reaching the eye than if the brightener were not present. Commercial optical brighteners are dye-like molecules, with planar π-electron systems, and having some affinity for the intended substrate. The stilbenedisulphonic acid residue (**8**), for example, is the basic fluorescent unit of several optical brighteners.

SO$_3$H

R—CH=CH—R

SO$_3$H

8

The fluorescence efficiency of a dye can be enhanced by trapping the dye in a rigid matrix, such as an organic polymer, and this effect has been used to produce fluorescent pigments, of value in high visibility paints and inks. Thus a fluorescent dye (usually a planar, cyanine-type chromogen, in which the rigidity of the molecule is enhanced by bridging groups, e.g. the xanthene dye **9**, Rhodamine B) is incorporated as a true monomolecular solution in a hydrophobic thermoplastic resin, and the resin is ground into a fine powder. The powder is used as a pigment in the usual way, and in daylight the dye fluoresces with a high intensity, and imparts a characteristic brilliance to a surface. As a much higher proportion of visible light reaches the eye from such a pigment than from a non-fluorescent one, the surface is more easily distinguished under poor lighting conditions.

$(C_2H_5)_2\ddot{N}$ —— O —— $\overset{+}{N}(C_2H_5)_2$ Cl$^-$

COOH

9

part FOUR

Once a molecule is in an excited electronic state, it can lose energy by a variety of processes. One of these is the emission of a photon, a phenomenon called luminescence. Chapter 4·1, 'Luminescence instrumentation', describes how the spectral distributions of the two types of emission, fluorescence and phosphorescence, are measured. This chapter also deals with methods of measuring the lifetimes of excited states and the proportion of excited molecules that emit a photon (i.e. the quantum yields of fluorescence and phosphorescence). Another way in which an excited molecule can lose energy is to transfer it directly to another, initially unexcited, molecule without the emission of a photon. Chapter 4·2, 'Applications of energy transfer to macromolecules', describes one particular mechanism for energy transfer and how studies of the extent of such energy transfer can provide information about the stereochemistry of biological macromolecules.

Chapters 4·3–4·7 all deal with various aspects of atmospheric photochemistry. There is much concern at the present time that some of mankind's activities, if unchecked, could seriously affect the well-being of life on Earth. The massive release of chlorofluorocarbons into the atmosphere is thought by many to threaten the effectiveness of the ozone layer in the stratosphere that shields us from harmful ultraviolet radiation from the Sun. Chapter 4·3, 'Evolution and present composition of the Earth's atmosphere' sets the scene by describing how the present atmosphere has most probably evolved. Chapter 4·4, 'The stratospheric ozone cycle', deals with the various complex cycles of reactions involved in maintaining the level of ozone in the stratosphere and in its potential reduction by chlorofluorocarbons. Chapter 4·5, 'Kinetics of reactions of stratospheric importance', goes on to examine how quantitative estimates can be made of the concentration of ozone in the stratosphere under various conditions. Chapter 4·6, 'Chlorofluorocarbons and stratospheric ozone', is an updated prognosis by one of the pioneers in the field of the current threat posed by the presence of increasing amounts of chlorofluorocarbons in the atmosphere. Finally, Chapter 4·7, 'Mechanisms of photochemical air pollution', deals with pollution of that part of the atmosphere closest to the Earth's surface, the troposphere. It describes the way in which photochemical smog arises as a result of a complex series of reactions involving sunlight, nitrogen oxides and organic compounds derived from unburnt hydrocarbon fuel.

4·1   Luminescence instrumentation

by Graham Fleming (University of Chicago)

For many compounds, measurements of luminescence provide some of the most sensitive and selective methods of analysis, and techniques for measuring fluorescence and phosphorescence have become highly developed. In addition, luminescence measurements provide important information about the properties of excited states, because the emitted light originates from excited electronic states. Thus measurement of luminescence intensity allows the change in concentration with time of the emitting chemical species to be monitored, while the wavelength distribution of the luminescence provides information on the nature and energy of the emitting species. This chapter describes how such measurements are made, and how molecular parameters (rate constants, quantum yields) are obtained from the measurements. To begin, we discuss the sensitivity and specificity of luminescence detection.

1   Sensitivity and specificity of luminescence detection

The measurement of luminescence is a significantly more sensitive technique for the detection of molecular species than absorption spectrophotometry. Fluorescence techniques are capable of detecting concentrations as low as one part in 10^{10}, a sensitivity some 10^3 times greater than most absorption spectrophotometric methods. The reason for this enhancement in sensitivity is that luminescence measurement is a null technique; that is, it involves the detection (or not) of photons. In contrast, conventional absorption spectrophotometry involves a determination of the difference between two measurements of light intensity, one derived from a cuvette (cell) containing solvent only and the other from a cuvette containing solute and solvent. At low concentrations of solute these two signals will be very similar: the measurement of a small difference between two nearly equal signals is always subject to large percentage error.

Luminescence spectroscopy, in particular fluorescence spectroscopy, is now used widely for analytical measurements (e.g. the determination of aspirin in blood) and has extensive applications in industries as diverse as printing, oil, the manufacture of tobacco, beer, detergents and insecticides. The sensitivity of luminescence is also exploited in scientific research, for example in the study of the excited states of molecules in vapours so dilute that individual molecules suffer no collisions during their excited state lifetimes.

Luminescence techniques are also highly specific for two major reasons. First, some selectivity is obtained because there is great variation in the extent to which different compounds luminesce. Second, luminescence is described by two spectra, the emission spectrum and the excitation spectrum, rather than the single spectrum of absorption spectrophotometry; two different chemical species that have very similar absorption spectra will probably have different emission spectra, and so luminescence techniques can be used to analyse complex mixtures of emitting species, as are found, for example, in crude oil.

2 Instrumentation

In this section we describe the basic components of an instrument designed to measure luminescence. These components are shown in block diagram form in Figure 1 and consist of (1) a light source, (2) wavelength selectors, (3) a sample compartment and (4) a light detection system. The detector is placed at 90° to the path of the incident light so that little of the exciting light reaches the detector. Luminescence is emitted in all directions and is thus registered by the detector.

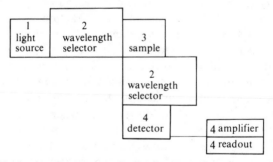

FIGURE 1   The basic components of a luminescence instrument. The numbers by the components are those used in the text.

2.1   Fluorescence

The individual components used in a typical fluorescence spectrometer (*spectrofluorimeter*) will now be described in more detail. The measurement of phosphorescence has some extra features which are discussed in Section 2.2.

The light source is usually a high-pressure xenon arc lamp (typically 150 W), emitting a reasonably smooth continuous spectrum from the ultraviolet to the infrared. A typical emission spectrum from a xenon lamp is shown in Figure 2.

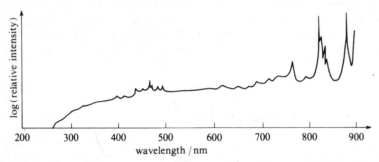

FIGURE 2   The emission spectrum of a xenon lamp. (source: Oriel Corporation, 1979)

Grating monochromators are normally used to select a narrow band of wavelengths, both from the light source for excitation of the sample (excitation monochromator) and from the fluorescence emitted by the sample (emission monochromator). A fluorescence spectrum is recorded by using a motor to change the angle of one of the diffraction gratings (and hence selecting different wavelengths). If the excitation wavelength is kept constant and the emission monochromator scanned, the emission (or normal fluorescence) spectrum is obtained; if the emission monochromator is kept fixed and the excitation monochromator scanned, the excitation spectrum is obtained. For a single-component sample, the excitation spectrum will normally be equivalent to the absorption spectrum (when corrected for variation with the wavelength of the lamp output and detection sensitivity).

The sample compartment normally contains a cell holder and two lenses, one to focus the excitation light on to the sample and the other to collect the fluorescence and focus it on to the entrance slit of the emission monochromator. Provision is normally made for temperature control of the sample.

The light emitted by the sample is usually detected by a photomultiplier tube. The photomultiplier amplifies the light signal by up to a million times. The photomultiplier output is further amplified and used to drive the pen of a chart recorder. The chart paper is then driven in synchrony with the wavelength drive on the excitation or emission monochromator. Figure 3 shows a schematic drawing of a commercial spectrofluorimeter.

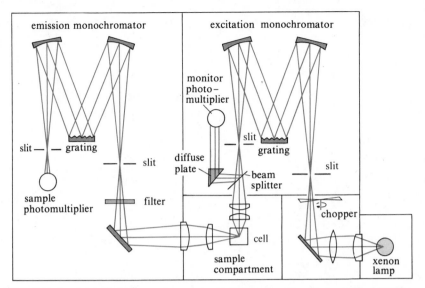

FIGURE 3 Optical layout of a commercial spectrofluorimeter (Perkin-Elmer MPF4). The light from the xenon lamp is mechanically chopped so that a.c. amplification of the detected luminescence can be used. The monitor photomultiplier is used to correct for fluctuations in the xenon lamp intensity. (source: Perkin-Elmer)

2.2 Phosphorescence

Normally, when a fluorescence spectrum is measured, there is no accompanying phosphorescence. This is because, at room temperature, triplet states are rather short-lived, mainly because of efficient bimolecular quenching by (a) other excited triplets, (b) oxygen molecules and (c) impurities that have diffused through the solvent to the excited molecule. At low temperatures, diffusion is inhibited and phosphorescence is readily observed. The usual method is to place samples in small quartz tubes, which are then immersed in liquid nitrogen in a quartz Dewar flask.

Unfortunately, in addition to the phosphorescence, fluorescence will normally be present in the emission. The phosphorescence and fluorescence spectra can be separated by exploiting the fact that phosphorescing states (e.g. triplet states of organic molecules) are much longer lived than fluorescing states (e.g. singlet states), and thus phosphorescence persists long after the fluorescence emission has decayed. One simple technique known as the rotating-can phosphoroscope is shown in Figure 4. An alternative method is to use two beam choppers that are exactly out of phase, one in the excitation beam and the other in the emission beam. Thus fluorescence is unable to reach the detector and only phosphorescence is observed.

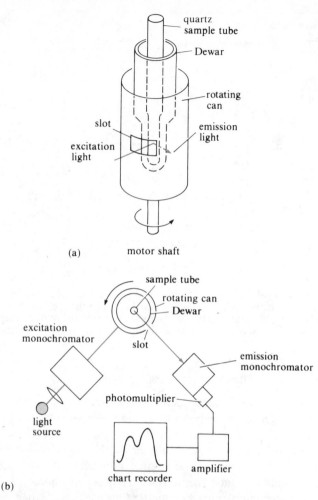

FIGURE 4 The rotating-can phosphoroscope. The sample is immersed in a Dewar flask. The rotation of the slotted can ensures that the path to the detector is blocked when the exciting light reaches the sample (a) and open when the exciting light is blocked (b).

3 Total luminescence spectroscopy

The total information present in both excitation and emission spectra requires three-dimensional representation; two dimensions for excitation and emission wavelengths and the third for intensity information. Figure 5 (p. 90) shows how such a total luminescence spectrum compares with the conventional spectra. The greater information content in (c) compared with a simple superposition of the two spectra in (a) has led to the use of total luminescence spectroscopy in the analysis of complex mixtures, such as crude oils, enabling the origin of crude oil spilled at sea to be identified.

4 Quantum yields and lifetimes from luminescence measurements

The lifetime of an excited state is determined by the sum of the rates of all the processes depopulating that state. If the excited state is a singlet state, then

$$\tau_S = \frac{1}{k_{tot}^S} = \frac{1}{k_f + \sum k_{nr}} \tag{1}$$

where τ_f is the observed lifetime of the decay of emission intensity I_f:

$$I_f = k_f[S_1]_0 \exp(-t/\tau_S) \tag{2}$$

k_f is the rate constant for the radiation process (fluorescence), $\sum k_{nr}$ is the sum of the rate constants for all the non-radiative processes depopulating the excited state, and $[S_1]_0$ is the concentration of the first excited state, S_1, at $t = 0$. The fluorescence quantum yield, ϕ_f, is defined as the fraction of excited molecules that decay by emitting light. This fraction is the ratio of the rate of radiative decay to the total decay rate:

$$\phi_f = \frac{k_f}{k_f + \sum k_{nr}} = k_f \times \tau_S \tag{3}$$

Thus, by a measurement of τ_S and ϕ_f, the radiative decay rate constant and the sum of the non-radiative decay rate constants can be obtained by application of equations (3) and (1) in turn. We will now describe how these quantum yields and lifetimes are obtained experimentally.

4.1 Fluorescence quantum yields

Direct determination of absolute values for fluorescence quantum yields is not commonly carried out, because it is very difficult to be sure that all the emitted light has been collected. The standard practice is to determine a fluorescence quantum yield by comparison with a standard of known quantum yield. Two widely used standards are quinine sulphate in 0.5 mol l^{-1} sulphuric acid, for which $\phi_f = 0.5$ at 5×10^{-3} mol l^{-1} at $25°C$, and sodium fluorescein $(10^{-6}$ mol l^{-1} in 0.01 mol l^{-1} NaOH) for which $\phi_f = 0.90$.

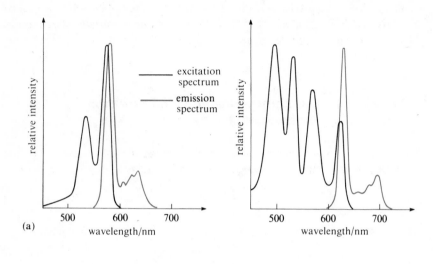

(a)

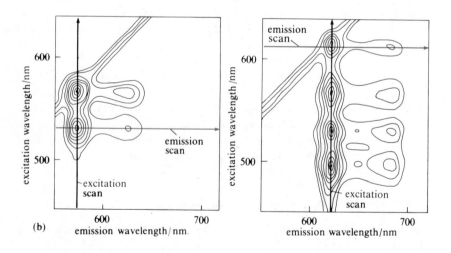

(b)

FIGURE 5   Total luminescence spectra of two single chemical species and their mixture. (a) Conventional fluorescence excitation and emission spectra for the two different species. (b) The total fluorescence spectrum of each species, shown as contours of equal fluorescence intensity.

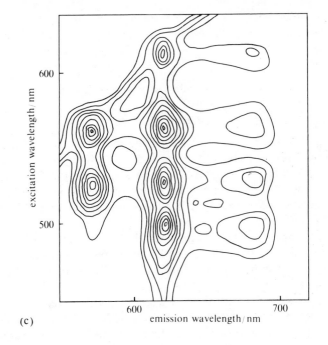

(c)

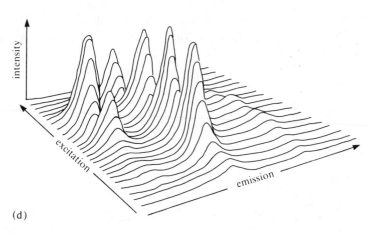

(d)

FIGURE 5 (c) A contour map of the mixture of the two. Again the contours represent regions of equal fluorescence intensity. (d) The projection of the contour map in (c) into three dimensions. (source: Johnson, Callis and Christian, 1977)

Once a reliable standard has been obtained, the fluorescence quantum yield can be determined by comparison of the area under the fluorescence spectrum of the molecule under study with that of the reference molecule.

$$\frac{\phi_f}{\phi_{f(ref)}} = \frac{n^2 \times (\text{area under sample spectrum})}{n_{ref}^2 \times (\text{area under reference spectrum})}$$

$$= \frac{n^2 \int_0^\infty F(\bar{v})\,d\bar{v}}{n_{ref}^2 \int_0^\infty F_{ref}(\bar{v})\,d\bar{v}} \tag{4}$$

where n and n_{ref} are the refractive indices of the specimen solution and the standard solution, respectively, and are included to correct for the optical geometry of the solution. The terms $F(\bar{v})$ and $F_{ref}(\bar{v})$ are the fluorescence intensities (as a function of wavenumber) of the specimen and reference. A number of precautions are necessary if reliable results are to be obtained from equation (4). These are:

1 Very dilute samples must be used, typically 10^{-5}–10^{-6} mol l^{-1}. The major reason for this is to avoid the possibility of fluorescence emitted by one molecule being absorbed by another molecule of the same compound in the solution (reabsorption).

2 Photomultipliers exhibit variations in sensitivity with wavelength which depend on the material from which the photocathode is constructed. These variations can lead to distortions in the observed spectra. As an example, Figure 6 shows the fluorescence spectrum of coproporphyrin measured using two different photomultipliers. The variation in wavelength sensitivity of the photomultiplier can be corrected in a number of ways, for example by using a

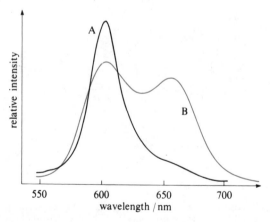

FIGURE 6   The change in the observed luminescence spectrum produced by variations in photomultiplier sensitivity with wavelength. Curve A is the fluorescence spectrum of coproporphyrin detected with a blue-sensitive photomultiplier. Curve B is the fluorescence spectrum of coproporphyrin detected with a red-sensitive photomultiplier. (source: West, 1975)

standard lamp, and many commercial fluorimeters have a built-in 'corrected spectrum' capability. If such correction facilities are not available, it is most important to choose a fluorescent reference molecule whose spectrum closely resembles that of the molecule under examination.

4.2 Phosphorescence quantum yields

Because the triplet state is not normally excited directly but is produced via intersystem crossing from the singlet state, we must take account of the fact that not all absorbed photons produce a state capable of phosphorescence. The triplet quantum yield is

$$\phi_T = \frac{k_{isc}^{ST}}{k_{isc}^{ST} + k_{ic}^{S} + k_f} = k_{isc}^{ST}\tau_S \tag{5}$$

where k_{isc}^{ST} and k_{ic}^{S} are the rates of intersystem crossing and internal conversion, respectively. By analogy with fluorescence, the fraction of triplet states that phosphoresce is

$$\theta_p = \frac{k_p}{k_p + \Sigma k_{nr}^{T}} \tag{6}$$

θ_p is called the *phosphorescence quantum efficiency*. Thus the phosphorescence quantum yield, ϕ_p, is

$$\phi_p = \phi_T \theta_p \tag{7}$$

and represents the fraction of photons emitted from T_1 when S_1 is excited.

It is difficult to determine the phosphorescence quantum yield directly by spectrophosphorimetry because excitation and observation are intermittent and the concentration of the triplet state varies with time. A value of ϕ_p can be determined more easily by methods similar to those described for the fluorescence quantum yield, by measuring the total luminescence (fluorescence and phosphorescence) spectra under steady excitation. If ϕ_f is known then the value of ϕ_p can be determined from the relative areas under the two corrected spectra.

4.3 Phosphorescence lifetimes

The lifetime of a molecule in the triplet state can be obtained directly from a measurement of the phosphorescence lifetime. Phosphorescence lifetimes observed from a sample at low temperature are usually longer than one microsecond and may even be several seconds. This means that a range of comparatively simple techniques are available for the measurement of phosphorescence lifetimes. The most simple and direct method is to excite the molecules with a short (say 1 μs) flash and follow the decay of the phosphorescence signal directly using a combined photomultiplier and oscilloscope. The accompanying fluorescence signal will decay too rapidly to be observed, and the decay of the detected luminescence intensity as a function of time will give the phosphorescence lifetime. The method used in most commercial instruments to obtain phosphorescence lifetimes is based on the rotating-can phosphoroscope, described earlier and shown in Figure 4.' During the dark period (when the slot is away from the light source) no molecules can be excited and the phosphorescence intensity, I_p, decays as

$$I_p = (I_p)_0 \exp(-t/\tau_T) \tag{8}$$

where $(I_p)_0$ is the phosphorescence intensity at the start of the dark period ($t = 0$) and τ_T is the triplet (or phosphorescence) lifetime. The phosphorescence is detected with a photomultiplier, the current from the photomultiplier at any instant being proportional to I_p. The value of τ_T can then be obtained by observing the photomultiplier signal as a function of time, using an oscilloscope whose sweep is triggered in synchrony with the rotating can of the phosphorimeter. This method is clearly identical in principle with the simple flash technique described earlier, with the slot acting as a shutter for the excitation lamp, but now the signal is obtained as a series of pulses.

4.4 Fluorescence lifetimes

The basic arrangement in Figure 1 remains the same for the measurement of fluorescence lifetimes. The light source is now a short flash of light, and the detection system must be able to respond quickly enough to enable the fluorescence decay to be observed directly. The most widely adopted technique for measurement of fluorescence lifetimes is called 'time-correlated single-photon counting', which we now briefly describe.

The flashlamp produces weak, repetitive pulses of light of the order of a few nanoseconds. Each pulse produces a weak fluorescence emission. The fluorescence photons are emitted over a range of times after excitation, with more photons being emitted earlier, and fewer emitted later as the excited state decays. Single-photon counting relies on the fact that certain photomultipliers are able to give measurable output pulses after a single photon strikes the photocathode. This allows the delay time between the excitation pulse and the arrival of individual photons to be determined. So by counting the number of photons that arrive within a given time interval (e.g. 3.2–3.3 ns after excitation) the fluorescence decay curve can be built up.

A block diagram of a typical apparatus is shown in Figure 7. The key to the method lies in the time-to-amplitude converter (TAC). The TAC is a device that charges a capacitor linearly, and produces a voltage pulse whose amplitude is proportional to the time interval between start and stop. The operation of the TAC is shown in Figure 8. The TAC is triggered by a pulse

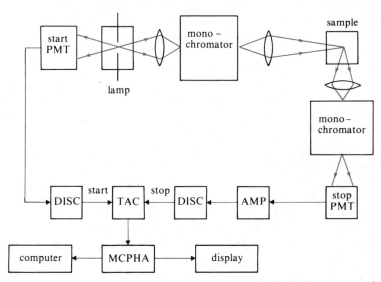

FIGURE 7   Schematic arrangement for time-correlated single-photon counting. PMT, photomultiplier tube; AMP, amplifier; DISC, discriminator; TAC, time-to-amplitude converter; MCPHA, multichannel pulse-height analyser. The function of the discriminators is to reject pulses outside a certain amplitude range and so improve the signal-to-noise ratio of the technique. The output from the multichannel pulse-height analyser can be displayed on an oscilloscope or processed by a computer.

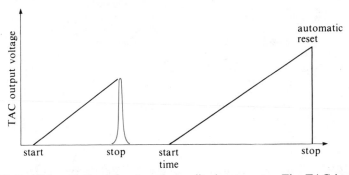

FIGURE 8   The operation of a time-to-amplitude converter. The TAC begins to charge linearly when the start pulse arrives. The voltage of the TAC output is proportional to the time interval between start and stop pulses. If no stop pulse arrives within a set time after the TAC has been started, an automatic reset sets the TAC voltage back to zero ready for another start pulse.

from the flashlamp, detected by the start photomultiplier (PMT) and stopped each time a fluorescence photon reaches the stop PMT. The voltage pulse produced by the TAC is fed to the multichannel pulse-height analyser (MCPHA), which sorts the output pulses by voltage. For example, if the

MCPHA is set so that each channel corresponds to a time interval of 0.1 ns, a fluorescence photon arriving 3.26 ns after excitation would register a count in channel 33; (assuming channel 1 covers the time interval 0–0.1 ns, channel 33 would cover the time interval 3.2–3.3 ns). Repetitive operation of the TAC produces a probability histogram for the detection of fluorescence photons, which is, in fact, the fluorescence decay curve. The fluorescence lifetime is obtained from this curve, from its definition as the time required for the fluorescence intensity to decrease by a factor of 1/e.

If a picosecond laser (see Chapter 2·1) is used as the light source, instead of a nanosecond flashlamp, the time resolution of the technique can be significantly improved. Figure 9 shows the fluorescence decay of the dye molecule Rose Bengal, obtained using a picosecond dye laser as the excitation source. The fluorescence lifetime, τ_f, of this molecule is 524 ps, and it is obtained from the experimental data by fitting the observed decay with an equation of the type $I_f = c \exp(-t/\tau_f)$ and varying c and τ_f until the best fit is found.

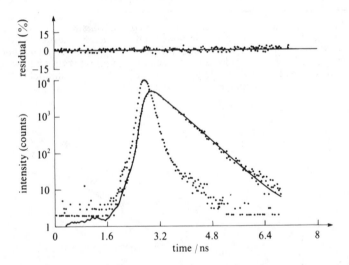

FIGURE 9   Time-resolved fluorescence decay of Rose Bengal in methanol, measured by the time-correlated single-photon counting technique. The time scale is 27.5 ps per channel, and data have been collected in 256 channels. The narrow dotted curve is the instrument response function obtained by scattering the exciting laser pulses from a non-fluorescent scatterer (in this case milk). This measurement determines the instrumental time resolution, because all the photons should arrive at the same time, and it is used to remove the distortion produced in the fluorescence curve by the finite time resolution of the instrument. The broad dotted curve is the experimental fluorescence decay. The solid line through the broad curve is a fit to the experimental curve from which the fluorescence lifetime is obtained as 524 ps. The residual plot at the top of the diagram shows the percentage differences between the experimental curve and the calculated fitted curve. Note that the intensity scale is logarithmic.

5 Applications of lifetime measurements

Direct determination of the fluorescence decay profile provides more information about the system than do steady-state methods such as quantum yield determinations, and is currently the area where most effort is devoted in luminescence spectroscopy. It is particularly valuable where complex kinetics occur—for example, if one fluorescent species is formed from another, the emission from the second species will appear ('grow in') as the first decays. Fluorescence lifetime measurements do not require measurements of absolute intensity, as is the case for fluorescence quantum yield determination. Lifetime determinations may, therefore, be more reliable when sample conditions are variable, for example in remote sensing of luminescence from oil slicks in the sea observed by laser excitation from an aeroplane.

4·2 Applications of energy transfer to macromolecules

by Antony Rest (University of Southampton)

An electronically excited molecule M* is able to lose its excitation energy and return to the ground state in a number of ways. A substance that accelerates the decay of an electronically excited state to the ground state or to a lower electronically excited state is described as a *quencher*. Thus, if the original excited state is luminescent, quenching will be observed as a reduction in the quantum yield of light emission. There are many quenching processes, as shown in Figure 1. Photophysical quenching can be divided into self-quenching, in which the quenching species is M, and impurity quenching, where the quencher is some other chemical species, Q.

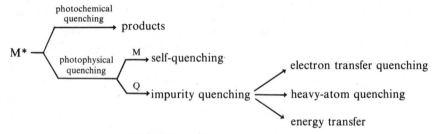

FIGURE 1   Quenching processes.

In this chapter we shall be concerned only with quenching by *energy transfer*. In the process of electronic energy transfer, an excited molecule (or part of a molecule) relaxes to its ground (or lower) state with simultaneous transfer of its electronic energy to another molecule (or another part of the same molecule) which is thereby promoted to an excited state. The former species is termed a *donor* (D) and the latter an *acceptor* (A), so that we have:

$$D^* + A \longrightarrow D + A^* \tag{1}$$

What is observed is quenching of the emission (or photochemistry) associated with D* and its replacement by the emission (or photochemistry) characteristic of A*.

The principal mechanisms of *electronic energy transfer* are summarised in Figure 2. *Radiative energy transfer* depends on the capture of photons emitted by the donor:

$$D^* \longrightarrow D + h\nu \tag{2}$$

$$h\nu + A \longrightarrow A^* \tag{3}$$

Such energy transfer can occur over distances immense on a molecular scale, e.g. 100 nm. *Non-radiative energy transfer* induced by *Coulombic* interactions is also a relatively long-range process, in that it can occur over distances which are much larger than molecular dimensions, i.e. 5 nm (5000 pm) or more, whereas the *electron exchange* interaction mechanism requires close approach (about 1–1.5 nm), though not necessarily actual contact, of the donor and acceptor species.

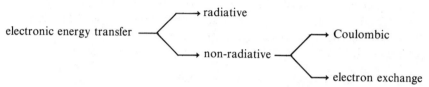

FIGURE 2   Principal mechanisms of electronic energy transfer.

Non-radiative energy transfer has a major biological significance in photosynthesis (see Chapter 6·3), where light is harvested by large numbers of chlorophyll molecules and energy is transferred in a stepwise fashion to centres at which photochemical reactions occur.

1   Principles of energy transfer

Various factors affect the extent and rate of energy transfer between the donor and the acceptor, whether they are in separate molecules or in different parts of the same molecule: (a) the distance between them; (b) their orientations relative to each other; (c) their spectroscopic properties; (d) the optical properties of the medium; (e) the effect of molecular collisions on the motion of the donor and acceptor in the period during which the donor is excited.

The quantitative contributions of these various factors to the probability of electronic energy transfer have been theoretically evaluated by the German physicist Theodor Förster. According to Förster's theory, the rate of energy transfer, k_{et}, in units of s^{-1}, and the efficiency of transfer, e, are given by:

$$k_{et} = 8.8 \times 10^{17} \, r^{-6} \, \kappa^2 \, J \, n^{-4} \, k_f \qquad (4)$$

$$e = r^{-6}/(r^{-6} + R_0^{-6}) \qquad (5)$$

The factor R_0 is the distance, in nanometres, between the donor and the acceptor at which the efficiency of transfer is 50%. This is given by:

$$R_0 = 9.7 \times 10^3 (J \, \kappa^2 \, \phi_0 \, n^{-4})^{-1/6} \qquad (6)$$

In these expressions some of the variables can be classified as *geometric* :

r, the distance between the centres of the donor and the acceptor,

κ^2, the orientation factor for dipole–dipole interaction;

and some as *spectroscopic*:

n, the refractive index of the medium between the donor and the acceptor,

k_f, the rate constant for fluorescence emission by the donor,

ϕ_0, the quantum yield of fluorescence of the donor in the absence of the acceptor,

J, the spectroscopic overlap integral (see p. 102).

Efficient energy transfer requires that the fluorescence spectrum of the donor should overlap the absorption spectrum of the acceptor. This leads to the description sometimes used of the phenomenon as *resonant energy transfer* (Figure 3). The spectroscopic overlap integral, J, is given by:

$$J = \int_0^\infty \frac{F_D(\bar{v})\epsilon_A(\bar{v})}{\bar{v}^4} \, d\bar{v} \qquad (7)$$

where $F_D(\bar{v})$ is the fluorescence intensity of the donor in the infinitessimally small wavenumber range $\bar{v}$ to $(\bar{v} + d\bar{v})$, normalised so that $\int_0^\infty F_D(\bar{v})d\bar{v} = 1$, and $\epsilon_A(\bar{v})$ is the absorption coefficient (l mol^{-1} cm^{-1}) of the acceptor at the wavenumber $\bar{v}$, as shown in Figure 4.

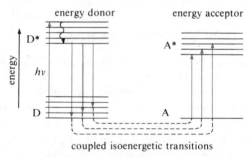

FIGURE 3   Energy level scheme showing the coupling of isoenergetic donor and acceptor transitions necessary for non-radiative energy transfer. (source: Barltrop and Coyle, 1978)

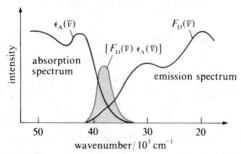

FIGURE 4   The spectroscopic overlap integral, J, is the shaded area (see equation 7). (source: Barltrop and Coyle, 1978)

2 Applications of energy transfer

2.1 General considerations

The dependence on distance of energy transfer for macromolecules was verified by Lubert Stryer, an American scientist, using a well-defined model system in which the donor–acceptor pairs were separated by known distances. Excitation of the naphthyl group in the series of compounds shown in Figure 5 led to the characteristic lower energy luminescence of the dansyl group. The result of a plot of energy transfer efficiency versus distance is shown in Figure 5, where it can be seen that the experimental points (circles) can be fitted by a r^{-6} function (line). This led Stryer to propose that non-radiative energy transfer could be used as a *spectroscopic ruler* for biological macromolecules to determine the distance between different component parts.

Applications of the spectroscopic ruler are related to R_0, the donor–acceptor separation at which 50% efficiency of energy transfer occurs while the other 50% is dissipated by all other processes including emission from the donor. This distance depends on four parameters of the energy transfer system (see equation 6). Any uncertainties in these parameters will lead to

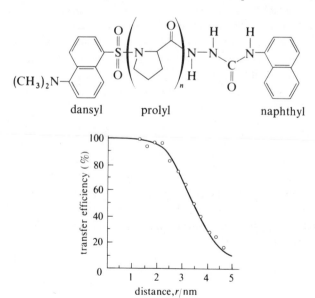

dansyl   prolyl   naphthyl

FIGURE 5   The efficiency of energy transfer as a function of the distance between naphthyl and dansyl groups at the end of a polyprolyl 'rod', $(prolyl)_n$. The observed efficiencies for values of n from 1 to 12 are shown as circles. The line is calculated from the assumption that the efficiency depends on r^{-6}. (source: Stryer, 1968)

uncertainties in R_0 and hence in r, so that, in order to assess the usefulness and validity of energy transfer as a spectroscopic ruler, an appreciation of the uncertainties is needed.

Refractive index. The effective refractive index of the medium between the donor and acceptor is not easy to measure when these are different parts of the same molecule. Various workers use values for n ranging from 1.3 to 1.6, but such a range of values has a relatively small effect. A value of 1.5 for n has been recommended for the interaction of aromatic amino acids in proteins.

Donor quantum yield. It is generally rather difficult to obtain the value of ϕ_0, the quantum yield of the donor in the absence of the acceptor. One approach is to use the typical quantum yield for the donor in the simplest possible protein (or polypeptide), or a model compound, e.g. the series of compounds in Figure 5. As a first approximation, the donor quantum yield in a simple model compound, containing no acceptor, can be used. Values of ϕ_0 for tyrosine range from 0.02 to 0.07 and those for tryptophan range from 0.06 to 0.15. Taking an average value is unsatisfactory. It is rather fortunate, therefore, that R_0 depends on the sixth root of ϕ_0 and is not critically sensitive to uncertainties in ϕ_0.

Spectroscopic overlap integral. Absorption spectra, as a rule, vary relatively little with change of solvent or temperature, but emission spectra may be very sensitive to environment. The integral J can be determined by graphical integration, as shown in Figure 4. It is simpler, and sufficiently accurate for most purposes, to calculate J on the assumption that the absorption and emission bands are represented by Gaussian distributions with standard deviations σ_A and σ_D:

$$\epsilon_A(\bar{v}) = \epsilon_{A\,(max)} \exp[-\{(\bar{v} - \bar{v}_A)/\sigma_A\}^2] \tag{8}$$

$$F_D(\bar{v}) = \epsilon_{D\,(max)} \exp[-\{(\bar{v} - \bar{v}_D)/\sigma_D\}^2] \tag{9}$$

where $\epsilon_{D\,(max)}$ and $\epsilon_{A\,(max)}$ are the maximum molar absorption coefficients of the longest wavelength absorption bands of the donor and acceptor molecules, respectively, and $\bar{v}_D$ and $\bar{v}_A$ are the wavenumber maxima of the donor emission and the acceptor absorption spectra. Values for σ_A and σ_D are calculated by considering the overlapping sides of the absorption and emission bands (Figure 4). It turns out that it is immaterial whether they represent accurately the opposite sides of the bands, because the overlap there is zero. With the Gaussian approximations

$$J = \epsilon_{A\,(max)}\epsilon_{D\,(max)}\frac{\sqrt{\pi}}{\left(\dfrac{1}{\sigma_A^2} + \dfrac{1}{\sigma_D^2}\right)} \exp[-(\bar{v}_A - \bar{v}_D)^2/(\sigma_A^2 + \sigma_D^2)] \tag{10}$$

Orientation factor. Dipole–dipole energy transfer has an angular dependence expressed by κ^2, the orientation factor, which is given by:

$$\kappa^2 = (\cos \alpha - 3 \cos \beta \cos \gamma)^2 \tag{11}$$

where α is the angle between the donor and acceptor transition moments, β is the angle between the donor moment and the line joining the centres of the donor and acceptor, and γ is the corresponding angle between the acceptor moment and the line joining the centres of the donor and acceptor. In many cases of practical interest, the donor and acceptor molecules undergo essentially free rotation during the lifetime of the donor. Then an average value of κ^2, $\overline{\kappa^2}$, can be used, where $\overline{\kappa^2} = 2/3$. Such a case would lead to R_0 being quoted as $\bar{R}_0$. The question arises as to how to treat κ^2 if there is not free rotation because the range of possible values for κ^2 (0–4) would seem to vitiate the usefulness of energy transfer for estimating distances in biological macromolecules and polymer molecules. In practice this is not so, because of the effect on κ^2 of partial rotational freedom, the existence of electronic transitions polarised along more than one direction, and the nature of the probability distribution function. It turns out that uncertainties in the distance over which energy transfer occurs, which are introduced by the orientation factor, are usually less than 20%. The problem is readily handled by measuring the extent of rotational mobility of the donor or acceptor to ensure that it is adequate, and by using more than one donor–acceptor pair. For spectroscopically isotropic ions (see later), there is almost no uncertainty in the orientation factor, even if they are rotationally immobile.

2.2 Experimental approaches

The use of energy transfer as a spectroscopic ruler depends on having placed, or being able to place, a fluorescent energy donor at a specific site and a suitable energy acceptor at another specific site. Furthermore, the spectroscopic characteristics of the donor and the acceptor must be sufficiently distinct so that the number of photons absorbed and emitted by each, can be readily determined. Experimentally, the distance r between a donor and an acceptor is obtained from measurements of the efficiency of energy transfer e (equation 5), and this can be determined in three ways.

The first way is by measuring the decreased quantum yield, ϕ_A, of the fluorescent donor in the presence of the acceptor compared with that, ϕ_0, without the acceptor, in a steady-state fluorescence experiment. In this case the energy transfer efficiency is given by:

$$e = 1 - (\phi_A/\phi_0) \tag{12}$$

The second way is by measuring the decreased fluorescence lifetime, τ_A, of the excited donor in the presence of the acceptor compared with that, τ_0, without the acceptor. In this case:

$$e = 1 - (\tau_A/\tau_0) \tag{13}$$

The third way is from the excitation spectrum corresponding to fluorescence from the acceptor, provided it is sufficiently fluorescent. Let $G(\bar{v})$ be the magnitude of the corrected excitation spectrum of the acceptor at $\bar{v}$; the corresponding absorption coefficients of the donor and the acceptor will be $\epsilon_D(\bar{v})$ and $\epsilon_A(\bar{v})$, respectively. Then, if $G(\bar{v})$ is measured at $\bar{v}_1$, where the donor has no absorption, and at $\bar{v}_2$, where the absorption coefficient of the donor is large compared with that of the acceptor, the efficiency is given by

$$e = [G(\bar{v}_2)/G(\bar{v}_1) - \epsilon_D(\bar{v}_2)/\epsilon_A(\bar{v}_1)] \times [\epsilon_A(\bar{v}_1)/\epsilon_D(\bar{v}_2)] \tag{14}$$

The first two methods are the most commonly used, and these assume that the presence of the acceptor does not alter the quantum yield of the donor except by the energy transfer process itself. The third method can be used even if the local environment of the donor is different in the presence of an acceptor, provided that the absorption spectra of both the donor and acceptor groups are known. At all events it is desirable that the transfer efficiencies measured by two different methods should agree.

2.3 Specific examples

One pertinent example relating to vision involved the specific labelling of bovine rhodopsin at three sites, A, B and C (Figure 6).

At site A, a sulphydryl (SH) group was alkylated with derivatives of acetamide containing a fluorescent group $\textcircled{F}$:

$$\textcircled{F}-NH\overset{O}{\overset{\|}{C}}CH_2I + HS-R \longrightarrow \textcircled{F}-NH\overset{O}{\overset{\|}{C}}CH_2-S-R \tag{15}$$

At site B, a different sulphydryl group was labelled with fluorescent disulphides, such as didansyl-L-cystine, via the reaction

$$\textcircled{F}-S-S-\textcircled{F} + HS-R \longrightarrow \textcircled{F}-S-S-R \tag{16}$$

At site C, an acridine group was attached.

The transfer efficiencies determined from the quantum yield and excited state lifetime of the donor showed that the apparent distances between 11-*cis*-retinal and sites A, B and C are 7.5, 5.5 and 4.8 nm, respectively. Different donors gave nearly the same apparent distances for site A, viz. 7.3, 7.5 and 7.7 nm, which suggests that the apparent distances closely approximate to the actual ones. The estimated distance between site A and 11-*cis*-retinal interestingly suggested that rhodopsin has an elongated shape, because a spherical molecule of that molecular weight would have had a diameter of only 4.5 nm. Subsequent neutron and X-ray scattering studies have shown that rhodopsin is at least 7.5 nm long.

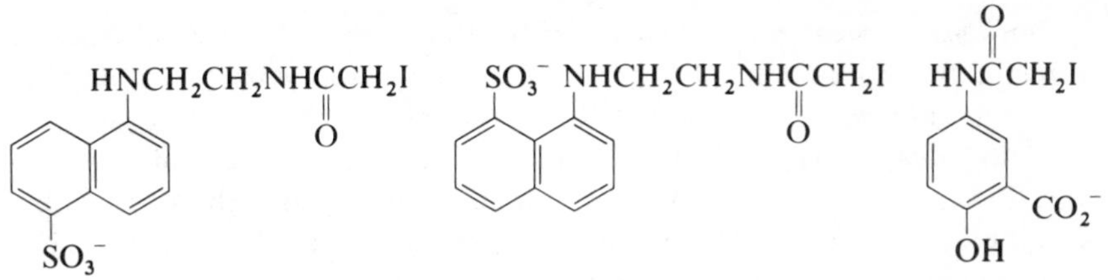

site A: derivatives of acetamide

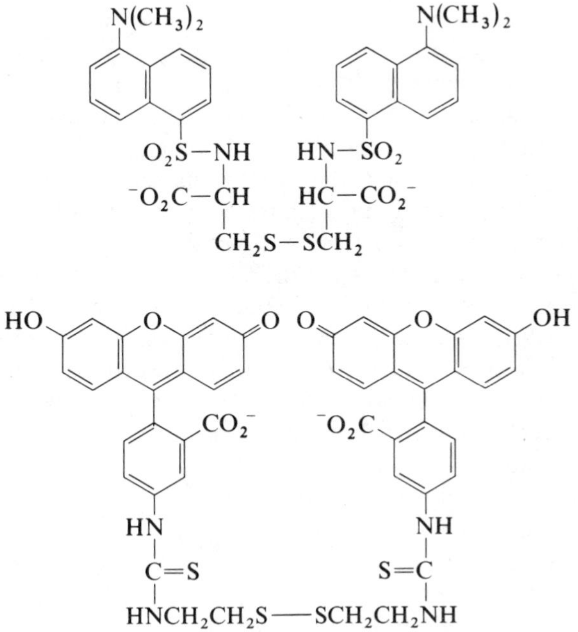

site B: disulphides

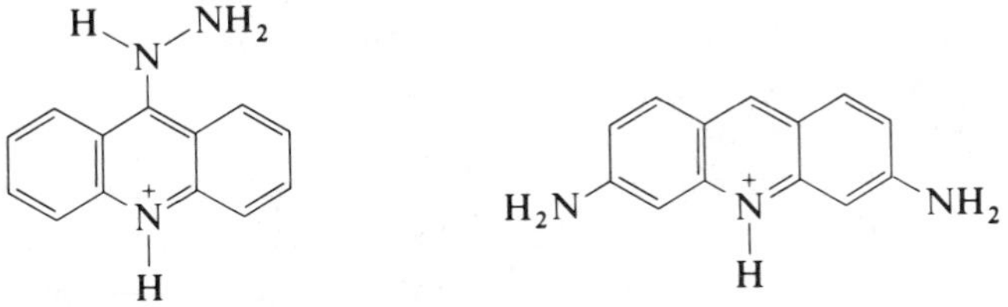

site C: acridines

FIGURE 6   Fluorescent labelling reagents.

Fluorescent trivalent lanthanide ions can serve as probes of the structure of metal-binding proteins. Thermolysin, a heat-stable enzyme, contains a Zn^{2+} ion at its active site and four Ca^{2+} ions at other locations. One of the Ca^{2+} ions was replaced by Tb^{3+}. The Zn^{2+} ion at the active site was replaced by a Co^{2+} ion so that there was an acceptor absorption to overlap with the Tb^{3+} emission. The bound Tb^{3+} ion was excited by energy transfer from the amino acid residue tryptophan, and the Tb^{3+} in turn transferred its excitation energy to the Co^{2+} ion with an efficiency of 89%. The R_0 distance for the donor–acceptor pair Tb^{3+}/Co^{2+} is not known precisely because of uncertainties in the ϕ_0 value of Tb^{3+} fluorescence. However, taking the commonly accepted value of $\phi_0 = 0.51$ gives an R_0 value of 1.96 nm. This estimated value, when used in conjunction with the observed transfer efficiency of 89%, indicates that the distance between Tb^{3+} and Co^{2+} (i.e. between Ca^{2+} and Zn^{2+}) is 1.37 nm. The validity of replacing Ca^{2+} by Tb^{3+} was demonstrated by a separate X-ray crystallographic study on thermolysin, and Co^{2+} is the common replacement probe for Zn^{2+} in carbonic anhydrase and carboxypeptidase. In the latter two enzymes only the Zn^{2+} and Co^{2+} forms are biologically active. In this case κ^2 can safely be taken as 2/3 because of the spherical symmetry of the donor and acceptor ions.

When a solution containing two similar methyl methacrylate copolymers, one labelled with naphthyl groups as donors and the other with anthryl groups as acceptors, is irradiated in the donor absorption band, the relative emission intensity from the two groups reflects the efficiency of energy transfer. This efficiency was found to be considerably lower for the labelled polymers than for similar concentrations of donors and acceptors when they were not attached to polymer chains. Two effects would be expected to contribute to this difference:

1 Small molecules diffuse faster when unimpeded by polymer chains, and this increases the probability of encounters between donor–acceptor pairs;

2 Intermolecular energy transfer between polymer chains could be affected by requirements for mutual interpenetration of molecular coils and chains.

Elimination of diffusion effects by studies of the donors and acceptors in poly(methyl methacrylate) films enabled energy transfer studies to provide evidence for interpenetration of flexible polymer chains.

In the applications mentioned so far, energy transfer has been used to estimate distances that do not change appreciably during the excited state lifetime of the donor. However, changes in distances occurring during the excited state lifetime can also be investigated. The underlying principle is that energy transfer may be enhanced by diffusion because a donor–acceptor pair that are too far apart for efficient transfer at the instant of excitation may diffuse towards each other during the excited state lifetime. Oligomers of 2-hydroxyl-L-glutamine (1; $n = 4$–9) containing a naphthalene donor at one end and a dansyl acceptor at the other, were studied by nanosecond fluorimetry. The mean end-to-end distance of this series ranges from 1.52 nm ($n = 4$) to 2.16 nm ($n = 9$), values that are comparable with the R_0 value of 2.2 nm. Correction for viscosity effects gave nanosecond emission kinetics for the donor that are about an order of magnitude lower than that expected for the unattached donor–acceptor pairs. It was concluded, therefore, that the polypeptide backbone possesses appreciable internal friction that resists the relative rotation and translation of the ends (viz. the interpenetration of polymer chains mentioned earlier), and also that the magnitude of the internal friction is greater for the shorter chain molecules.

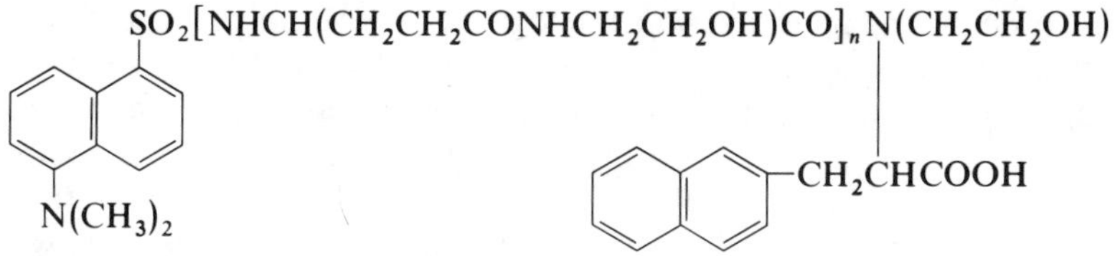

$$SO_2[NHCH(CH_2CH_2CONHCH_2CH_2OH)CO]_n N(CH_2CH_2OH)$$

1

The examples that we have discussed are all of the heterogeneous type of energy transfer, where the donor molecule (or part of a molecule) has a different electronic structure from the acceptor molecule (or part of a molecule). By contrast, in the homogeneous type of energy transfer, the donor and the acceptor have the same electronic structure. The Förster theory had been considered inapplicable to situations involving homogeneous energy transfer, e.g. the natural light-harvesting system of chlorophylls in photosynthesis. However, a modification of the Förster equation, obtained from studies of the emission properties of chlorophyll, has enabled critical transfer distances to be determined from either fluorescence intensity data or lifetime data for homogeneous systems.

4·3 Evolution and present composition of the Earth's atmosphere

by David Phillips (The Royal Institution, London)

1 Evolution from primitive constituents

With hydrogen so predominant in the cosmos (Chapter 1·2), other elements in a gas cloud are likely to be present as their hydrides. Thus, besides molecular hydrogen and the noble gases, there is likely to be found in relatively small amounts methane, ammonia, and water vapour, plus some hydrogen sulphide and phosphine. It should be recognised that this composition will be found on a cosmic scale: thus, it is believed to represent the composition of the interstellar medium. Such a gas cloud would be bathed in weak radiation from nearby stars, and therefore itself represents a photochemical reactor. That photochemical synthesis occurs under these circumstances is now well established.

Table 1 Lifetimes of molecules in unobscured interstellar regions, calculated from laboratory measurements

Molecule	Lifetime/years
COS	10
H_2CO	30
$CH_3C{\equiv}CH$	30
NO	100
H_2O	65

Table 1 gives the calculated ground-state lifetimes with respect to photochemical decomposition of some molecules observed by radioastronomy in unobscured regions of interstellar space. Given effective molecular velocities comparable with those of gas clouds themselves, 10–100 km s^{-1}, the total distance travelled by a molecule in a lifetime of 100 years is only 3×10^{13} to 3×10^{14} m. Because cloud diameters are typically of the order of 3×10^{15} to 3×10^{17} m, and intercloud distances much greater, the conclusion seems reasonable that these molecules are the result of photochemical synthesis in situ. One of the largest molecules yet observed in the interstellar medium is $H(C{\equiv}C)_4CN$, again presumed to be the result partly of photochemical synthesis. Table 2 shows examples of elementary reactions through which reactive species, such as the ·CN radical, could be produced in interstellar molecular clouds.

Table 2 Elementary reactions in interstellar gas clouds† (source: Brown, 1979)

Ionisation	*Photorecombination*
$H_2 + p \rightarrow H_2^+$ (or H^+)	$C^{.+} + H_2 \rightarrow (\cdot CH_2^+)^* \rightarrow \cdot CH_2^+ + hv$
$H_2^+ + H_2 \rightarrow H_3^{.+} + H\cdot$	
$He + p \rightarrow He^+$	*Dielectronic recombination*
	$CH^+ + e \rightarrow C + H\cdot$
Ion–molecule	$\cdot CH_2^+ + e \rightarrow \cdot CH + H\cdot$
$H_3^+ + C \rightarrow CH^+ + H_2$	
$H_3^+ + O \rightarrow OH^+ + H_2$	*Photoionisation*
$C^{.+} + \cdot OH \rightarrow CO + H^+$	$\cdot CH + hv \rightarrow CH^+ + e$
$C^{.+} + NH \rightarrow \cdot CN + H^+$	$CH_2 + hv \rightarrow \cdot CH_2^+ + e$
$O^{.+} + H_2 \rightarrow OH^+ + H\cdot$	
$N^+ + H_2 \rightarrow \cdot NH^+ + H\cdot$	*Neutral–neutral*
$CH^+ + O \rightarrow CO + H^+$	$O + \cdot CH \rightarrow CO + H\cdot$
$CH^+ + N\cdot \rightarrow \cdot CN + H^+$	$O + CH_2 \rightarrow \cdot OH + \cdot CH$
	$N\cdot + \cdot OH \rightarrow NO\cdot + H\cdot$
	$C + NO\cdot \rightarrow CO + N\cdot$

† In this table, p = proton and e = electron.

The present composition of the atmospheres of planetary bodies with solid cores may differ from the primitive composition owing to outgassing from rocks and, for bodies of small mass, loss of lighter molecular species, especially hydrogen, from the gravitational field. On *Mercury* this process is complete, there being total absence of any atmosphere. *Venus* has a highly evolved atmosphere in which complete outgassing of the rocks has occurred. The atmosphere is dense, hot and turbulent, with atmospheric pressure some 85 times that on *Earth*, a surface temperature of 750 K, and a period of rotation of the atmosphere of some 4 days compared with a planetary period of some 8 Earth months. The composition of the Venusian atmosphere is shown in Table 3. Clouds are present in the atmosphere, which are now known to be aerosols of concentrated sulphuric acid. Photochemistry has played an important role in establishing the Venusian atmosphere, and some important reactions are illustrated in Figure 1. One of the important points to note about this evolved atmosphere is that in the 4.5×10^9 years since the planets were formed, all of the CO_2 should have been lost by photolysis, and yet CO remains only a minor constituent, with CO_2 by far the most abundant chemical species. This is also true of the atmosphere of *Mars*. Some possible reactions accounting for the back conversion of CO to CO_2 are

Table 3   The composition of the Venusian atmosphere (source: McEwan and Phillips, 1975)

Major constituents	Relative abundance (%)	Minor constituents	Abundance (relative to CO_2)
CO_2	97	CO	4.6×10^{-5}
H_2O	0.4–1	HCl	6×10^{-7}
N_2	2	HF	1.5×10^{-9}
		O_2	8×10^{-5}
		C_3O_2	10^{-5}
		O_3	10^{-8}

shown (for the atmosphere of Mars) in Figure 2. On Venus, reactions of chlorine atoms, not shown in Figures 1 and 2, may also contribute.

The atmosphere of Mars, our neighbouring planet further from the Sun, is still evolving, with rocks still outgassing and H_2 being lost rapidly. The

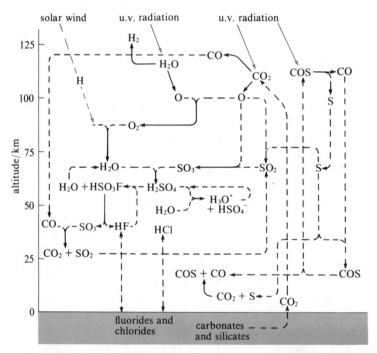

FIGURE 1   Some of the reactions that occur in the Venusian atmosphere. Dashed lines represent transport rather than reactions. Note that the solar wind consists of particles physically transported from the Sun. (From Young, L. and Young, A., *Venus*. Copyright © 1975 by Scientific American Inc. All rights reserved)

atmosphere is thin, with a pressure only 0.5% of that on Earth, and is principally CO_2. Because the surface temperature is only 140–250 K, water is present in solid form. Some reactions of importance in the Martian atmosphere are illustrated in Figure 2.

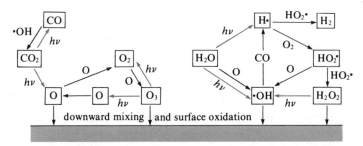

FIGURE 2 Some of the reactions that occur in the Martian atmosphere. (from Leovy, C. B., *The atmosphere of Mars*. Copyright © 1977 by Scientific American Inc. All rights reserved)

The evolution of the Earth's atmosphere has taken a radically different turn from that of our neighbouring planets, in that the present atmosphere contains large mole fractions of oxygen and nitrogen. The primitive Earth atmosphere, 4.5×10^9 years ago, possibly resembled the composition of, say, Jupiter, as a typical non-evolved system, so it is necessary to explore sources of molecular oxygen.

2 Sources of molecular oxygen

The Earth's primary atmosphere was certainly lost, because there is a deficiency of the noble gases compared with the cosmic abundance. What remained was a result of outgassing. Thus from early times there was abundant liquid water, and hence water vapour which could be photolysed by radiation in the far-ultraviolet region (UV-B and UV-C), which reached the surface of the Earth at that time. The appropriate reactions are:

$$H_2O + h\nu \longrightarrow H\cdot + \cdot OH \qquad \lambda < 242 \text{ nm} \qquad (1)$$

$$H_2O + h\nu \longrightarrow H\cdot + \cdot OH^* \qquad \lambda < 135.6 \text{ nm} \qquad (2)$$

$$H_2O + h\nu \longrightarrow H_2 + O(^1D) \qquad \lambda < 123.6 \text{ nm} \qquad (3)$$

$$\cdot OH + \cdot OH \longrightarrow H_2O + O \qquad (4)$$

$$O + O + M \longrightarrow O_2 + M \qquad (5)\dagger$$

† For reactions between two atoms, simultaneous collision with a third molecular species, M, is required to carry away excess energy otherwise the atoms merely rebound and do not form a diatomic molecule.

111

These reactions undoubtedly did occur, and could also have been responsible for the relatively small concentrations of oxygen detected, for instance, in the Venusian atmosphere. The process could not continue indefinitely to build up oxygen, however, because the product itself is sensitive to the same ultraviolet radiation:

$$O_2 + h\nu \longrightarrow O(^3P) + O(^3P) \qquad \lambda < 245 \text{ nm} \qquad (6)$$

$$O_2 + h\nu \longrightarrow O(^3P) + O(^1D) \qquad \lambda < 175 \text{ nm} \qquad (7)$$

$$O_2 + h\nu \longrightarrow O(^3P) + O(^1S) \qquad \lambda < 134.2 \text{ nm} \qquad (8)$$

After an initial build-up period, the oxygen would compete with water for the incoming ultraviolet light, and a steady-state concentration of oxygen would be reached. In order to calculate the rate of oxygen production, the absorption coefficients of oxygen and water need to be measured accurately over the solar spectral range; the quantum yields of photodissociation of oxygen and water as a function of wavelength also need to be known. Then by an iterative procedure, the steady-state concentration of oxygen resulting from this photolytic source can be computed. Such computations must also take into account other mechanisms of oxygen loss, such as reaction with minerals at the surface of the Earth to produce oxides. The American scientists Berkner and Marshall have given the estimate that this would be a factor of 10^{-4} of the present atmospheric level (PAL) of oxygen.

There is an alternative school of thought which has suggested that the build-up of atmospheric oxygen in even the earliest pre-Cambrian times was due to the biological activity of living organisms (algae) that were capable of photosynthesis. Life is believed to have appeared on Earth between 3.0×10^9 and 4.0×10^9 years ago, and photochemistry almost certainly played a prominent role in the creation of the molecular species necessary for the evolution of life. That there was an early source of atmospheric oxygen is beyond dispute, because many pre-Cambrian rocks, including some of the oldest known sediments, contain primary oxidised iron minerals. Neither is it in dispute that the very rapid growth of the level of atmospheric oxygen from the primitive levels (around 0.0001 PAL) to the present level is a result of photosynthesis. This growth has occurred most quickly from the Cambrian period (600 million years ago) to the present (see Figure 3). The principal argument is, therefore, whether or not photosynthesis was of importance in the very earliest period of the evolution of the atmosphere.

Although the majority view currently appears to favour photosynthesis during this period, others have argued convincingly against this. Photosynthesis in green plants today involves two photochemical reactions in sequence, known as photosystems I and II. Photosystem I does not involve

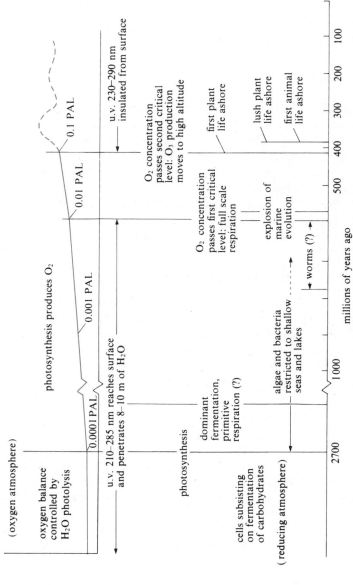

FIGURE 3   A model for the relationship between the availability of oxygen and the evolution of life in the sea and on land. (source: Berkner and Marshall, 1964)

release of oxygen, and is functionally similar to bacterial photosynthetic routes in which hydrogen sulphide (or other agents) act as electron donors:

$$CO_2 + 2H_2S \longrightarrow H_2O + \frac{1}{n}(CH_2O)_n + 2S \tag{9}$$

Photosystem II is the oxygen-releasing reaction:

$$CO_2 + H_2O \longrightarrow \frac{1}{n}(CH_2O)_n + O_2 \tag{10}$$

The assumption that blue-green algae capable of existing in the original anaerobic environment necessarily developed *both* photosystem I and photosystem II (hence pointing to a biotic source of early oxygen) is challenged by the observation that several blue-green algae can thrive in an environment without oxygen *solely* utilising photosystem I using H_2S as the electron donor, as in reaction (9). There are powerful evolutionary arguments against the development of photosystem II at the expense of photosystem I in the largely anoxygenic primitive atmosphere, and such a development may thus be thought to be unlikely, although this point is contentious.

3 Photosynthetic oxygen

Whatever the original source of oxygen, once photosystem II developed then the oxygen concentration began to increase irreversibly: (Nitrogen also is of biological origin. The reasons for this are quite straightforward, and relate simply to the extent of the habitat available for viable plant life in the prevailing conditions). It should be recalled that without oxygen the surface of the Earth was bathed in UV-B and UV-C radiation which is lethal to most life-forms. However, on production of any oxygen, ozone would be formed through reactions (6)–(8), followed by:

$$O_2 + O + M \longrightarrow O_3 + M \tag{11}$$

Ozone absorbs UV-C radiation strongly (Figure 4). At an oxygen concentration of 0.01 PAL or less, there is insufficient ozone to attenuate the incoming UV-C radiation significantly, and it can thus be argued that some other filter for this 'germicidal' radiation was required. This is most likely to have been liquid water, a column 10 metres in depth being sufficient to remove almost all of the most harmful radiation. One may, therefore, speculate that life evolved at the bottom of some stagnant pool of at least this depth. As oxygen production increased, however, the column of water required as additional filter would diminish, and thus over the period from 2.5×10^9 years ago to the Cambrian period (600 million years ago) the

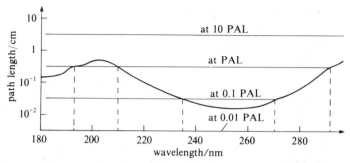

FIGURE 4   Ozone path length, in centimetres, required to attenuate solar ultra-violet radiation such that the intensity at the Earth's surface is 1 erg cm^{-2} s^{-1} in a 5 nm band. Horizontal lines represent equivalent ozone path lengths at oxygen levels of 0.01, 0.1, 1 and 10 PAL. (source: Berkner and Marshall, 1964)

available habitat for life (and hence the rate of oxygen production) would have slowly increased.

At about 0.01 PAL, a small enough column of water (a few centimetres) would have been required in addition to the available ozone to filter out UV-C for life in the oceans to have become viable despite the turbulent action of waves. The enormously increased habitat would have caused a rapid increase in the rate of oxygen production over the ensuing period until, at about 0.1 PAL, little or no water was required. (Only in the wavelength region 194–210 nm is ozone deficient in its absorbing properties; see Figure 4.) Thus life ashore would have been possible from this point on, again resulting in an accelerating build-up of oxygen to present atmospheric levels. The period from 500 million years ago to the present is characterised by an oscillating concentration of oxygen, representing the balance between production of oxygen and consumption of carbon dioxide, which through the 'greenhouse' effect, maintains the temperature of the surface of the Earth a few degrees higher than would be the case without CO_2. Periods of 'over-production' of oxygen thus correspond to periods of reduced CO_2 concentration, and thus colder (ice-age) periods.

Berkner and Marshall's model of the evolution of the atmosphere, summarised in Figure 3, may have defects, but remains an extremely useful basis for the qualitative understanding of the evolution of the atmosphere to the present oxygenic system. It is of paramount importance to understand that the atmosphere has evolved dramatically from its primitive composition, and that the present concentrations of oxygenic constituents represent a state of quasi-equilibrium. Whether or not this state of affairs could be altered on a short time-scale by the industrial activities of mankind is scrutinised in other chapters.

115

4 Evolution of life

In Chapter 1·2 it was reasoned that the gases constituting a 'primary' atmosphere would be largely methane, ammonia, hydrogen sulphide, phosphine, and molecular hydrogen, with carbon dioxide and water vapour present from the outgassing of rocks. With the exception of carbon dioxide, it is clear from radioastronomy that these gases are widely distributed throughout the Universe, and that photochemical reactions of these constituents are responsible for the synthesis of the much larger chemical species that have been observed by radioastronomy in deep space. It is also generally accepted that the evolution of the Earth's atmosphere took its unique course with the appearance of life on the planet. It is pertinent to consider the photochemical reactions that can occur following ultraviolet irradiation of a primitive atmosphere, to see if a plausible model can be developed for the creation of the large molecules considered to be essential precursors to life.

This process can be resolved into two problems: the synthesis of the small molecules necessary for life, and the combination of these small molecules into the much larger molecules which are the precursors of nucleic acids and proteins. Some components of the early Earth atmosphere are the same as are found in interstellar gas clouds. Thus reactions of the type shown in Table 2 could, therefore, have occurred readily in such a primitive atmosphere, producing hydrogen cyanide, formaldehyde (methanal), etc., just as are observed today in space by radioastronomy.

Attempts have been made to recreate this process in the laboratory, the classic experiment being that of the American chemists Miller and Urey. In this, a flask containing boiling water and the constituents of the primitive atmosphere, notably methane and ammonia, was irradiated with ultraviolet light, or subjected to an electrical discharge to simulate lightning. After a period of irradiation a substantial fraction of the methane was found to have been converted into organic materials, which on analysis revealed the presence of amino acids. These experiments have given rise to the conventional picture that amino acids were synthesised from the primitive atmospheric constituents. Formaldehyde is also a product of such reactions.

The question then arises of the polymerisation of these materials to give the larger molecules necessary for life. There are many models for this process. Because the process is a dehydration reaction, it has been argued, for example, that it could have taken place on the shoreline of the primitive Earth by absorption of the organic compounds on to a clay surface, which would then have been acted on by solar heat. An alternative explanation is that a number of prebiotic condensing agents in aqueous solution could have achieved the necessary condensation reactions. Thus cyanamide, $N\equiv CNH_2$, when irradiated in the presence of the amino acids glycine and leucine, yields amongst other products diglycine, triglycine, leucylglycine and glycylleucine. This theory seems more plausible to some researchers, in that the condensation reactions can take place in the oceans or lakes and not merely on the shores.

The theory that amino acids, formed as in the Miller–Urey experiment, represent the basic building blocks of life has been strongly challenged by Matthews and co-workers, working at the University of Illinois, who argue that hydrogen cyanide will, under the conditions of the primitive Earth, condense as shown in Scheme 1 to yield heteropolyamidines (**1**). When in contact with cold water these yield heteropolypeptides **2** and **3**, but when vigorously hydrolysed with boiling water, as in the original Miller–Urey experiment, they *degrade* to amino acids. In this scheme, therefore, polymers of hydrogen cyanide represent the basic building blocks of life, and amino acids mere degradation products.

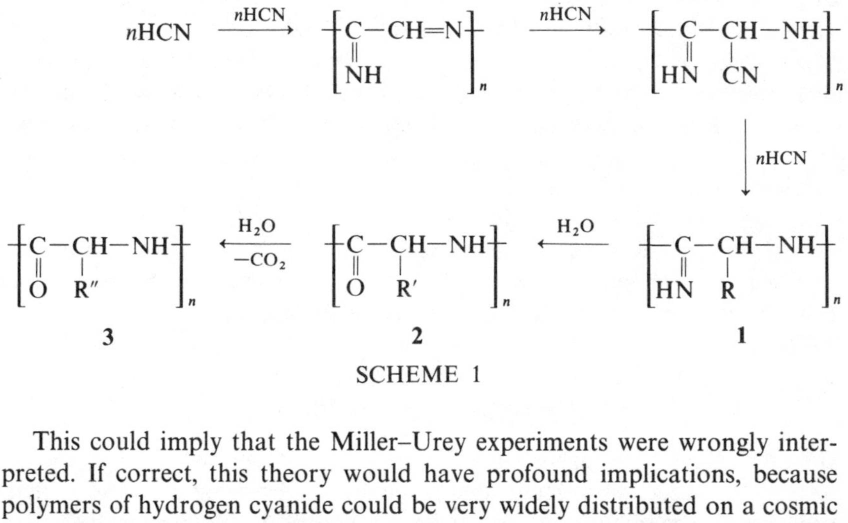

$$n\text{HCN} \xrightarrow{n\text{HCN}} \left[\begin{array}{c} \text{C}-\text{CH}=\text{N} \\ \| \\ \text{NH} \end{array}\right]_n \xrightarrow{n\text{HCN}} \left[\begin{array}{c} \text{C}-\text{CH}-\text{NH} \\ \| \quad | \\ \text{HN} \quad \text{CN} \end{array}\right]_n$$

$$\Big\downarrow n\text{HCN}$$

$$\left[\begin{array}{c} \text{C}-\text{CH}-\text{NH} \\ \| \quad | \\ \text{O} \quad \text{R}'' \end{array}\right]_n \xleftarrow[-\text{CO}_2]{\text{H}_2\text{O}} \left[\begin{array}{c} \text{C}-\text{CH}-\text{NH} \\ \| \quad | \\ \text{O} \quad \text{R}' \end{array}\right]_n \xleftarrow{\text{H}_2\text{O}} \left[\begin{array}{c} \text{C}-\text{CH}-\text{NH} \\ \| \quad | \\ \text{HN} \quad \text{R} \end{array}\right]_n$$

$$\textbf{3} \qquad\qquad\qquad \textbf{2} \qquad\qquad\qquad \textbf{1}$$

SCHEME 1

This could imply that the Miller–Urey experiments were wrongly interpreted. If correct, this theory would have profound implications, because polymers of hydrogen cyanide could be very widely distributed on a cosmic scale, with significant probability of life-forms being present in other regions of the cosmos. The similarity of photochemical synthesis in simulated primitive Earth atmospheres and in interstellar gas clouds has led to the rather extreme view that the organic molecules necessary for the creation of life were, in fact, synthesised in space; interaction then developed as far as viruses and bacteria, which were transported to Earth through the intermediary of comets. This view is not widely supported.

Clearly there are many possible models for the evolution of life, some more plausible than others, but that photochemical reactions took part in the prebiotic syntheses seems highly likely.

4·4 The stratospheric ozone cycle

by David Phillips (The Royal Institution, London)

In Chapter 4·3 we speculated as to the reasons for the unique feature of the Earth's atmosphere, namely the high concentration of molecular oxygen present compared with other planets, and we discussed possible processes through which the atmosphere may have evolved from a primitive system to its present state. Implicit in these arguments was the thesis that as the concentration of molecular oxygen built up, so in the stratosphere (between 15 and 100 km above the surface) the concentration of trimeric oxygen (ozone, O_3), also gradually increased, thus shielding the surface of the Earth from harmful ultraviolet radiation. In this chapter we take a more detailed look at the processes by which the ozone layer is maintained, and examine the long-term stability of the system. In particular, we try to assess whether or not any of mankind's current activities could lead to an attenuation of present ozone levels. The decade of the 1970s saw an enormous increase in the activities of research scientists interested in the stratosphere, and the understanding of the basic mechanisms now has a firmer foundation of kinetic measurements. Nevertheless, the controversy over perturbations arising from human activities remains lively. We seek in this chapter merely to present the problem, without adopting a particular stance in the controversy.

1 The Chapman mechanism

The English geophysicist Sydney Chapman is the recognised father of aeronomy, and it was he who first explained the rather surprising observation that a temperature minimum existed at an altitude of around 15 km from the Earth's surface (Chapter 1·2, Figure 2). Chapman realised that most of the ultraviolet radiation incident on the planet would be absorbed in the upper regions of the atmosphere, where it would ultimately be dissipated as heat.

The principal atmospheric constituent, molecular nitrogen, absorbs only in the far ultraviolet and so is much less involved in the photochemical process than molecular oxygen, which has two absorption regions (Figure 1). Absorption in the Schumann–Runge continuum results in the reaction

$$O_2 + h\nu \longrightarrow O(^3P) + O(^1D) \qquad \lambda < 175 \text{ nm} \qquad (1)$$

The Schumann–Runge absorption band corresponds to an allowed electronic transition and thus absorption is strong, preventing radiation of these wavelengths from penetrating below about 70 km. As a further result of the absorption, above about 120 km most oxygen is present in the form of atoms.

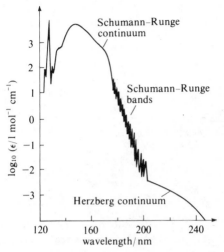

FIGURE 1   The absorption spectrum of oxygen. (sources: Heddle and Ditchburn, 1953; and Inn, Watanabe and Zelikoff, 1953)

Absorption by oxygen in the relatively weak Herzberg continuum produces two ground-state (^3P) atoms:

$$O_2 + hv \longrightarrow O(^3P) + O(^3P) \qquad \lambda < 245 \text{ nm} \qquad (2)$$

and because of the weakness of this electronic transition, this process persists down to an altitude of about 30 km. Subsequent reactions of the atoms can lead to ozone formation (reaction 3) or reformation of molecular oxygen (reaction 4):

$$O + O_2 + M \longrightarrow O_3 + M \qquad \Delta H = -100 \text{ kJ mol}^{-1} \qquad (3)\dagger$$

$$O + O + M \longrightarrow O_2 + M \qquad \Delta H = -493 \text{ kJ mol}^{-1} \qquad (4)$$

The ozone formed in reaction (3) can further react with oxygen atoms (reaction 5), or absorb incoming solar radiation in the 215–295 nm region (reaction 6), as indicated in Figure 2.

$$O + O_3 \longrightarrow 2O_2 \qquad \Delta H = -390 \text{ kJ mol}^{-1} \qquad (5)$$

$$O_3 + hv \longrightarrow O_2 + O \qquad (6)$$

It is evident from the enthalpies of reaction of this cycle of five reactions, now known as the Chapman mechanism, that a great deal of heat is dumped into the stratosphere, and this provides the explanation for the temperature inversion at the tropopause. From a knowledge of the laboratory rate constants

---

† As with reactions between two atoms, reactions involving small molecules sometimes need a third species (M) to carry away the excess energy of the reaction.

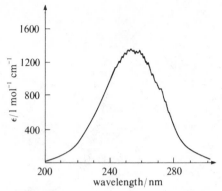

FIGURE 2   The absorption spectrum of ozone. (source: Calvert and Pitts, 1966)

for reactions (3), (4) and (5), the absolute intensity distribution of sunlight as a function of altitude, and the absorption coefficients of molecular oxygen and ozone, it is possible to compute the profile of ozone concentration as a function of altitude above the Earth's surface. The process is made rather difficult because rate constants are not easy to measure, but some recent

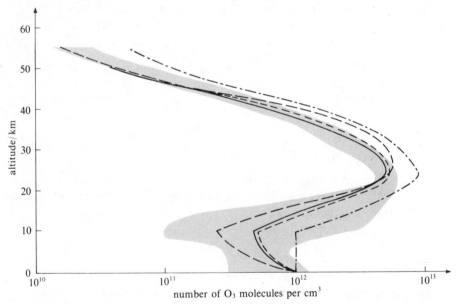

FIGURE 3   The concentration of ozone as a function of altitude. The red band represents the range of observed values. The four black curves are calculated from various models. The curve —·—·— is derived from the Chapman mechanism (oxygen-only system); the curve ——— is from the oxygen–hydrogen system; the curve – – – – is from the oxygen–hydrogen–nitrogen system; and the continuous curve is from the oxygen–hydrogen–nitrogen–chlorine system. (source: Chang, 1980)

results are shown in Figure 3. It can be seen that the ozone profile computed on the basis of the Chapman mechanism mimics the profile observed by rocket-borne instrumentation surprisingly well, except that it is too large.

These results show that the Chapman mechanism, although substantially correct, is inadequate for explaining quantitatively the ozone layer. There must be reactions occurring that cause a reduction in ozone concentration relative to the 'classical' predicted level. This realisation caused aeronomists to turn their attention to other chemical species present in the atmosphere, in the hope of understanding their role in the complete cycle. Some suggested mechanisms will be reviewed in turn.

2 Reactions involving oxides of hydrogen

Because ozone is a reactive molecule, even minor constituents of the atmosphere may contribute greatly to the destruction of ozone, and hydrogen-containing species derived from water, methane, and hydrogen itself could be important. If hydrogen atoms could be produced in the stratosphere, then the chain

$$H\cdot + O_3 \longrightarrow \cdot OH + O_2 \qquad \Delta H = -326 \text{ kJ mol}^{-1} \qquad (7)$$

$$\cdot OH + O \longrightarrow O_2 + H\cdot \qquad \Delta H = -64 \text{ kJ mol}^{-1} \qquad (8)$$

would be equivalent to reaction (5). However, the rate constants for these reactions are such that the loss of ozone occurs at a rate some 10^3 times larger than that of reaction (5). The question is: can hydrogen atoms be created in the stratosphere?

Because hydrogen and methane absorb only in the far ultraviolet, photodissociation of these constituents is unimportant. Although water vapour can be dissociated to H· and ·OH radicals by light of the same wavelengths (< 175 nm) as is absorbed by oxygen in the Schumann–Runge region, the greater concentration of oxygen compared with water vapour in the atmosphere makes this route also relatively unimportant.

The principal source of chain carriers for reactions (7) and (8) turns out to be the reaction of electronically excited oxygen atoms $O(^1D)$ with CH_4, H_2O, or H_2 molecules to produce hydroxyl radicals. One source of $O(^1D)$ is the photolysis of oxygen through reaction (1).

Reactive species such as H· and ·OH eventually meet up with other such atoms or radicals in termination reactions. Two fast termination steps of the ·OH radical are:

$$\cdot OH + \cdot OH \longrightarrow H_2O + O \qquad (9)$$

$$\cdot OH + HO_2\cdot \longrightarrow H_2O + O_2 \qquad (10)$$

Reactions of ·OH with CH_4 and H_2 are unimportant at stratospheric temperatures, because both reactions have activation energies of around 16 kJ mol^{-1} whereas other reactions have lower activation energies. However, hydroxyl radicals may destroy ozone through the cycle (11) and (12) involving HO_2·, the hydroperoxyl radical:

$$·OH + O_3 \longrightarrow HO_2· + O_2 \qquad (11)$$

$$HO_2· + O_3 \longrightarrow ·OH + 2O_2 \qquad (12)$$

The HO_2· radical is also involved in another pair of reactions which effectively form an ·OH radical from atoms of hydrogen and oxygen.

$$H· + O_2 + M \longrightarrow HO_2· + M \qquad (13)$$

$$HO_2· + O \longrightarrow ·OH + O_2 \qquad (14)$$

All this serves to illustrate the complexity of modelling the atmosphere in that a very large number of reactions must be included. Figure 4 illustrates the main reactions involved in an oxygen–hydrogen system. Models based on such a scheme are in general agreement about the effect of species containing hydrogen on the ozone cycle: above an altitude of 45 km they play a controlling role (see Figure 3) whereas below 45 km the presence of these chemical species cannot explain the observed ozone concentration profile. It is clear, therefore, that below 45 km, reactions of other chemical species must be of importance.

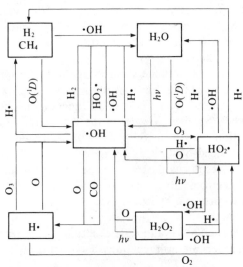

FIGURE 4   Reaction paths in the oxygen–hydrogen system. The major components are shown in boxes. (source: McCormac, 1973)

3   Reactions involving oxides of nitrogen

The American scientist Paul Crutzen was the first to suggest that reactions involving oxides of nitrogen might critically affect the ozone concentration, largely through the chain reactions (15) and (16):

$$NO\cdot + O_3 \longrightarrow NO_2\cdot + O_2 \qquad \Delta H = -200 \text{ kJ mol}^{-1} \qquad (15)$$

$$NO_2\cdot + O \longrightarrow NO\cdot + O_2 \qquad \Delta H = -192 \text{ kJ mol}^{-1} \qquad (16)$$

Again, this sequence of reactions is identical in result to reaction (5), but the cycle has a very much larger effective rate constant than reaction (5). Nitric oxide and nitrogen dioxide together are referred to as NO_x. The principal source of NO_x in the stratosphere is the reaction of $O(^1D)$ with N_2O:

$$O(^1D) + N_2O \longrightarrow NO\cdot + NO\cdot \qquad (17)$$

$$O(^1D) + N_2O \longrightarrow N_2 + O_2 \qquad (18)$$

These two reactions have approximately equal probabilities. The N_2O is transported to the stratosphere from the troposphere, where it has biological origins.

Major loss processes for NO_x appear to be reactions (19) and (20). During daylight hours reaction (21) is also important. This leads to the regeneration of ozone, because oxygen atoms can combine with O_2 through reaction (3) to form ozone.

$$NO_2\cdot + \cdot OH + M \longrightarrow HNO_3 + M \qquad (19)$$

$$NO\cdot + \cdot OH + M \longrightarrow HNO_2 + M \qquad (20)$$

$$NO_2\cdot + h\nu \longrightarrow NO\cdot + O \qquad (21)$$

Because reaction (21) can be brought about even by visible radiation, photolysis of NO_2 can occur at any altitude. This means that any process that produces nitrogen dioxide will lead to ozone formation, a fact that has not escaped the notice of residents of many conurbations, particularly those of Los Angeles.

Subsequent to reaction (19), photolysis of the nitric acid probably produces $\cdot OH$ and NO_2, thus reversing reaction (19). Nitric acid thus simply retards the chain process, but because HNO_3 can be removed by downward transport into the troposphere where it is removed by rain, the catalytic destruction of ozone is undoubtedly impaired by reaction (19).

Some of the important processes in the NO_x cycle of stratospheric reactions are summarised in Figure 5.

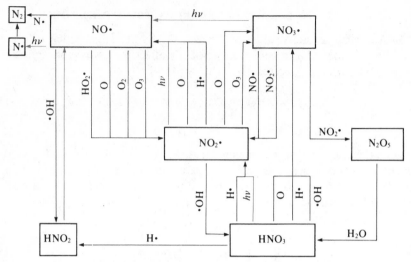

FIGURE 5   The NO_x reaction cycle. (source: McCormac, 1973)

Although these NO_x and HO_x reactions are capable of modelling the observed ozone concentration profile (see Figure 3), it is necessary to include all cycles that may be of importance in order to understand the rates of overall processes and the interactions of the different cycles. For this reason, the ClO_x cycle must be discussed.

4   Reactions involving oxides of chlorine

It is only comparatively recently that attention has been focused on the possibility that compounds containing chlorine may occur *naturally* in the troposphere, and may thence be transported to the stratosphere. Gaseous chlorine occurs principally as chloromethane, which is presumed to have predominantly marine origins, although some arises from 'slash-and-burn' tropical agriculture. Another source of natural chlorine is HCl, of importance only at low altitudes. Chlorine atoms can be produced by reaction (22) and analogous reactions, and in the stratosphere by photolysis.

$$\cdot OH + HCl \longrightarrow H_2O + Cl\cdot \qquad (22)$$

The rapid reaction (23) then follows:

$$Cl\cdot + O_3 \longrightarrow ClO\cdot + O_2 \qquad (23)$$

At higher altitudes, the $ClO\cdot$ formed can react further with oxygen atoms to regenerate the chlorine atom:

$$ClO\cdot + O \longrightarrow Cl\cdot + O_2 \qquad (24)$$

This pair of reactions, (23) and (24), constitute a chain which effectively removes *two* ozone molecules per cycle, because oxygen atoms can be considered to be the precursors of ozone through reaction (3). As before, the effect of reactions (23) and (24) is the same as that of reaction (5), except that the chlorine atom has a very large catalytic effect and the rate constant is enhanced by several orders of magnitude. Thus, any chlorine present in the stratosphere will certainly lead to a reduced concentration of ozone. The sinks for chlorine are thought to be abstraction reactions with CH_4, H_2, H_2O_2, HNO_3, etc. (e.g. reaction 25). However, reaction of hydroxyl radicals with the HCl that is produced returns the chlorine to the cycle (reaction 22).

$$Cl\cdot + CH_4 \longrightarrow HCl + \cdot CH_3 \qquad (25)$$

Because the ClO_x and NO_x cycles occur in the same regions of the stratosphere, they interact. Thus, below 30 km reaction (26) is of importance:

$$ClO\cdot + NO\cdot \longrightarrow Cl\cdot + NO_2\cdot \qquad (26)$$

Chlorine nitrate, $ClONO_2$, might provide a temporary reservoir for chlorine atoms through reactions (27) and (28). The equilibrium concentrations of these chemical species clearly depend on the rate constant for reaction (27), and the photochemical rate parameters for reaction (28) (see Chapter 4·5).

$$ClO\cdot + NO_2\cdot + M \longrightarrow ClONO_2 + M \qquad (27)$$

$$ClONO_2 + h\nu \begin{cases} \longrightarrow Cl\cdot + NO_3\cdot & (a) \\ \longrightarrow ClO\cdot + NO_2\cdot & (b) \\ \longrightarrow ClONO + O & (c) \end{cases} \qquad (28)†$$

Current models are in broad agreement that small concentrations of chlorine in the stratosphere (from whatever source) play a significant role in establishing a steady-state concentration of ozone. If the interactions of all three cycles, HO_x, NO_x, and ClO_x, are included in a model of ozone concentration, the resulting curve is the solid line in Figure 3.

5 Perturbations to ozone concentrations from human activities

In the past decade, one question that scientists have been considering is the possibility that a change in the overall ozone concentration in the stratosphere could result from human activities. It is evident from the preceding discussion that the present level of ozone results from a balance between its

† The products of this reaction have not yet been positively identified, but it seems most likely that (a) is correct.

photochemical formation and its destruction through catalytic cycles of reactions, principally involving HO_x, NO_x, and ClO_x. The simple analogy may be drawn of a level of water in a bathtub being maintained by having the taps running and the plughole open, where a state of dynamic equilibrium exists. The question being posed is: what will the ozone level be if more catalytic species are introduced into the stratosphere? Will it be equivalent to a pinhole in the bathtub, and thus negligible, or equivalent to kicking the side of the bathtub away, which would be catastrophic? It is not a simple matter to quantify such effects, because, to continue with the analogy, the level of the water in the bathtub is not naturally constant, but varies geographically, seasonally and diurnally (daily). It is thus extremely difficult to measure small changes, which might be harbingers of impending disaster, against the background of large-amplitude oscillations. The difficulties in such measurements, and their importance, are discussed in Chapter 4·6. Here we simply consider ways in which additional catalytic species could be introduced into the stratosphere.

The HO_x cycle plays an important although not exclusive role in the maintenance of the ozone concentration in the critically important 7–20 km region. A change in the amount of HO_x (mainly as water) could therefore attenuate the ozone concentration, and one way this could be brought about is through a change in the stratospheric heat balance, caused in part via the 'greenhouse effect' of CO_2 produced by combustion. A change of 4 K would change the stratospheric water concentration by a factor of 2, and such effects are of current interest to climatic modellers.

In the early 1970s there was much concern that injection of copious amounts of NO_x from nuclear weapon tests and large fleets of high-flying supersonic transport aircraft could drastically reduce the ozone concentration through the NO_x catalytic cycle. Such concern has now abated with an improved quantitative understanding of the NO_x cycle, and the realisation that at least in the near future, the numbers of such aircraft will be small. Indeed, recent predictions have indicated that small additional amounts of NO_x introduced into the stratosphere may well cause a small (about 1%) increase in the ozone level through the interactions of the HO_x and NO_x cycles:

$$HO_2{\cdot} + NO{\cdot} \longrightarrow {\cdot}OH + NO_2{\cdot} \tag{29}$$

The current large subsonic fleet of jet aircraft may well influence the ozone catalytic cycles through emissions of NO_x and water.

Another possibility is that perturbation of the current level of ozone could occur through injection of chlorine-containing compounds into the stratosphere. This could be done directly, through the production of HCl exhaust gases in the NASA space shuttle (though this would be in very small amounts) or indirectly through the release of chlorine into the troposphere followed by transport to the stratosphere. It is of course the latter possibility that has been widely discussed in recent years with reference to the release of chlorofluorocarbons into the troposphere on a relatively large scale. Once these molecules have been transported to the stratosphere, photodissociation typified by reaction (30) produces catalytic chlorine atoms.

$$CCl_2F_2 + h\nu \longrightarrow \cdot CClF_2 + Cl\cdot \qquad (30)$$

Some of the questions that must be answered therefore, are:

1   What is the rate of release of man-made chlorine into the troposphere?
2   What are the residence times of chlorine compounds in the troposphere, and what are their sinks?
3   What is the rate of transport of these materials into the stratosphere?
4   Is the downward propagation through the atmosphere of effects caused by an increase in ClO_x well enough understood for the effects on the total ozone column to be predicted?
5   What are the consequences of reduced ozone levels for living organisms, including humans, on the surface of the planet?
6   Are the known and unknown consequences of ozone depletion of such potential significance that they should be prevented now, rather than attempts be made to ameliorate them if and when they appear?

There is not as yet a concensus of opinion concerning these important, perhaps vital, questions. In Chapter 4·6 the views of one scientist intimately concerned with research in this field are presented. Although these views are challenged by some, it must be said that many originally sceptical aeronomists now concede the validity of these arguments, and we should therefore study the case seriously.

4·5 Kinetics of reactions of stratospheric importance

by David Phillips (The Royal Institution, London)

As discussed in Chapter 4·4, two of the important reactions in the Chapman mechanism, reactions (1) and (2), are photochemical:

$$O_2 + hv \longrightarrow O + O \tag{1}$$

$$O_3 + hv \longrightarrow O_2 + O \tag{2}$$

Any understanding of the atmosphere must be concerned with measurement of the rates of these reactions in the atmosphere, and for modelling purposes, in the laboratory. Laboratory measurements are in principle simple, and a comparison of the atmosphere with the laboratory photochemical reactor is made in Section 3. The rates of photochemical processes in the atmosphere are conveniently represented by a rate coefficient j, which is analogous to the rate constant k for a non-photochemical reaction.† Thus the rate of reaction (1) is $j_1[O_2]$. However, from the functional form of j (derived in Section 3.2) it can be seen that j is dependent on the excitation wavelength, the distribution of the incident intensity and the path length, and thus varies markedly with altitude. Some typical j values for reactions (1) and (2) at different altitudes are listed in the Appendix to this chapter (p. 139).

1 Kinetics of the Chapman mechanism

To see the principles involved in calculating the ozone concentration at different altitudes, we shall begin with the simplest case, the Chapman mechanism. The complete Chapman mechanism is:

$$O_2 + hv \longrightarrow O + O \tag{1}$$

$$O_3 + hv \longrightarrow O_2 + O \tag{2}$$

$$O + O_2 + M \longrightarrow O_3 + M \tag{3}$$

$$O_3 + O \longrightarrow O_2 + O_2 \tag{4}$$

$$O + O + M \longrightarrow O_2 + M \tag{5}$$

† Many authors use J as the symbol for rate coefficient. The subscript numbers refer to the equations involved.

128

Ozone is produced by reaction (3) and consumed by reactions (2) and (4), so the net rate of formation of ozone is given by equation (6), where [M] is the concentration of air:

$$\frac{d[O_3]}{dt} = k_3[O][O_2][M] - j_2[O_3] - k_4[O][O_3] \tag{6}$$

The corresponding expression for the net rate of formation of oxygen atoms is:

$$\frac{d[O]}{dt} = 2j_1[O_2] + j_2[O_3] - k_3[O][O_2][M] - k_4[O][O_3] - 2k_5[O]^2[M] \tag{7}$$

Note that there is a factor of 2 in the first and last terms because two oxygen atoms are produced or consumed each time. The concentration of oxygen atoms in the stratosphere is very low, so the last term can be neglected by comparison with the others because it involves two oxygen atoms. Also this means that the steady-state approximation may be applied to equation (7), and the net rate of formation of oxygen atoms taken as zero, to give:

$$2j_1[O_2] + j_2[O_3] - k_3[O][O_2][M] - k_4[O][O_3] = 0 \tag{8}$$

Then adding equations (6) and (8) gives:

$$\frac{d[O_3]}{dt} = 2j_1[O_2] - 2k_4[O][O_3] \tag{9}$$

Further, at equilibrium the net rate of formation of ozone is also zero, therefore from equation (9):

$$j_1[O_2] = k_4[O][O_3] \tag{10}$$

Hence the concentration of oxygen atoms is given by:

$$[O] = j_1[O_2]/k_4[O_3] \tag{11}$$

Also, a combination of equation (10) and equation (8) gives:

$$j_1[O_2] + j_2[O_3] - k_3[O][O_2][M] = 0 \tag{12}$$

Substituting equation (11) into equation (12) gives:

$$j_1[O_2] + j_2[O_3] - k_3 j_1[O_2]^2[M]/k_4[O_3] = 0 \tag{13}$$

From the data in the Appendix, at 25 km (the height of maximum concentration of ozone) j_1 has a value of 3.79×10^{-12} s^{-1} and j_2 a value of 4.57×10^{-4} s^{-1}. From Table 1, [O$_2$] is 1.5×10^{17} molecules cm^{-3} and [O$_3$] is 3.2×10^{12} molecules cm^{-3} at 25 km. Hence it is apparent that $j_2[O_3] \gg j_1[O_2]$ and so the term $j_1[O_2]$ can be neglected and equation (13) reduces to:

$$k_3 j_1[O_2]^2[M] - k_4 j_2[O_3]^2 = 0 \tag{14}$$

129

Thus

$$[O_3]_{eq} = [O_2](k_3 \, j_1 [M]/k_4 j_2)^{1/2} \tag{15}$$

So from a knowledge of the altitude dependence of j_1 and j_2, and laboratory measurements of k_3 and k_4, the altitude profile of ozone concentration can be computed.

Table 1 Typical temperatures and concentrations of air, oxygen and ozone in the stratosphere (source: Nicolet, 1972)

Altitude/ km	Temperature/ K	Air/ molecules cm^{-3}	Oxygen/ molecules cm^{-3}	Ozone/ molecules cm^{-3}
15	211	3.9×10^{18}	7.8×10^{17}	1.0×10^{12}
20	219	1.9×10^{18}	3.8×10^{17}	2.9×10^{12}
25	227	7.7×10^{17}	1.5×10^{17}	3.2×10^{12}
30	235	3.6×10^{17}	7.2×10^{16}	2.9×10^{12}
35	252	1.7×10^{17}	3.4×10^{16}	2.0×10^{12}
40	268	8.1×10^{16}	1.6×10^{16}	1.0×10^{12}
45	274	4.3×10^{16}	8.6×10^{15}	3.2×10^{11}
50	274	2.3×10^{16}	4.6×10^{15}	1.0×10^{11}

2 Effect of NO$_x$ and ClO$_x$

We established in Chapter 4·4 that the oxygen-only scheme proposed by Chapman is inadequate, and that minor constituents such as NO_x and ClO_x can have a significant effect on the ozone concentration. This can be demonstrated semi-quantitatively as follows, beginning with the NO_x cycle:

$$NO\cdot + O_3 \longrightarrow NO_2\cdot + O_2 \tag{16}$$

$$\underline{NO_2\cdot + O \longrightarrow NO\cdot + O_2} \tag{17}$$

$$\text{net } O_3 + O \longrightarrow 2O_2$$

Another reaction in which NO_2 is converted into NO is:

$$NO_2\cdot + h\nu \longrightarrow NO\cdot + O \tag{18}$$

With addition of the NO_x cycle of reactions, the rate of formation of ozone is now given by:

$$\frac{d[O_3]}{dt} = k_3[O][O_2][M] - j_2[O_3] - k_4[O][O_3] - k_{16}[NO\cdot][O_3] \tag{19}$$

Similarly, the rate of formation of oxygen atoms is given by:

$$\frac{d[O]}{dt} = 2j_1[O_2] + j_2[O_3] + j_{18}[NO_2\cdot] - k_3[O][O_2][M]$$

$$- k_4[O][O_3] - k_{17}[O][NO_2\cdot] \tag{20}$$

We can write an analogous equation for the rate of formation of NO_2:

$$\frac{d[NO_2\cdot]}{dt} = k_{16}[NO\cdot][O_3] - k_{17}[O][NO_2\cdot] - j_{18}[NO_2\cdot] \tag{21}$$

If the steady-state approximation applies, then net rates of formation of O and NO_2 are zero. Then adding equations (19), (20) and (21) gives:

$$\frac{d[O_3]}{dt} = 2j_1[O_2] - 2k_4[O][O_3] - 2k_{17}[O][NO_2\cdot] \tag{22}$$

In equation (22) the first term corresponds to ozone production, while the others correspond to ozone removal. Comparison with equation (9) shows clearly that the NO_x cycle increases the rate of destruction of ozone, while the rate of formation is unaffected. Furthermore, given that at an altitude of 25 km, $[NO_2\cdot]$ is typically 2×10^9 molecules cm^{-3}, it is apparent (see Appendix) that $k_{17}/k_4 = 1.2 \times 10^4$ and $[O_3]/[NO_2\cdot] = 1.6 \times 10^3$, and so $k_{17}[O][NO_2\cdot]$ is greater than $k_4[O][O_3]$ by a factor of about 8. Thus the rate of loss of ozone is considerably greater in an atmosphere containing NO_x than one without; the ratio, termed the catalytic ratio ρ, being given by (23).

$$\rho(NO_x) = 1 + k_{17}[NO_2]/k_4[O_3] \tag{23}$$

This naturally leads to the concentration of ozone in the steady state being reduced.

A similar analysis can be followed for the ClO_x cycle of reactions:

$$Cl\cdot + O_3 \longrightarrow ClO\cdot + O_2 \tag{24}$$

$$\underline{ClO\cdot + O \longrightarrow Cl\cdot + O_2} \tag{25}$$

$$\text{net } O_3 + O \longrightarrow 2O_2$$

This gives the following catalytic ratio:

$$\rho(ClO_x) = 1 + k_{24}[ClO\cdot]/k_4[O_3] \tag{26}$$

In this case k_{24} is about five times greater than k_{17}, and thus the effect of ClO_x in catalysing the combination of ozone with atomic oxygen is even more pronounced than the effect of NO_x.

3 The atmosphere in comparison with the laboratory reactor

To compute the altitude profile of ozone concentration, in addition to the concentrations of the various chemical species, the appropriate k and j values need to be known. The k values can be determined by laboratory measurements, but how are the j values obtained?

We have referred to the atmosphere as a photochemical reactor that can be compared with a conventional steady-state photochemical reactor in the laboratory. In the laboratory reactor, monochromatic radiation of intensity I_0, in the form of a parallel beam, is incident normally on a vessel with transparent windows. The intensity, I_t, of the light transmitted through the cell is dependent on three factors: (i) the absorption coefficient, ϵ_λ, of the single absorbing molecular species at the wavelength, λ, of light being used, (ii) the concentration, c, of the absorber, and (iii) the path length, l. The relationship between these factors is called the Beer–Lambert law, and is given by:

$$\log_{10}\left(\frac{I_0}{I_t}\right) = \epsilon_\lambda c l \qquad (27)$$

The amount of light absorption in the cell, I_a, in the absence of reflection from windows, is simply $I_0 - I_t$. Replacing I_t in equation (27), inverting, and changing to natural logarithms, yields:

$$\log_e\left(1 - \frac{I_a}{I_0}\right) = -2.303\,\epsilon_\lambda c l \qquad (28)$$

For small absorptions, this can be simplified† to:

$$I_a = 2.303\,I_0\,\epsilon_\lambda c l \qquad (29)$$

In this we have used the absorption coefficient, ϵ_λ, which is defined in terms of logarithms to the base 10, and the concentration in molar terms. In aeronomy, concentrations (n) are usually given in units of particles (atoms, molecules or ions) per cm^3, and in order to accommodate this habit, we will transform equation (29) into the equivalent relationship using the absorption cross-section σ_λ in place of ϵ_λ, thus giving:

$$I_a = I_0\sigma_\lambda n l \qquad (30)‡$$

(The 2.303 term is omitted because σ_λ is defined in terms of natural logarithms.) If a photochemical reaction has a quantum yield of ϕ, the rate of the photochemical process is then:

$$\text{rate} = \phi I_0\,\sigma_\lambda n l \qquad (31)$$

---

† $\log_e[1 - (x/a)] \simeq -x/a$ for small values of x/a.
‡ To convert ϵ/l mol^{-1} cm^{-1} (log base 10) into σ/cm^2 $molecule^{-1}$ (log base e), multiply by 3.82×10^{-21}. To convert σ into ϵ, multiply by 2.62×10^{20}.

It is important to recognise the restrictions imposed on a system in order that this simple rate equation should apply: (i) weak absorption of light; (ii) monochromatic exciting light; (iii) uniform concentration of the absorber; (iv) normal incidence of light; (v) single absorbing chemical species.

Let us consider the complications introduced if we progressively remove these restrictions, in the hope of gaining an insight into the complexities of obtaining rate coefficients for atmospheric photochemical reactions.

Strong absorption. If strong absorption occurs, equation (31) must be replaced by its logarithmic form:

$$\text{rate} = \phi I_0 \exp(-\sigma_\lambda nl) \tag{32}$$

For the sake of simplicity it is convenient to assume that in the atmosphere the medium is optically thin, and that the simplified equation (31) is thus valid.

Polychromatic light source. If a polychromatic light source is used, then the quantum yield of reaction will in principle be wavelength dependent, as will the absorption cross-section, σ_λ, and of course the incident intensity, I_λ. The overall rate coefficient j for the reaction must then correspond to the integration of equation (31) over all wavelengths:

$$j = \int_{\lambda=0}^{\infty} \phi_\lambda I_\lambda \sigma_\lambda l \, d\lambda \tag{33}$$

In the laboratory example this integration can be carried out numerically.

Effect of variation of atmospheric pressure. The pressure, p, of atmospheric gas declines exponentially with increase in altitude, and reference to the Beer–Lambert law (equation 27) shows that the rate at which light is absorbed, because it is dependent on the concentrations of absorbing chemical species, must be very strongly dependent on altitude. The effect is illustrated in Figure 1. For a constant gas pressure, as in a laboratory reactor, the intensity of light would decline exponentially with decrease in altitude (curve B), whereas in the real atmosphere, most of the light is absorbed in a relatively narrow layer of the atmosphere (shown shaded in Figure 1).

Variation in solar zenith angle. The angle that the Sun's rays make with the normal to the Earth's surface is called the solar zenith angle, χ, (Figure 2). This angle varies throughout the day and seasonally, which has the effect of altering the path length for light absorption. Thus the rate at which light is absorbed is strongly dependent on the zenith angle.

Figure 3 shows that as the zenith angle increases, the 'layer' in the atmosphere in which a particular photochemical reaction occurs moves to higher altitudes.

Competitive absorption. To return to the laboratory reactor, the irradiation of mixtures of gases often results in simultaneous absorption by more

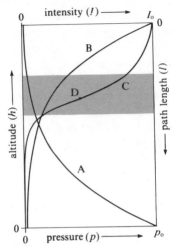

FIGURE 1   The absorption of light in the atmosphere. Curve A shows the variation of gas pressure with altitude. Curve B shows the variation of light intensity with depth at *constant* gas pressure. Curve C shows the variation of intensity with depth when the pressure increases exponentially (as in curve A). The rate of absorption of light is given by the slope of curve C, and this is at a maximum near the altitude of point D. (source: McEwan and Phillips, 1975)

than one chemical species. The rate of photochemical reaction of one of the species is thus dependent on the fraction, F, of light intensity that is absorbed by that species; this is given by:

$$F = \frac{\sigma_1 n_1}{(\sigma_1 n_1 + \sigma_2 n_2 \cdots \sigma_m n_m)} \tag{34}$$

where $1, 2, \ldots, m$ are all the different species present. In the atmosphere, competitive absorption by atmospheric constituents requires in principle the estimation of fractional absorption by each component in the same way. It can thus be seen that precise evaluation of j for a particular atmospheric reaction is difficult. Accepted recent values are given in the Appendix (p. 139).

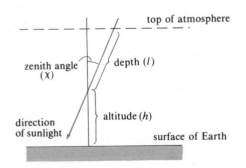

FIGURE 2   The definition of the solar zenith angle. (source: McEwan and Phillips, 1975)

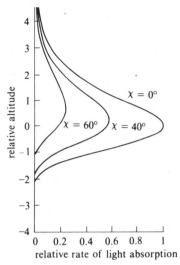

FIGURE 3   The absorption of light at different solar zenith angles. As the value of χ increases, so the absorption maximum (the peak of the curve) moves to à higher altitude. In this diagram, zero relative altitude corresponds to the maximum rate of absorption (1.0) for $\chi = 0°$. (source: McEwan and Phillips, 1975)

4   Transport processes

In the derivation of the steady-state ozone concentration in Section 1 it was assumed that transport processes (eddy diffusion) were unimportant. This is only valid if the time-scale for a system to come to chemical equilibrium is short (less than a year). It turns out that the equilibrium time-scale for ozone is given by:

$$\tau_{eq} = \frac{[O_3]_{eq}}{2j_1[O_2]} \tag{35}$$

If τ_{eq} is longer than a year, physical transport processes become appreciable and have to be included in any modelling. Figure 4 shows that above 15 km, τ_{eq} is less than one year, whereas below it is longer, and transport processes are of prime importance.

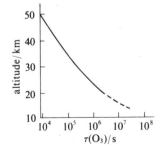

FIGURE 4   The equilibrium time-scale, in seconds, for ozone in a pure oxygen atmosphere, as a function of altitude for an overhead Sun. The time-scale is about a day at 50 km and more than a year below 15 km. (source: Okabe, 1978)

135

5 Effects of variation in temperature

The photochemical generation of reactive chemical species, particularly atoms and radicals, results in large numbers of non-photochemical reactions proceeding in the atmosphere. Attempts to understand the atmosphere as a kinetic reactor thus rely on accurate laboratory measurements of rate constants, k, for a myriad thermal reactions. In particular, the temperature dependence of the rate constant is of importance, and this is usually reported in the form of the Arrhenius parameters A and E:

$$k = A \exp(-E/RT) \tag{36}$$

Measurements are often fitted empirically to equation (36) over a limited temperature range. Curiously there are many reactions of importance in the atmosphere for which the activation energy, E, is of opposite sign to that normally found; that is, a negative temperature coefficient is encountered. Rate parameters for 62 non-photochemical reactions of stratospheric importance are given in the Appendix (p. 140). It is clear that as the rates of many of these reactions are temperature dependent, a good knowledge of the temperature of the region of the atmosphere of concern is required, and because the temperature in the atmosphere varies greatly with altitude, rates will be strongly altitude dependent in some cases. In general, as stratospheric temperatures are not high, thermal reactions of importance are those with low activation energies.

6 Formulation of models

We are now in a position to see how kinetic models of atmospheric reactions can be formulated. In principle, all that is required is the writing of an equation (like equation 6) for each component, i, of the atmosphere, taking into account transport processes, and recognising that in such equations the production rates and loss rates will, in general, be complex functions involving photochemical rate coefficients and rate constants multiplied by concentrations. The solution of the set of coupled differential equations for all components will then lead to evaluation of the concentrations of all components. Such calculations can in principle be carried out as a function of altitude, solar zenith angle, value of the coefficient of eddy diffusion, etc. Of course, when it is recognised that even a simple model of the stratosphere uses 17 photochemical and some 62 thermal reactions (see Appendix) it is easily seen that a complete solution of this problem is out of the question. Many simplifying approximations have thus to be introduced. These may commonly be the neglect of large numbers of reactions, as in the analysis in Sections 1 and 2, although this is perilous.

As an example of modelling we can quote that used by the American scientist Paul Crutzen for stratospheric ozone in the 16–50 km altitude region. The model is one-dimensional, so that transport is vertical only. A constant solar zenith angle of 44° 25', such that sec $\chi = 1.4$, was adopted, and for numerical computations the atmosphere was divided into layers of 1 km thickness. The results of this calculation are shown in Figure 5 to be in reasonable agreement with observation.

A simpler approach has been taken by Johnston and Podolske. These authors recognised that among the scores of simultaneous reactions in the stratosphere there are some cycles which have a 'null' effect on a component of interest, in this case ozone. One such 'null' cycle involving chlorine and nitrogen is:

$$Cl\cdot + O_3 \longrightarrow ClO\cdot + O_2 \qquad (37)$$

$$ClO\cdot + NO\cdot \longrightarrow Cl\cdot + NO_2\cdot \qquad (38)$$

$$NO_2\cdot + h\nu \longrightarrow NO\cdot + O \qquad (39)$$

$$O + O_2 + M \longrightarrow O_3 + M \qquad (40)$$

net null

The treatment takes the complex 79-component mechanism for stratospheric reactions given in the Appendix and transforms the usual continuity equation for ozone to a form where every term is the *rate-determining* step in one or more *catalytic* cycles or sequences which form or destroy ozone, and thus

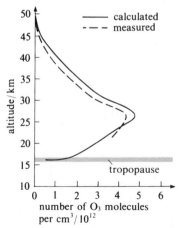

FIGURE 5   Calculated and measured vertical profiles of ozone concentration. (source: Crutzen, 1974)

137

eliminates *null* cycles. The treatment certainly does not displace more rigorous model calculations, but is supplementary, and is extremely useful in that in some cases the simple one-step calculation allows firm conclusions to be reached concerning specific problems in the atmosphere when more complete models are insoluble.

7 Appendix
(source: Johnston and Podolske, 1978)

This Appendix lists typical reactions that are considered in the modelling of stratospheric chemistry. Reactions circled are those discussed in Chapters 4·3–4·6 that are involved in catalytic cycles leading to the destruction of ozone.

Values of j/s^{-1} (global average)

Photochemical reactions	15 km	25 km	35 km	45 km
① $O_2 + h\nu \longrightarrow O + O$	2.92×10^{-15}	3.79×10^{-12}	9.40×10^{-11}	4.32×10^{-10}
② $O_3 + h\nu \longrightarrow O_2 + O$	4.12×10^{-4}	4.57×10^{-4}	4.95×10^{-4}	5.09×10^{-4}
③ $O_3 + h\nu \longrightarrow O_2 + O(^1D)$	1.54×10^{-5}	7.32×10^{-5}	5.04×10^{-4}	2.96×10^{-3}
④ $NO_2^{\cdot} + h\nu \longrightarrow NO^{\cdot} + O$	8.27×10^{-3}	9.21×10^{-3}	9.62×10^{-3}	9.83×10^{-3}
5 $N_2O + h\nu \longrightarrow N_2 + O(^1D)$	2.44×10^{-12}	3.80×10^{-9}	7.00×10^{-8}	2.06×10^{-7}
6 $NO^{\cdot} + h\nu \longrightarrow N^{\cdot} + O$	7.30×10^{-37}	7.45×10^{-17}	1.27×10^{-8}	3.43×10^{-7}
7 $HNO_3 + h\nu \longrightarrow \cdot OH + NO_2^{\cdot}$	4.25×10^{-7}	1.78×10^{-6}	1.59×10^{-5}	4.36×10^{-5}
8 $H_2O_2 + h\nu \longrightarrow 2\cdot OH$	2.23×10^{-5}	2.98×10^{-5}	4.52×10^{-5}	8.03×10^{-5}
9 $HO_2^{\cdot} + h\nu \longrightarrow \cdot OH + O$	—	—	—	—
10 $NO_3^{\cdot} + h\nu \longrightarrow NO^{\cdot} + O_2$	—	—	—	—
11 $NO_3^{\cdot} + h\nu \longrightarrow NO_2^{\cdot} + O$	—	—	—	—
12 $H_2CO + h\nu \longrightarrow H^{\cdot} + HCO^{\cdot}$	—	—	—	—
13 $H_2CO + h\nu \longrightarrow H_2 + CO$	—	—	—	—
⑭ $CCl_2F_2 + h\nu \longrightarrow \cdot CClF_2 + Cl^{\cdot}$	5.81×10^{-12}	1.16×10^{-8}	2.45×10^{-7}	8.00×10^{-7}
⑮ $CCl_3F + h\nu \longrightarrow \cdot CCl_2F + Cl^{\cdot}$	1.34×10^{-10}	1.89×10^{-7}	3.31×10^{-6}	8.66×10^{-6}
⑯ $ClONO_2 + h\nu \longrightarrow ClO^{\cdot} + NO_2^{\cdot}$	—	—	—	—
17 $HOONO_2 + h\nu \longrightarrow HO_2^{\cdot} + NO_2^{\cdot}$	—	—	—	—

Thermal reactions	A/cm^3 molecule^{-1} s^{-1}	$E/\text{J mol}^{-1}$
⑱ $O + O_2 + M \longrightarrow O_3 + M$	1.07×10^{-34}	$-4\,200$
⑲ $O + O_3 \longrightarrow O_2 + O_2$	1.9×10^{-11}	$19\,100$
⑳ $O_3 + NO\cdot \longrightarrow NO_2\cdot + O_2$	2.1×10^{-12}	$12\,100$
㉑ $O + NO_2\cdot \longrightarrow NO\cdot + O_2$	9.1×10^{-12}	0
22 $N_2O + O(^1D) \longrightarrow N_2 + O_2$	5.5×10^{-11}	0
㉓ $N_2O + O(^1D) \longrightarrow NO\cdot + NO\cdot$	5.5×10^{-11}	0
24 $N\cdot + O_2 \longrightarrow NO\cdot + O$	5.5×10^{-12}	$26\,800$
25 $N\cdot + NO\cdot \longrightarrow N_2 + O$	8.2×10^{-11}	$3\,400$
26 $N\cdot + NO_2\cdot \longrightarrow 2NO\cdot$	2.0×10^{-11}	$6\,700$
27 $O(^1D) + H_2O \longrightarrow 2\cdot OH$	2.3×10^{-10}	0
28 $O(^1D) + CH_4 \longrightarrow \cdot OH + \cdot CH_3$	1.3×10^{-10}	0
㉙ $O_3 + \cdot OH \longrightarrow O_2 + HO_2\cdot$	1.5×10^{-12}	$8\,300$
㉚ $O + \cdot OH \longrightarrow H\cdot + O_2$	1.0×10^{-10}	$2\,100$
㉛ $O_3 + HO_2\cdot \longrightarrow \cdot OH + O_2 + O_2$	1.0×10^{-13}	$12\,700$
32 $O + HO_2\cdot \longrightarrow \cdot OH + O_2$	1.0×10^{-10}	$2\,100$
33 $H\cdot + O_2 + M \longrightarrow HO_2\cdot + M$	2.1×10^{-32}†	$-2\,400$
㉞ $H\cdot + O_3 \longrightarrow \cdot OH + O_2$	1.2×10^{-10}	$4\,700$
35 $HO_2\cdot + HO_2\cdot \longrightarrow H_2O_2 + O_2$	5.0×10^{-12}	$4\,200$
36 $\cdot OH + HO_2\cdot \longrightarrow H_2O + O_2$	5.1×10^{-11}	0
37 $\cdot OH + NO_2\cdot + M \longrightarrow HNO_3 + M$	*	—
38 $\cdot OH + HNO_3 \longrightarrow H_2O + NO_3\cdot$	8.0×10^{-14}	0
39 $\cdot OH + H_2O_2 \longrightarrow H_2O + HO_2\cdot$	1.0×10^{-11}	$6\,200$
40 $N_2 + O(^1D) + M \longrightarrow N_2O + M$	3.5×10^{-37}†	0
41 $N\cdot + NO_2\cdot \longrightarrow N_2O + O$	2.0×10^{-11}	$6\,700$
42 $NO\cdot + O + M \longrightarrow NO_2\cdot + M$	1.55×10^{-33}†	$-4\,900$
43 $HO_2\cdot + NO\cdot \longrightarrow \cdot OH + NO_2\cdot$	8.0×10^{-12}	$-2\,100$
44 $\cdot OH + \cdot OH \longrightarrow H_2O + O$	1.0×10^{-11}	$4\,600$
45 $N\cdot + O_3 \longrightarrow NO\cdot + O_2$	5.0×10^{-12}	$5\,400$
46 $NO_2\cdot + O_3 \longrightarrow NO_3\cdot + O_2$	1.2×10^{-13}	$20\,400$
47 $\cdot OH + CH_4 \longrightarrow H_2O + \cdot CH_3$	2.35×10^{-12}	$14\,200$
48 $\cdot OH + \cdot OH + M \longrightarrow H_2O_2 + M$	1.25×10^{-32}†	$-7\,500$
49 $H_2O_2 + O \longrightarrow \cdot OH + HO_2\cdot$	2.75×10^{-12}	$17\,700$
50 $O(^1D) + M \longrightarrow O + M$	2.0×10^{-11}	-900
51 $\cdot CH_3 + \frac{11}{4}O_2 \longrightarrow \frac{1}{2}H_2O + 2HO_2\cdot + CO$	—	—
52 $\cdot CH_3 + O_2 + M \longrightarrow CH_3OO\cdot + M$	2.6×10^{-31}†	$4\,200$
53 $CH_3OO\cdot + NO\cdot \longrightarrow CH_3O\cdot + NO_2\cdot$	3.3×10^{-12}	$4\,200$

Thermal reactions	A/cm^3 molecule^{-1}s^{-1}	$E/\text{J mol}^{-1}$
54 $CH_3O\cdot + O_2 \longrightarrow H_2CO + HO_2\cdot$	1.6×10^{-13}	27 400
55 $\cdot CH_3 + O_2 \longrightarrow H_2CO + \cdot OH$	3.0×10^{-16}	—
56 $HCO\cdot + O_2 \longrightarrow CO + HO_2\cdot$	6.0×10^{-12}	—
57 $\cdot OH + CO \longrightarrow CO_2 + H\cdot$	1.4×10^{-13}	0
58 $\cdot OH + H_2 \longrightarrow H_2O + H\cdot$	3.6×10^{-11}	21 500
59 $O(^1D) + H_2 \longrightarrow \cdot OH + H\cdot$	9.9×10^{-11}	0
60 $\cdot OH + H_2CO \longrightarrow H_2O + HCO\cdot$	1.4×10^{-11}	—
61 $O_3 + O(^1D) \longrightarrow O_2 + O_2$	1.2×10^{-10}	0
62 $O_3 + O(^1D) \longrightarrow O_2 + O + O$	1.2×10^{-10}	0
⑥③ $Cl\cdot + O_3 \longrightarrow ClO\cdot + O_2$	2.7×10^{-11}	2 100
⑥④ $ClO\cdot + O \longrightarrow Cl\cdot + O_2$	7.7×10^{-11}	1 100
⑥⑤ $ClO\cdot + NO\cdot \longrightarrow Cl\cdot + NO_2\cdot$	2.2×10^{-11}	$-1\,700$
66 $Cl\cdot + H_2 \longrightarrow HCl + H\cdot$	3.5×10^{-11}	19 000
67 $Cl\cdot + HO_2\cdot \longrightarrow HCl + O_2$	3.0×10^{-11}	0
68 $Cl\cdot + CH_4 \longrightarrow HCl + \cdot CH_3$	7.3×10^{-12}	10 500
69 $Cl\cdot + H_2O_2 \longrightarrow HCl + HO_2\cdot$	1.7×10^{-12}	3 200
70 $\cdot OH + HCl \longrightarrow H_2O + Cl\cdot$	3.0×10^{-12}	3 500
71 $ClO\cdot + NO_2\cdot + M \longrightarrow ClONO_2 + M$	5.1×10^{-33}†	$-8\,600$
72 $CCl_2F_2 + O(^1D) \longrightarrow ClO\cdot + \cdot CClF_2$	2.0×10^{-10}	0
73 $CCl_3F + O(^1D) \longrightarrow ClO\cdot + \cdot CCl_2F$	2.3×10^{-10}	0
74 $ClONO_2 + O \longrightarrow O_2 + ClO\cdot + NO\cdot$	4.5×10^{-12}	7 000
75 $HO_2\cdot + NO_2\cdot + M \longrightarrow HOONO_2 + M$	1.0×10^{-32}†	0
76 $HOONO_2 + O \longrightarrow \cdot OH + NO_2\cdot + O_2$	—	0
77 $2NO\cdot + O_2 \longrightarrow 2NO_2\cdot$	3.3×10^{-39}†	$-4\,400$
⑦⑧ $O + O + M \longrightarrow O_2 + M$	4.8×10^{-33}†	0
79 $NO\cdot + NO_3\cdot \longrightarrow 2NO_2\cdot$	1.9×10^{-11}	0

† Units of cm^6 molecule^{-2} s^{-2}

* This is given as $(4.0 \times 10^{-12} \times [M])/(1.12 \times 10^{18} + [M])$

4·6 Chlorofluorocarbons and stratospheric ozone

by F. Sherwood Rowland (University of California)

The fully halogenated chlorofluorocarbons, such as CCl_2F_2 and CCl_3F, were originally synthesised 50 years ago in the culmination of a search for an inert chemical compound useable for refrigeration. During the 1930s, CCl_2F_2 rapidly replaced the chemically noxious or flammable gases then in use, and is now the most widely employed refrigerant gas in the world. The combination in the chlorofluorocarbons of inertness and volatility has since proven valuable in many additional commercial applications, most of which share the characteristic that sooner or later the gases are released and spread through the troposphere. The same chemical inertness continues when these compounds are exposed to the atmosphere, and no important removal processes affect the chlorofluorocarbons in the troposphere.

Diatomic chlorine, Cl_2, absorbs visible radiation (hence its green colour) and is decomposed by it within an hour or so during daylight hours. Molecules such as HCl, while transparent to visible and near-ultraviolet radiation, are highly soluble in water and are removed from the troposphere during rainfall. Still other compounds are destroyed in the troposphere by chemical reactions, often those involving hydroxyl radicals. However, the chlorofluorocarbons are transparent in the visible and near-ultraviolet regions of the solar spectrum, essentially insoluble in water, chemically inert toward the reactive species found in the troposphere, and can survive there unchanged for many decades.

Appreciable photochemical reactivity occurs for the chlorofluorocarbons only after upward diffusion into the mid-stratosphere, where they are exposed to the short-wavelength ultraviolet radiation that does not penetrate to lower altitudes. The absorption of this ultraviolet radiation by a chlorofluorocarbon molecule releases highly reactive chlorine atoms which proceed to react rapidly with the other chemical compounds found in the stratosphere, most often through removal of an oxygen atom from an ozone molecule. This chapter is concerned with the chemical, physical and biological consequences of this interaction between chlorine and ozone in the stratosphere.

The most widely used chlorofluorocarbon compounds currently are CCl_2F_2 and CCl_3F, with 1981 world-wide production rates of approximately 400 000 and 300 000 tonnes per annum, respectively. These colourless, odourless molecules are often identified in industrial shorthand as molecules FC-11 (CCl_3F) and FC-12 (CCl_2F_2), with a prefix such as Propellant-12 or

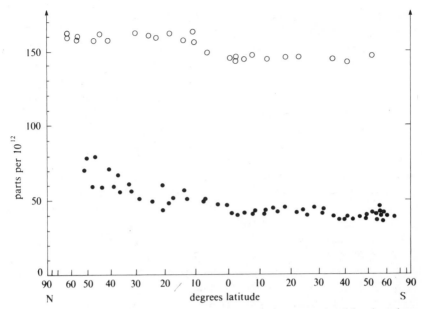

FIGURE 1 Levels of CCl₃F (FC-11) in the atmosphere at ground level as determined in 1971 (by Lovelock; *filled circles*) and 1979 (by Rowland, Tyler and Montague; *open circles*). The 1979 measurements represent a world-wide atmospheric burden of CCl₃F of approximately 4×10^9 kg, almost equal to the estimated amount manufactured and released to the atmosphere in the entire world to that date.

Refrigerant-12 which identifies its intended use, or a trade-name such as Freon-11 (du Pont Co.) or Arcton-11 (I.C.I.). A mixture of FC-11 and FC-12 makes an effective propellant for aerosol sprays; FC-11 is a blowing agent in the manufacture of plastic foams; etc. The concentrations of both CCl_3F and CCl_2F_2 are steadily increasing in the Earth's atmosphere. The extent of this increase is shown for CCl_3F in Figure 1.

1 The chemistry of chlorofluorocarbons in the atmosphere

Molecules such as CCl_3F and CCl_2F_2 eventually rise randomly into the stratosphere, mixed in large volumes of air with all of the other atmospheric components. All these gases are protected while in the troposphere against exposure to solar radiation with wavelengths shorter than 295 nm because this energetic radiation is efficiently absorbed at higher altitudes by stratospheric ozone. (The same protection is provided as well to all earth-bound biological species, including man, and has led to the descriptive term, 'ozone shield'.) However, as molecules rise above this absorbing ozone, they are progressively exposed to the more energetic parts of the solar spectrum, beginning around 25 km altitude with the wavelengths between 200 and 220 nm.

Neither CCl_2F_2 nor CCl_3F is transparent to 200 nm radiation, and absorption of this radiation leads immediately to bond rupture, releasing one atom of chlorine plus a residual radical:

$$CCl_2F_2 + hv \longrightarrow Cl\cdot + \cdot CClF_2 \qquad (1)$$

$$CCl_3F + hv \longrightarrow Cl\cdot + \cdot CCl_2F \qquad (2)$$

This photodecomposition between 25 and 40 km is the most important atmospheric removal process for these chlorofluorocarbon molecules. On the average, a period of about 50–80 years elapses between the release of molecules of CCl_3F at ground level and photochemical destruction at these altitudes. The molecules of CCl_2F_2 absorb ultraviolet radiation less strongly, and have an estimated average lifetime of about 90–150 years. The residual radicals from reactions such as (1) and (2) interact quickly with atmospheric oxygen, eventually releasing all of the chlorine either as $Cl\cdot$ or $ClO\cdot$. Chlorine atoms released in the stratosphere react with ozone by reaction (3), forming $ClO\cdot$. The $ClO\cdot$ radicals often react with O atoms by reaction (4), especially at altitudes above 30 km, releasing $Cl\cdot$ again and completing one cycle of the ClO_x catalytic chain.

$$Cl\cdot + O_3 \longrightarrow ClO\cdot + O_2 \qquad (3)$$

$$ClO\cdot + O \longrightarrow Cl\cdot + O_2 \qquad (4)$$

The stratospheric chain carriers in the various catalytic cycles ($Cl\cdot$, $ClO\cdot$, $NO\cdot$, $NO_2\cdot$, $H\cdot$, $\cdot OH$, $HO_2\cdot$) are all radicals, and are able to interact with one another through reactions such as (5)–(10):

$$ClO\cdot + NO\cdot \longrightarrow Cl\cdot + NO_2\cdot \qquad (5)$$

$$Cl\cdot + CH_4 \longrightarrow HCl + \cdot CH_3 \qquad (6)$$

$$\cdot OH + HCl \longrightarrow Cl\cdot + H_2O \qquad (7)$$

$$ClO\cdot + NO_2\cdot + M \longrightarrow ClONO_2 + M \qquad (8)$$

$$ClO\cdot + HO_2\cdot \longrightarrow HOCl + O_2 \qquad (9)$$

$$HO_2\cdot + NO\cdot \longrightarrow \cdot OH + NO_2\cdot \qquad (10)$$

Sometimes, two chain carriers react to form chemically stable molecules, such as $ClONO_2$ and $HOCl$ by reactions (8) and (9), providing temporary havens from the continuing chain processes. However, both of these molecules absorb strongly at wavelengths longer than 295 nm and undergo rapid photodissociation at all altitudes. The formation of HCl by reaction of $Cl\cdot$

with CH_4 shifts the radical chain carrier from $Cl\cdot$ to $\cdot CH_3$, as in reaction (6), only for the $Cl\cdot$ to be returned to the ClO_x chain again by reaction (7). On the average, each $Cl\cdot$ atom released into the stratosphere at an altitude of 30 km removes several tens of thousands of ozone molecules before arriving back in the troposphere in the chemical form of HCl many months later.

Tropospheric measurements during 1980 in remote locations away from urban sources showed substantial concentrations of several organochlorine compounds, including (in parts per 10^{10} by volume) CH_3Cl (6), CCl_2F_2 (3), CCl_3F (1.7), CCl_4 (1.2), and CH_3CCl_3 (1.4). Among these organochlorine compounds, only CH_3Cl is likely to have existed in the atmosphere in any significant concentration in the year 1900, because the others are almost entirely the product of human activities during the twentieth century.

Production of CCl_3F, CCl_2F_2, and CH_3CCl_3 has been increasing by 10 to 15% per annum on average over the past 25 years, corresponding to doubling of the atmospheric release rate every 5 to 7 years. (Production of CCl_3F and CCl_2F_2 has levelled off since the early 1970s.) Measurements at ground level have shown rapid increases during the 1970s in the atmospheric concentrations of CCl_2F_2, CCl_3F (Figure 1) and CH_3CCl_3. Examination of infrared spectrograms made from balloons at an altitude of 30 km has also shown steady increases in the concentration of CCl_3F in the lower stratosphere since 1968. Estimates of the atmospheric lifetimes of CCl_3F and CCl_2F_2 can be made from these tropospheric increases, and consistently indicate atmospheric lifetimes of at least several decades, confirming that no major tropospheric removal processes exist. On the other hand, the molecules of CH_3CCl_3 last for only about 7 years because of their reactivity toward hydroxyl radicals in the troposphere.

Because the concentration of ClO_x in the stratosphere is determined by the total concentration of inert chlorine-containing molecules in the troposphere, the observed increases in CCl_3F and CCl_2F_2 must inevitably be followed a few years later by an increase in stratospheric ClO_x, delayed only by the time required for upward mixing. The atmospheric chemistry of chlorine is relatively simple above 40 km because the intense ultraviolet radiation rapidly destroys most chemical bonds, and only $Cl\cdot$, $ClO\cdot$, and HCl can contain any appreciable fraction of the total chlorine. The average lifetime for a newly formed molecule of ozone between 40 and 50 km is controlled by the available removal processes, of which the ClO_x chain is one of the most important. With increasing stratospheric concentrations of $Cl\cdot$ and $ClO\cdot$, the lifetime of ozone at 40 km will decrease, and the average ozone concentration will decrease in turn. All of the atmospheric model calculations are in agreement that continued release into the atmosphere of CCl_3F and CCl_2F_2 at 1981 rates will eventually lead to a large decrease (30–50%) in the average world-wide ozone concentration at 40 km.

145

Because the absorption of ultraviolet radiation by ozone is the primary heat source for the stratosphere, a diminution in ozone concentration at 40 km will result in less heat being released there, and temperatures in the upper stratosphere will decrease. (Much of this radiation would then be absorbed at lower altitudes and would release heat there, further altering the profile of temperature versus altitude in the stratosphere.)

In the lower atmosphere, with most of the short-wavelength radiation absorbed at higher altitudes by oxygen and ozone, accurate description of the chemistry is much more complicated than at 40 km, and many more chemical species and many more chemical reactions need to be considered. The chemical transformation times can stretch out to many months, and the chemical distribution found in a particular volume of air then becomes dependent on the prior history of this air mass over that period of months—in other words, the observed chemistry becomes strongly dependent on the accompanying meteorology.

The response of the atmosphere to potential perturbations by mankind is also more complex at 20–30 km altitudes because of the intricate interactions among the ClO_x, NO_x, and HO_x chains, as evidenced by reactions such as (5)–(10) and the presence of molecules such as $HONO_2$, $ClONO_2$ and $HOCl$. When these molecules have appreciable lifetimes, an increase in NO_x can result in tying up HO_x as $HONO_2$, thereby reducing the efficiency of the HO_x chain in the removal of ozone at some altitudes. These feedback processes are made more complex, too, in predictions of the possible perturbations because diminution of ozone at 40 km permits increased penetration of ultraviolet radiation to 30 km and to 20 km, and the solar irradiation conditions are altered as well as the overall concentrations of the various chemical species.

2 Modelling and measurement

Such atmospheric interactions can be simulated by numerical models of varying complexity in the treatment of both chemical and meteorological processes. As more and more chemical species and chemical reactions are included, computational limitations restrict the meteorological details that can be included. The frequently used one-dimensional models consider variations in chemical concentrations and irradiation conditions only in the vertical dimension, using some average atmospheric condition otherwise (often those at 30°N latitude, averaged over all longitudes). Such calculations should work well at 40 km with the proper input for solar radiation, but are quite dependent for accuracy at 20 km on satisfactory representation of the average conditions of meteorological transport. In contrast, the existing three-dimensional (latitude, longitude, altitude) models can be made self-consistent from a meteorological standpoint (e.g., winds derived from atmospheric gradients in the input of solar radiation) only at the expense of chemical simulation at a primitive level because of computational limitations. The limitation is not solely computational, however, because fully valid three-dimensional models require a complex grid of simultaneous meteorological and chemical observations, which are simply not yet available.

The distribution of chlorine among the various chemical species is shown in Figure 2 for a typical one-dimensional model, using 1980 chlorine concentrations. Numerous different analytical techniques have been applied to the determination of stratospheric concentrations of the chemical species in Figure 2, and for the companion compounds in the HO_x and NO_x series. For example, both Cl· and ClO· have been determined in situ by atomic resonance fluorescence (before measurement, ClO· can be converted into Cl· by reaction with NO·); HCl has been measured both by balloon-borne infrared spectrometry and by collection on hydroxide-coated filters. In general, the

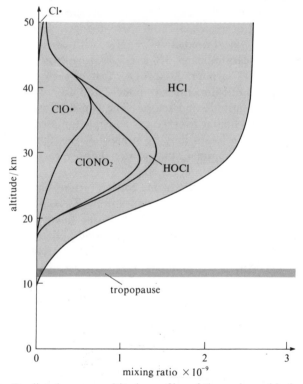

FIGURE 2 Predicted average altitude profiles of the various chlorine-containing chemical species according to a typical one-dimensional model for 1980. The mixing ratio is the ratio by volume of each component to the total in the atmosphere.

various experimental results for Cl·, ClO· and HCl are consistent with the calculations made with the one-dimensional models. In particular measurements some problems can arise, and intensive further experimentation is being carried out to provide more and more detailed chemical maps of the stratosphere for various latitudes, altitudes, times of day, seasons, etc. Molecules such as HOCl and $ClONO_2$ are calculated to be present only in low concentrations, and satisfactory measurements for these are still lacking.

Predictions of the future effects on stratospheric ozone concentrations of the continued release of chlorofluorocarbons have been made since 1974. The initial estimates suggested possible eventual losses of about 10% of the total ozone, and subsequent estimates have oscillated roughly about that figure. (The 1979 reports by the UK Department of the Environment and by the US National Academy of Sciences were in general agreement then on a range of 11–17%, and newer 1981 calculations with some revised estimates of lower stratospheric chemistry place the expected long-term depletion of ozone at about 10%.) In these predictive models, the chlorofluorocarbons accumulate in the troposphere, ClO_x increases in the stratosphere, and the average total ozone concentration decreases, with all these changes occurring on a time-scale of decades. A typical predictive scenario, with constant chlorofluorocarbon input each year, indicates 3% average ozone loss by the year 2000, 6% by 2035, and 10% around 2100 A.D. Most of such calculations have been performed with one-dimensional models, and do not give information about changes with latitude and season. The two-dimensional models (latitude, altitude) show similar average ozone depletion estimates, while suggesting that percentage losses may be somewhat less than average in the tropics and during the summer, and greater than average in polar regions and in the winter and spring.

Measurements of atmospheric ozone concentrations have been made for about 50 years in a few locations (e.g. Arosa in the Swiss Alps), and in many for 20 years or so. The observed levels of ozone fluctuate daily, and the monthly averages vary with both season and latitude. Observers have earlier sought to establish whether long-term oscillations or trends exist in these measured natural ozone levels, and have long suspected that the variations in the 11-year solar sunspot cycle may initiate variations in the atmospheric ozone content. (The emission of more ultraviolet radiation near 200 nm during maximum sunspot activity can cause the photodissociation of more oxygen, thereby causing more ozone to be formed.) The maximum sunspot activity during the current solar cycle was reached during 1980–1981.

The detection of any long-term changes in ozone caused by the release of chlorofluorocarbons must be carried out against this background of fluctuations in the natural level, as well as the possibility of effects from other human activities. Small changes in the observed levels of ozone can be calculated for the period 1960–1980 through increases in atmospheric CO_2, and from the release of NO_x accompanying increased use of commercial subsonic jet aircraft. Most evaluations conclude that changes in average ozone levels of 3–5% over a decade might be needed before the existence of such a change could be placed on a firm statistical basis. In contrast, the present level of ozone depletion from the release of chlorofluorocarbons is estimated as approximately 1%, well below this level of detectability. Recent satellite observations, however, indicate that the decrease in the ozone level at 40 km during the decade of the 1970s was indeed about 5%.

3   Consequences of ozone depletion

The possible consequences for the Earth and its inhabitants of future depletion of stratospheric ozone can be summarised into two physical consequences, and three areas of ecological concern. Ultraviolet radiation in the 290–320 nm range (UV-B radiation) is partially absorbed in the atmosphere by ozone, but a fraction of it penetrates all the way to the Earth's surface. (This partial penetration to the surface of UV-B is routinely used at Arosa and many other surface locations as the basis for daily measurements of ozone concentrations overhead.) If the total column of ozone were to decrease by 10%, then there would be an increase of about 20% in the amount of UV-B received at the surface. The second physical consequence has been discussed earlier—the predicted decrease in stratospheric temperature accompanying ozone depletion at 40 km altitude.

The three major environmental concerns are: (i) will an increase in UV-B have a deleterious effect on human beings? (ii) will an increase in UV-B have deleterious effects on any other plant or animal biological species? (iii) can changes in the amounts or distribution of stratospheric ozone influence the world climate?

The major effects of UV-B radiation on humans occur in the skin, which intercepts and absorbs the radiation. The incidence of human skin cancer has been correlated with the intensity of UV-B exposure, and an average ozone depletion of 10% is now predicted to cause a 30–50% increase in human skin cancer. One of the major experimental bases for this prediction is the well-established correlation of the incidence of skin cancer with latitude, as illustrated in Figure 3. The total intensity of UV-B is greater near the equator both because on average less ozone is found there, and also because the Sun is more nearly overhead so the radiation has a shorter path through the atmosphere. One of the forms of human skin cancer, malignant melanoma, is relatively rare but accounts for an important fraction of human mortality from skin cancer. While the relationship between UV-B exposure and mela-

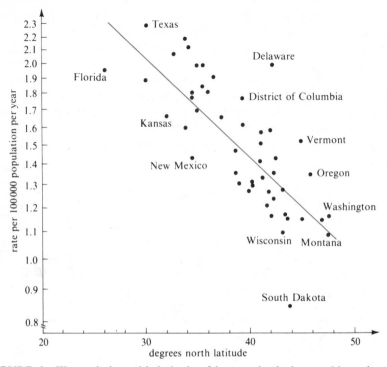

FIGURE 3   The variation with latitude of human death due to skin melanoma among white males in the United States (excluding Alaska and Hawaii) for 1960. (source: Scotto, Fears and Gori, 1975)

noma is less certain than for the other forms of skin cancer, both Scandinavian and American medical investigators have concluded that UV-B is a major causative factor for melanoma.

The possible effects of increased UV-B levels on other biological species are much more difficult to evaluate. Many animals and plants are certainly sensitive to the UV-B level in the environment, but very few field experiments have been performed which can provide details of the systematic response to be expected with increased UV-B levels. The biological complexity is deepened by the dependence of higher order species on the results of the competitions among the lower orders. With tiny species such as plankton, UV-B radiation is absorbed throughout and not just in the surface layers as with larger species. Alterations or disruptions in the ecological competition among species of plankton could then be passed upward through the food-chain. However, without satisfactory detailed models of biological competition in nature as it now exists, predictions of the overall biological consequences of future perturbations of ozone concentrations cannot be done with any degree of confidence.

Similarly, without satisfactory models for prediction of the current characteristics of climate, the possible perturbations to it from changes in the concentration of stratospheric ozone cannot be ascertained even on a qualitative basis. Most of the mass and most of the energy of the atmosphere are contained within the troposphere, and changes in the stratospheric temperature structure are unlikely to force direct tropospheric responses. However, the coupling of energy and momentum between the troposphere and the stratosphere is an intricate relationship, and the possibility is very much present that stratospheric changes can either trigger or turn off complex tropospheric interactions.

In sum, the depletion of stratospheric ozone has one known direct consequence—an expected increase in the incidence of human skin cancer. In addition, two potentially far more serious effects could be involved: (i) disruption of the ecological cycles of other biological species, including some of those involved in food-chains; (ii) changes in the Earth's climate. All this has led to efforts, notably in North America and Scandinavia, to curtail future emissions of CCl_2F_2 and CCl_3F to the atmosphere by regulations restricting their use. If the current pattern of atmospheric release were to be continued until ozone depletion had been definitely established to have occurred, then the level of depletion would probably need to reach an average ozone loss of 5% or greater because of the large fluctuations in natural levels. Even if direct release to the atmosphere of the chlorofluorocarbons (from aerosols, for example) were to be stopped suddenly at some point, the level of ozone depletion would continue to increase for another two decades. This would arise from later release of chlorofluorocarbons already in use (as refrigerants, for example), and from the atmospheric transport time required from ground release to 40 km. The time required after that for the atmosphere to return to its original level of ozone concentration is then controlled by the lifetime in the atmosphere of the chlorofluorocarbons—some 50–150 years on average for molecules of CCl_3F and CCl_2F_2. A return even to the present levels of chlorofluorocarbon concentration would require more than a century. Atmospheric repair of ozone depletion is therefore a very slow process; if the consequences of such depletion are severe, the world will have to contend with them throughout the twenty-first century and beyond.

4·7 Mechanisms of photochemical air pollution

by Richard Wayne (Oxford University)

In the stratosphere, naturally occurring oxides of nitrogen, NO_x, reduce the concentration of ozone to below that predicted by the oxygen-only mechanism of Chapman, and injection of man-made NO_x may thus lead to depletion of ozone. In contrast, release of NO_x into the troposphere may lead to the *production* of ozone. The driving force is photochemical, and because various other undesirable chemical species, including particles, are formed, pollution of this kind is referred to as 'photochemical smog' (smog = smoke + fog). A major contributing cause of photochemical smog is the emission from automobile exhausts, and in this chapter we concentrate exclusively on this source of pollution. *Any* combustion of fossil fuels, however, (e.g. in industrial power plants) can release similar pollutants. This chapter first presents some experimental facts about photochemical smog, and then goes on to discuss the probable chemistry of its formation and possible methods of control.

1 Photochemical smog

Photochemical air pollution was first recognised in the Los Angeles Basin. Subsequently, many other areas—particularly in the South West USA, but also, for example, Jerusalem, and even in the UK—have been found to suffer from similar pollution. There are several factors that cause the problem to be so severe in Los Angeles. The local topography often results in lighter warm air lying on top of heavier cold air—a very stable situation known as a 'temperature inversion', which leads to the trapping of pollutants. Intensely sunny days are frequent. Last, but not least, there is a very high density of automobile use.

What is observed on a smoggy day? By noon, there are high concentrations of ozone and nitrogen dioxide in the atmosphere, there is a brown haze because particles are present; a lachrymator (peroxyacetyl nitrate—PAN) causes the eyes to run. Figure 1 gives measured concentrations of various species as a function of time of day in a typical smog episode. Figure 2 shows the degradation in visibility caused by smog.

A number of adverse effects can be associated with the presence of the various pollutants. Human health can suffer. The lachrymatory effect of PAN may be only a nuisance, but ozone, nitrogen dioxide, and especially the particles, are irritants to the respiratory system that can cause severe illness. Plant growth may be impaired. Reduction in visibility can also be a hazard.

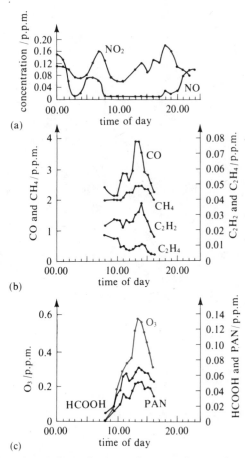

FIGURE 1   Diurnal variation of some primary and secondary pollutants in Pasadena, California, on 25 July 1973. (sources: (a) Los Angeles Air Pollution Control District; (b) and (c) Hanst, 1975)

The most important source of photochemical air pollution resulting from human activities appears to be the combustion of fossil fuels. The relatively high temperatures in the internal combustion engine convert some atmospheric nitrogen and oxygen into NO_x (mainly NO). Carbon monoxide and unburnt hydrocarbons are emitted, together with sulphur dioxide when the fuel has an appreciable sulphur content. The mixture of primary pollutants with air then undergoes chemical change on irradiation with sunlight, to give rise to the concentration changes and secondary pollutants shown in Figure 1. The temporal behaviour of various pollutant species in the atmosphere is well mimicked when a test chamber ('smog chamber') containing a mixture of hydrocarbon, nitric oxide and air is irradiated with near-ultraviolet light.

FIGURE 2   Photographs of Los Angeles in clear air (*above*) and after smog has formed under an inversion layer (*below*). (source: South Coast Air Quality Management District, California)

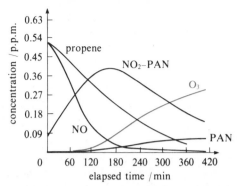

FIGURE 3   The variation with time of the concentrations of major and secondary pollutants during irradiation of a mixture of propene (0.53 p.p.m.) and NO_x (0.59 p.p.m.) in purified air at a pressure of 1 atm in a smog chamber. (source: Pitts, 1976)

Figure 3 shows some typical experimental results for propene as the hydrocarbon. Note that in the *absence* of hydrocarbon, the conversion of NO into NO_2 is much slower, much less ozone is formed, and, of course, the organic chemical species do not appear.

Our objective now is to see whether known chemistry can explain the conversion of the primary into the secondary pollutants.

2   Inorganic chemistry

The only known source of ozone in urban air is the reaction

$$O + O_2 + M \longrightarrow O_3 + M \tag{1}$$

To explain the formation of ozone we must, therefore, find a source of atomic oxygen. Energy considerations indicate that this source must be photochemical, but the solar radiation penetrating to near ground level is essentially all at wavelengths greater than about 310 nm. Relatively few chemical species can be photolysed at these wavelengths to give oxygen atoms, and the only likely candidate is NO_2:

$$NO_2\cdot + h\nu \longrightarrow NO\cdot + O \qquad \lambda < 430 \text{ nm} \tag{2}$$

The wavelength 430 nm is an approximate upper limit for the photolytic process. We shall return to this point in the section on Models.

Nitric oxide, rather than nitrogen dioxide, is the primary pollutant, so that if reaction (2) is the source of oxygen atoms and ultimately ozone, there must be some way of converting NO into NO_2. The well known process

$$2NO\cdot + O_2 \longrightarrow 2NO_2\cdot \tag{3}$$

155

is far too slow to be important at the relatively low concentrations of nitric oxide encountered in polluted atmospheres, because its rate depends on $[NO\cdot]^2$. The only elementary reaction that is fast enough is that with ozone itself:

$$NO\cdot + O_3 \longrightarrow NO_2\cdot + O_2 \qquad (4)$$

Consumption of ozone by nitric oxide in this reaction is responsible for the inhibition of ozone appearance in both polluted atmospheres and test chambers (cf. Figures 1 and 3) until nitric oxide has reached low concentrations. However, reaction (4) on its own cannot be responsible for conversion of NO into NO_2. Ozone is needed to effect the conversion, while nitrogen dioxide is necessary for ozone formation. It is apparent that the very simple chemistry of reactions (1), (2) and (4) alone cannot explain the observed behaviour.

An alternative rapid route for the oxidation of NO to NO_2 involves a catalytic chain reaction propagated by radical and atomic intermediates. Considering, for the moment, only inorganic chemical species, this chain might be written

$$\cdot OH + CO \longrightarrow H\cdot + CO_2 \qquad (5)$$

$$H\cdot + O_2 + M \longrightarrow HO_2\cdot + M \qquad (6)$$

$$\underline{HO_2\cdot + NO\cdot \longrightarrow \cdot OH + NO_2\cdot} \qquad (7)$$

$$\text{net} \quad NO\cdot + O_2 + CO \longrightarrow NO_2\cdot + CO_2 \qquad (8)$$

Recent kinetic data have shown that reactions (5) and (7) are both extremely rapid, and hydroxyl radicals have been detected in urban air.

Initiation of the chain involves generation of one or more of the reactive intermediates. One suggestion for the production of hydroxyl radicals is the photolysis of nitrous acid (HONO):

$$HONO + h\nu \longrightarrow \cdot OH + NO\cdot \qquad \lambda < 400 \text{ nm} \qquad (9)$$

Nitrous acid has been detected both in smog chamber experiments and in ambient air. One route to its formation (which does not demand consumption of a chain carrier) is

$$NO_2\cdot + NO\cdot + H_2O \rightleftharpoons 2HONO \qquad (10)$$

Although reaction (10) consumes an NO_2 molecule, the net result of (10) followed by $2 \times (9)$ is

$$NO_2\cdot + H_2O + 2h\nu \longrightarrow 2\cdot OH + NO\cdot \qquad (11)$$

so that two chain carriers are formed at the expense of one NO_2 molecule. Because kinetic chain lengths can be long (i.e. many catalytic cycles can occur before the carriers are lost), the net result may be the conversion of many NO molecules into NO_2.

3 Organic chemistry

Although the catalytic cycle of reactions (5)–(7) provides a way of oxidising NO to NO_2, the presence of hydrocarbons seems, as pointed out earlier, to be essential for ozone formation. We must now examine the organic chemistry of photochemical air pollution in terms both of the production of ozone and of the formation of secondary organic pollutants. Hydroxyl radicals are again the key species in currently accepted mechanisms.

Measured reaction rates indicate that when hydrocarbons are oxidised in a test chamber, the rate of attack by ·OH exceeds that by any other species at short reaction times (although for irradiations lasting hours, consumption by ozone and by HO_2· becomes comparable). The hydroxyl radical abstracts hydrogen from the hydrocarbon to form a radical that we will describe as RCH_2· (where R can be H or an organic group). Alkyl radicals can add O_2 to form peroxyalkyl radicals (RCH_2O_2·) that react with NO in a manner analogous to HO_2· radicals. Thus we can write a radical chain process that oxidises hydrocarbons at the same time as converting NO into NO_2:

$$\cdot OH + RCH_3 \longrightarrow H_2O + RCH_2\cdot \tag{12}$$

$$RCH_2\cdot + O_2 \longrightarrow RCH_2O_2\cdot \tag{13}$$

$$RCH_2O_2\cdot + NO\cdot \longrightarrow RCH_2O\cdot + NO_2\cdot \tag{14}$$

$$RCH_2O\cdot + O_2 \longrightarrow RCHO + HO_2\cdot \tag{15}$$

$$HO_2\cdot + NO\cdot \longrightarrow \cdot OH + NO_2\cdot \tag{7}$$

net $\quad RCH_3 + 2NO\cdot + 2O_2 \longrightarrow RCHO + 2NO_2\cdot + H_2O \tag{16}$

The aldehydes, RCHO, can undergo further oxidation to acids. Figure 1 shows that formic (methanoic) acid (HCOOH) is produced during an urban smog episode. Other studies have shown the presence of formaldehyde (methanal) and higher aldehydes.

Aldehydes may provide an important entry into the radical chain, via photolysis. One channel for the photodissociation of formaldehyde gives two radicals:

$$HCHO + h\nu \longrightarrow H\cdot + HCO\cdot \qquad \lambda < 370 \text{ nm} \tag{17}$$

Both the product radicals can generate HO_2·, which is a chain carrier, by reaction with oxygen:

$$H\cdot + O_2 + M \longrightarrow HO_2\cdot + M \tag{6}$$

$$HCO\cdot + O_2 \longrightarrow HO_2\cdot + CO \tag{18}$$

Higher aldehydes are probably less significant sources of chain carriers, because they require shorter-wavelength ultraviolet light for photolysis, but they, too, yield radical fragments that directly, or via reaction (18), provide chain initiators:

$$RCH_2CHO + hv \longrightarrow RCH_2\cdot + HCO\cdot \qquad \lambda < 350 \text{ nm} \qquad (19)$$

Smog chamber experiments support the idea that aldehydes are important. Addition of formaldehyde causes NO to be converted much more rapidly into NO_2, and ozone forms sooner and at higher concentrations. It is interesting, in this context, that formaldehyde is emitted directly into the air from automobile exhausts.

The formation of peroxyacetyl nitrate (PAN) may also depend on the presence of aldehydes. One possible sequence is

$$\cdot OH + CH_3CHO \longrightarrow H_2O + CH_3CO\cdot \qquad (20)$$

$$CH_3CO\cdot + O_2 \longrightarrow CH_3\underset{\underset{O}{\|}}{C}OO\cdot \qquad (21)$$

$$CH_3\underset{\underset{O}{\|}}{C}OO\cdot + NO\cdot \longrightarrow CH_3\underset{\underset{O}{\|}}{C}O\cdot + NO_2\cdot \qquad (22)$$

$$CH_3\underset{\underset{O}{\|}}{C}OO\cdot + NO_2\cdot \longrightarrow CH_3\underset{\underset{O}{\|}}{C}OONO_2 \qquad (23)$$

$$PAN$$

Note that reactions (20)–(22) are the analogues of reactions (12)–(14), with the alkyl radical $RCH_2\cdot$ replaced by $CH_3CO\cdot$.

4 Aerosol formation

Many of the undesirable effects of photochemical smog arise from the presence of suspended particulate matter. In this section we consider possible mechanisms by which particles may appear in polluted atmospheres. Some particles, such as soot or lead, are primary pollutants: that is, they are a result of direct emissions from the combustion process. However, in photochemical smog, secondary aerosol concentrations may exceed those of the primary particles. The most important aerosols are probably organic compounds and sulphates.

Nearly half the aerosol mass can be organic in severe photochemical smog, and of this organic fraction 95% is secondary in origin. A variety of long-chain aliphatic and aromatic compounds (including the carcinogen benzpyrene) are present, together with oxygenated species such as acids, esters, aldehydes, ketones, and peroxides. The mechanisms leading to the formation and growth of particles are not yet clear. It has, however, long been known that oxidation by ozone of hydrocarbons such as terpenes leads to polymerisation and aerosol formation. Indeed, the haze of the Smoky

Mountains, or of the Los Angeles basin *before* the advent of automobiles, has been ascribed to the reaction between oils from pine forests or citrus groves and the ozone naturally present in the troposphere.

Sulphate aerosol may carry with it a health hazard and certainly leads to reduced visibility. If we start from the premise that SO_2 is the primary pollutant from combustion of fossil fuels, we need to find a way to oxidise SO_2 to SO_3, which can then react with water:

$$SO_3 + H_2O \longrightarrow H_2SO_4 \tag{24}$$

In the absence of other pollutants, the reaction of SO_2 with O_2 in the dark may be neglected, and even photo-oxidation is a relatively slow process (less than 0.1% per hour). Observation shows that, in the Los Angeles area, oxidation of SO_2 may proceed 100 times faster than the simple photo-oxidation rate. The chemical species involved in photochemical smog formation are thus implicated in SO_2 oxidation: $\cdot OH$, $HO_2\cdot$, O, O_2, $RO\cdot$, $RO_2\cdot$, and NO_2 are obvious candidates. At present, insufficient is known about the rates or products of the reactions of these species with SO_2 for the reaction path to be described with certainty. One postulated route involves the $HOSO_2\cdot$ radical, formed by addition of $\cdot OH$ to SO_2:

$$\cdot OH + SO_2 + M \longrightarrow HOSO_2\cdot + M \tag{25}$$

$$HOSO_2\cdot + O_2 \longrightarrow HOSO_2O_2\cdot \tag{26}$$

$$HOSO_2O_2\cdot + NO\cdot \longrightarrow HOSO_2O\cdot + NO_2\cdot \tag{27}$$

followed either by dissociation of $HOSO_2O\cdot$ to SO_3 and $\cdot OH$, or by its direct reaction with water. Interestingly, this sequence also oxidises NO to NO_2. It is clear that, whatever the detailed mechanism, there is an interaction of SO_x, NO_x and hydrocarbon chemistry in photochemical air pollution.

5 Models

Validation of any proposed mechanism for photochemical smog formation requires the development of a mathematical model for the concentration–time dependence of all the reactive species. Such a kinetic model may then be used to predict concentrations of major and minor species for comparison with experimental observations—*if* these latter observations exist. Furthermore, the model can also be employed to determine what control methods might be effective, and possibly what standards of air quality should be set.

We have concentrated here on schemes that exemplify the underlying chemistry. A model approximating to the 'real' situation has to employ a staggering number of reactions: an attempt published in 1974 included 242 reactions after 100 minor processes had been excluded. Some simplification can be achieved by grouping together similar species, for example alkanes, alkenes, or aromatics. Nevertheless, good kinetic data are available for only a handful of the reactions. In some cases, rate constants are available at a single pressure or temperature: long extrapolations and guesses at the dependence on pressure and temperature need then to be made. The same problem arises over quantum yield data for photochemical processes. Here the quantum yield for formation of a particular product may be a function of wavelength, temperature and pressure. A case in point is the photolysis of NO_2 (reaction 2), as hinted at earlier. The O—NO bond energy suggests that the long-wavelength limit for photolysis ought to be around 390 nm; but internal energy in NO_2 can contribute to dissociation, so that between 390 nm and about 430 nm oxygen atoms are produced, with less than unit quantum efficiency. Because of the contribution from internal energy, the relationship between quantum efficiency and wavelength is temperature dependent. The difficulties are compounded because both the absorption coefficient and the solar irradiance change sharply in just that region where the quantum yield is sensitive to wavelength and temperature.

One matter not touched on at all, and about which virtually nothing is known, is the occurrence of heterogeneous reactions. All the processes we have discussed are homogeneous gas-phase reactions. But the existence of particles must alert us to the possibility of reactions on surfaces. Research into the detailed photochemical kinetics is obviously an urgent necessity for the development of reliable and useful models. Such research has been gathering momentum in the past decade, although much remains to be done.

6 Control

Finally, we should consider ways in which pollution from photochemical smog can be alleviated. There are two possible approaches: first, to eliminate or reduce the primary emissions, and second, to interfere deliberately with the chemistry.

Use of fuels such as hydrogen or methanol eliminates at once the hydrocarbon emission, although it would be extremely difficult at present to implement such a change commercially. Modification of the internal combustion engine to run at lower compression ratios and temperatures reduces the NO_x emission. Changes in carburation and ignition, and use of catalytic converters, can decrease the hydrocarbon content of exhaust gases. Although some such engine modifications have become law, especially in California, they appear unfortunately to be accompanied by reductions in efficiency. And sometimes the effects are the contrary of those intended. For example, reducing the amount of reactive hydrocarbon at a constant concentration of NO_x can *increase* the maximum ozone level.

Radical chains may be inhibited in laboratory systems by adding compounds that preferentially react with the chain carriers. Transferring such inhibition to the environment is fraught with difficulties and dangers. For a start, the amounts of inhibitor needed would be enormous. One proposed radical trap is diethylhydroxylamine (DEHA). Certainly it delays the conversion of NO into NO_2 in smog chamber experiments, although in the atmosphere this delay may only serve to increase the pollution downwind of the source later in the day. But, more important, the inhibitor or its reaction products may be toxic. Because DEHA is structurally similar to diethylnitrosoamine, a known carcinogen, deliberate exposure of the general public must be approached with the utmost caution.

part FIVE

Excited states of organic molecules can be deactivated by the various radiative and non-radiative processes; they can also undergo chemical reaction leading to new molecular structures. Because the excited state is considerably more energetic than the ground state, the synthesis of 'energy-rich' compounds is often possible using light as the energy source. Photochemical reactions also have the advantage of being selective, because the photons may be absorbed by just one molecular species in a mixture, and the absorbed energy within each molecule may be localised predominantly around a small number of the constituent atomic centres.

The following fourteen chapters make up the largest section of material in this book, and although the topics covered are quite diverse, their common feature is the application of organic photochemical reactions in areas of commercial or of academic importance. The fourteen chapters fall into three groups, the first dealing with synthetic uses of photochemistry, the second with polymers, and the third with photochemical reaction mechanisms.

Photochemistry is being used increasingly as a tool in organic synthesis, with ultraviolet radiation employed as a 'reagent' for making organic compounds. Two chapters cover such applications for a particular reaction type: 'Synthetic applications of photochemical *cis–trans* isomerisation' describes the uses of a reaction that can, for example, convert a *trans*-alkene into the higher energy *cis*-isomer, and 'Photohalogenation and related processes' deals with radical reactions, largely of hydrocarbon substrates, that are of considerable commercial importance. Three subsequent chapters cover synthetic applications more generally, ranging from those that are initially of academic importance ('Photochemistry in laboratory synthesis') to those of value in medium-scale ('Photochemistry in fine chemical manufacture') or large-scale ('Photochemistry in large-scale synthesis') manufacturing processes. A rather specialised application comes in the final chapter ('Photochemical isotope enrichment'), that of producing isotopically enriched compounds using laser radiation; although specialised as a synthetic application, this is of practical value in the enrichment of uranium isotopes for nuclear reactor fuels.

Photochemistry as it relates to organic polymers forms the subject matter for a second group of chapters. 'Photoinitiation of polymerisation' describes the formation of polymers using ultraviolet radiation; 'Photochemical cross-linking of polymers' follows on from this and deals with methods of extending existing polymer structures by photochemical means;

163

'Chemistry of the photodegradation of polymers' looks at the other side of the coin, that is ways in which polymer structures are broken down by light, either by design or as a consequence of the generally destructive effect of ultraviolet radiation on organic polymeric material. Many of the important materials of living organisms are organic macromolecules, and the effects of ultraviolet radiation at the molecular level in biological systems are the subject of a two-part chapter ('Biological effects of ultraviolet radiation'). The first part covers the photochemical reactions of nucleic acid bases, which are involved in many of the harmful effects of light on living matter; the second part deals with other effects, including some of the more beneficial aspects as far as human beings are concerned. In the chapter on 'Photopolymers for imaging and photoresists' there is a description of the widespread application of photochemically produced or photochemically modified polymers to imaging and information storage. As a complement to this use of photopolymers there is a separate chapter ('Non-conventional photoimaging') on some non-conventional (i.e. non-silver halide) methods of photoimaging that make use of the photochemistry of small organic molecules.

Chapters on applications in the investigation of the mechanisms of organic photochemical reactions complete this section of the book. Two topics are dealt with, namely the use of photosensitisers to promote and study the cis–trans isomerisation of alkenes ('Photosensitised cis–trans isomerisation'), and the use of flash photolysis as an investigative tool for organic reactions ('Applications of flash photolysis').

5·1

Synthetic applications of photochemical *cis–trans* isomerisation

by Gerry Pattenden (University of Nottingham)

Alkenes have a planar configuration, because this is the arrangement that allows for maximum overlap of the *p*-orbitals on the carbon atoms involved in the double bond. Rotation about the double bond from this planar configuration results in decreased overlap of the *p*-orbitals, and the potential energy increases. At 90° twist, the overlap is fully destroyed and the perpendicular orientation has maximum energy. These energy changes for rotation about the double bond in ethylene (ethene) are shown in Figure 1.

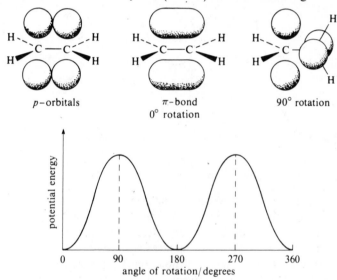

FIGURE 1   The planar ethene molecule, showing overlap of *p*-orbitals to produce the π-bond. Rotation through 90° prevents overlap of *p*-orbitals, and the potential energy increases.

Ethene has eclipsed hydrogen atoms at 250 pm apart and since the van der Waals' radius of hydrogen is about 100 pm, there is clearly no 'steric' strain in the molecule. The methyl group and the hydrogen atom on adjacent carbons in the *trans*-isomer of but-2-ene (1) are also separated by a distance greater than the van der Waals' distance of closest approach, but in *cis*-but-2-ene (2) weak (non-bonded) interactions occur between the methyl groups resulting in the molecule having higher energy than that of *trans*-but-

2-ene. Rotation about the double bond in *trans*-but-2-ene results then in 'overlap' strain and 'steric' strain; the associated energy changes are shown in Figure 2.

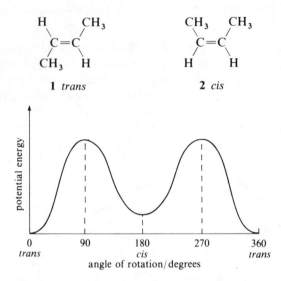

1 *trans*   **2** *cis*

FIGURE 2   Barriers to rotation about the double bond in *trans*- and *cis*-but-2-ene.

1   Thermal isomerisation

As a general rule, the *trans*-configuration of an alkene is thermodynamically more stable than the *cis*-form by an amount that reflects the steric, non-bonded interactions in the latter, and interconversion between the *cis*- and *trans*-forms occurs at a rate that increases with temperature. If we take the case of maleic acid (*cis*-butene-1,4-dioic acid) (**4**) and fumaric acid (*trans*-butene-1,4-dioic acid) (**3**), for example, although these acids are both stable at room temperature, the former isomer is smoothly converted into the latter when it is heated above 130 °C. Furthermore, when fumaric acid is heated to 230 °C (i.e. under conditions that allow dehydration of the maleic acid produced) it is converted into maleic anhydride (**5**). In a similar manner,

3   **4**   **5**

cis-stilbene (*cis*-1,2-diphenylethene) (**6**) is converted into *trans*-stilbene (*trans*-1,2-diphenylethene) (**7**) at temperatures around 250 °C. On the other hand, the *cis*-isomer (**8**) of the dye indigo changes rapidly into the more stable *trans*-form (**9**) at room temperature.

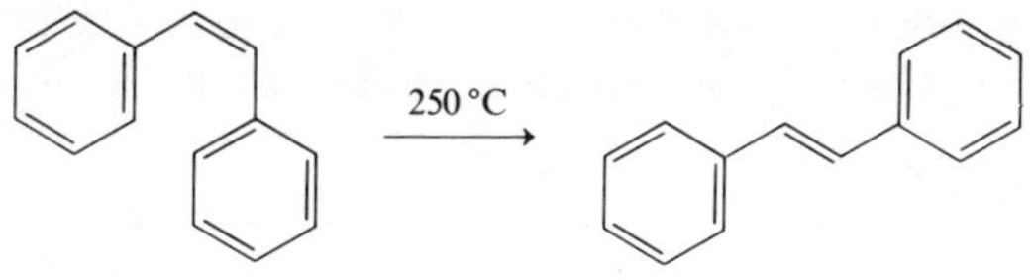

6   7

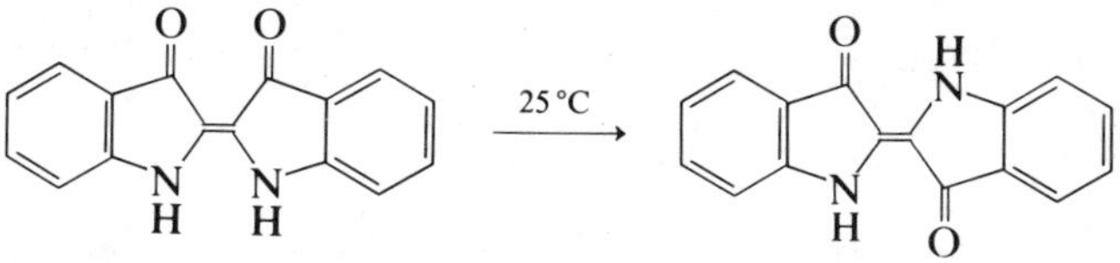

8   9

In the cases cited above, the energy difference between the isomeric pairs is sufficiently large that the less stable *cis*-form is changed almost completely into the more stable *trans*-form simply on heating. In other instances, however, the differences in stability are less, so that either form is converted into a mixture that contains comparable amounts of the two isomers. A case in point is that of *trans*-but-2-ene (**1**), which leads to an approximately 1 : 1 mixture of *cis*- and *trans*-isomers under a variety of thermal conditions.

2   Photochemical isomerisation

The *cis–trans* isomerisations brought about by the action of light are special in that with this method it is *often possible to transform the more stable geometrical form into the less stable form*. A typical example is afforded by the photoisomerisation of *cis*- and *trans*-stilbene, which is a much investigated reaction. Direct irradiation of *trans*-stilbene at 313 nm results in the formation of a photoequilibrium mixture of *cis*- and *trans*-isomers containing more than 90% of the *cis*-isomer. The composition of this photostationary state is determined mainly by the absorption coefficients of the two isomers at 313 nm, which are 2 300 (*cis*-isomer) and 16 300 (*trans*-isomer) l mol⁻¹ cm⁻¹. The difference between the absorption coefficients reflects, at least in part, the inhibition of resonance in the *cis*-isomer as a result of distortion from planarity due to non-bonded interactions between the two phenyl groups in this isomer. This distortion increases the energy of the system, not only in the ground state but also in the excited state. Indeed, the effect on the excited state is felt even more severely, and consequently the energy separation between the ground state and the excited state in the *cis*-isomer is that much larger (see Figure 3). The difference between the absorption coefficients of the isomers means that much more of the *trans*-isomer will be excited. Consequently, the *trans*-isomer is converted largely into the *cis*-isomer. Other examples of *cis–trans* isomerisations are collected in Table 1.

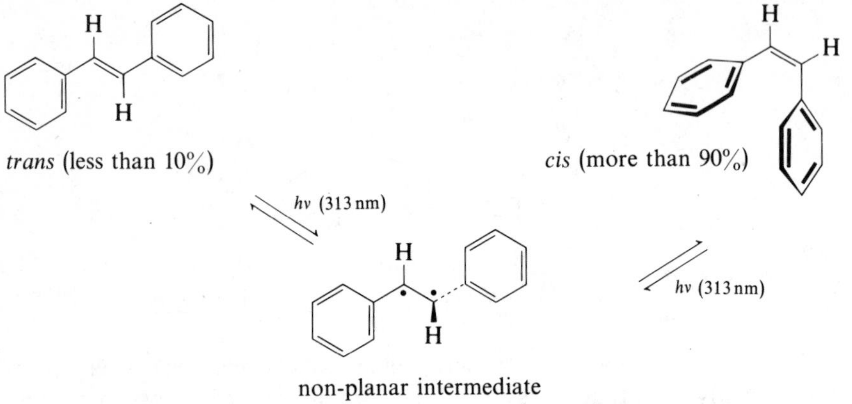
H
H
trans (less than 10%)
H
H
cis (more than 90%)
hν (313 nm)
H
H
hν (313 nm)
non-planar intermediate

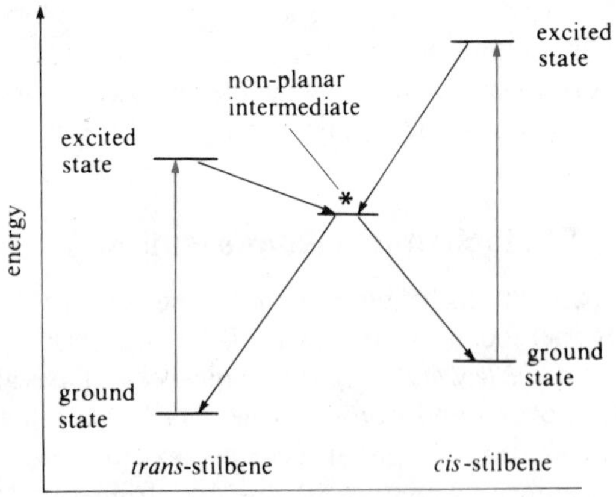
energy
excited state
ground state
non-planar intermediate
*
excited state
ground state
trans-stilbene
cis-stilbene

FIGURE 3 Energy levels for *trans*- and *cis*-stilbene in the ground state and excited state.

3 Triplet-sensitised isomerisation

Photochemical *cis–trans* isomerisations can also be brought about by energy transfer from a triplet sensitiser (e.g. benzophenone). Transfer of energy in this manner means that the alkene will be excited to its triplet state, which

Table 1 Examples of photochemical *cis–trans* isomerisation reactions

Isomer 1	Isomer 2	Percentage of isomer 2 at photoequilibrium
		85%
		91%
		87%
		88%
		51%

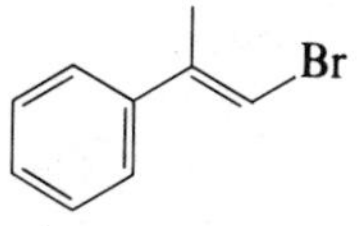

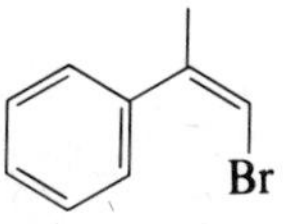

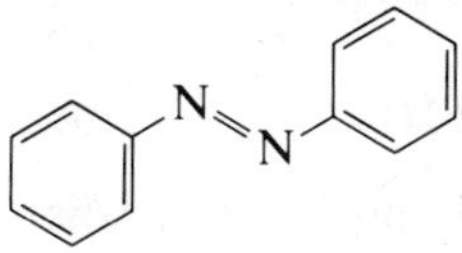

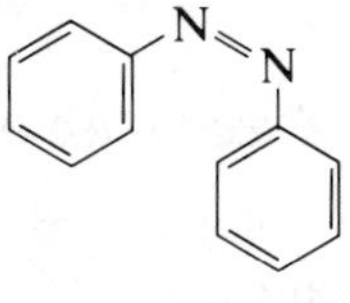

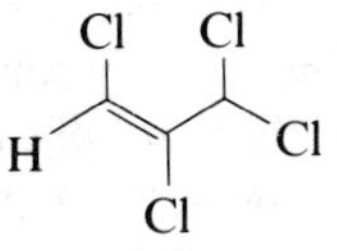

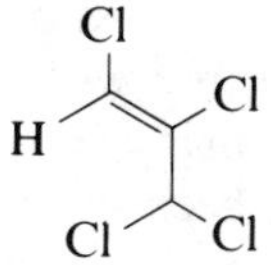

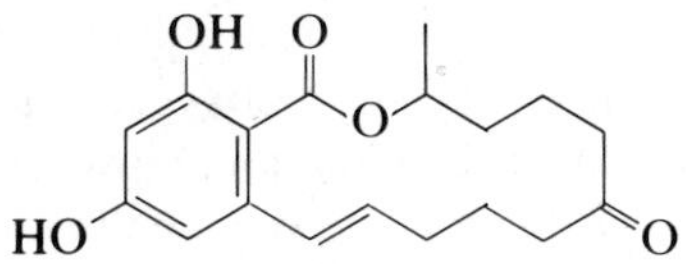

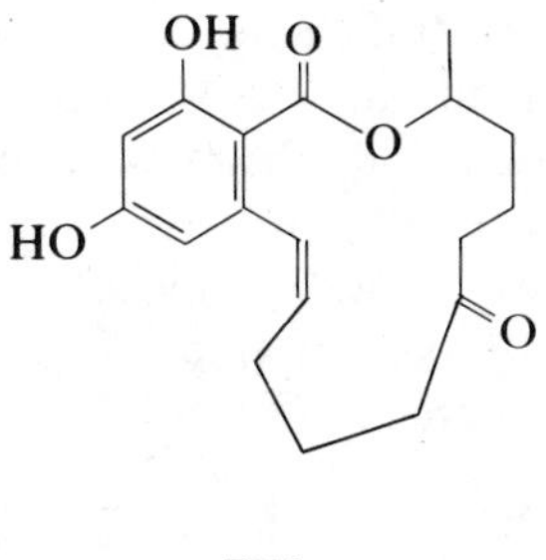

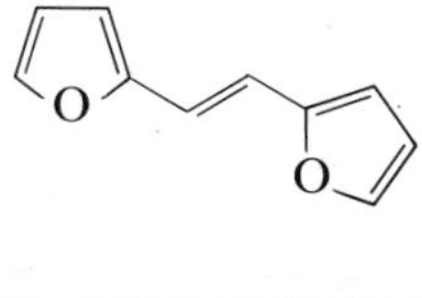

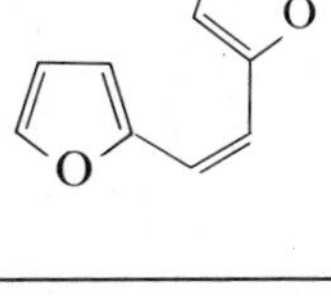

can then decay to either geometrical isomer (Scheme 1). Indeed, the ratio of *cis*- and *trans*-isomers produced in sensitised isomerisations is found to be dependent on the triplet energy of the particular sensitiser used (Chapter 5·3).

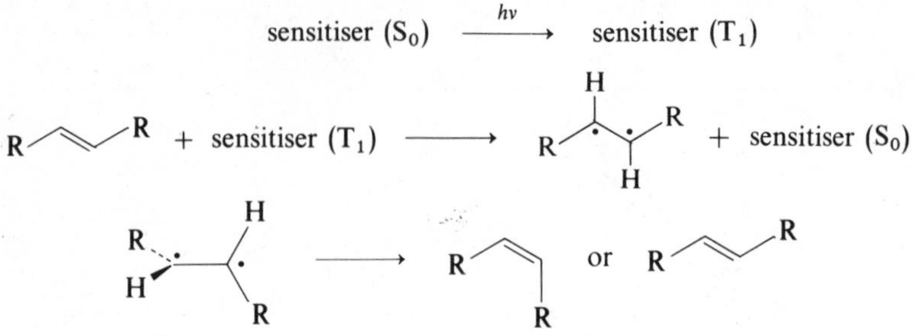

$$\text{sensitiser (S}_0) \xrightarrow{\;h\nu\;} \text{sensitiser (T}_1)$$

SCHEME 1   Photoisomerisation in the presence of a sensitiser.

4   Catalysed isomerisation

Heat and light are not the only agencies found to bring about *cis–trans* interconversions amongst alkenes. Various catalysts, of which halogens (with light) and strong acids are characteristic examples, are also found to be effective. Interestingly, the ratios of geometrical isomers produced by these methods are comparable with those obtained by thermal isomerisation procedures. Although many features of the mechanisms of catalysed isomerisations have still not been satisfactorily investigated or explained, it seems likely that the halogen-catalysed isomerisations all involve the initial production of halogen atoms $(X \cdot)$, which then add to the alkene double bond as depicted in Scheme 2. It is conceivable that the production of halogen atoms is due to the presence of traces of impurities, or to oxygen and peroxides, in the substrates or solvents. A more likely explanation, however, is that ordinary visible light is responsible for the dissociation of the halogen molecules into atoms. Indeed, photoisomerisation in the presence of iodine is a very commonly employed method for converting a less stable *cis*-isomer into the more stable *trans*-isomer (e.g. *cis*-stilbene into *trans*-stilbene).

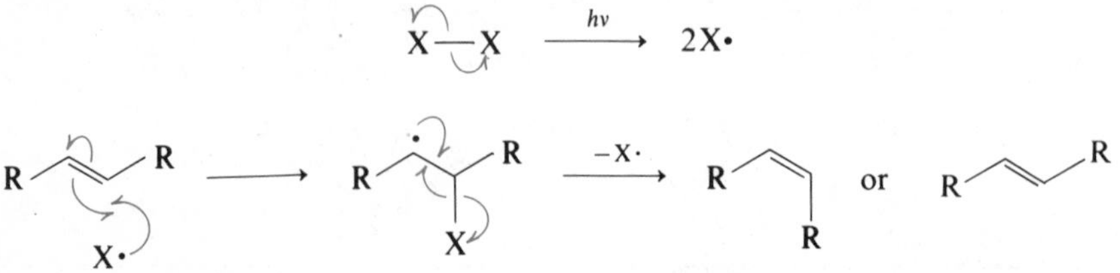

$$X-X \xrightarrow{\;h\nu\;} 2X\cdot$$

$$(X = Cl, Br \text{ or } I)$$

SCHEME 2   Photoisomerisation in the presence of halogen.

In catalysed *cis–trans* interconversions involving strong acids (e.g. dimethyl maleate into dimethyl fumarate in the presence of HBr) the catalyst is thought to act largely as a proton donor and not as a source of halogen atoms (Scheme 3).

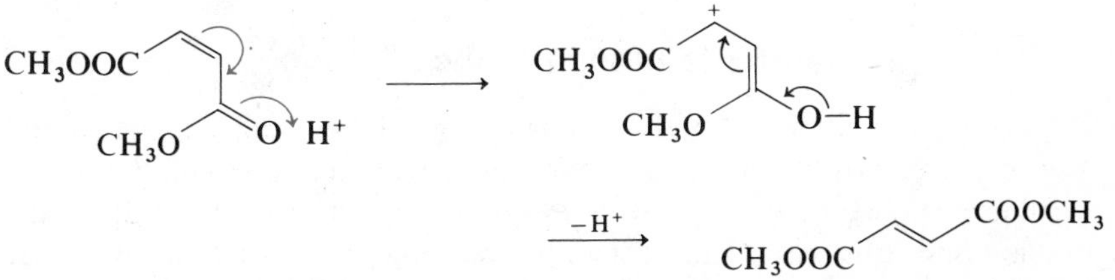

SCHEME 3   Isomerisation in the presence of hydrobromic acid.

5   Isomerisation in polyenes

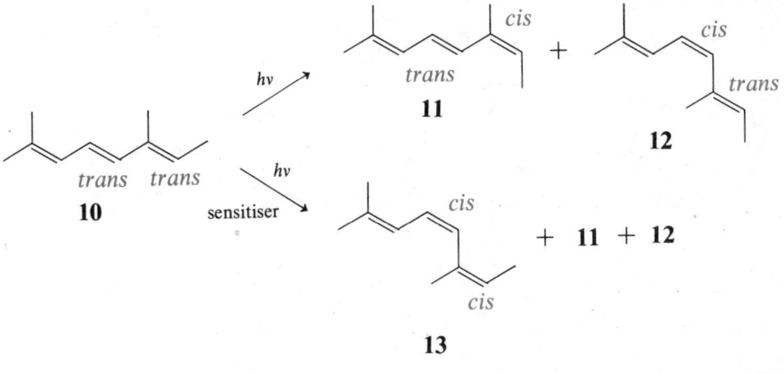

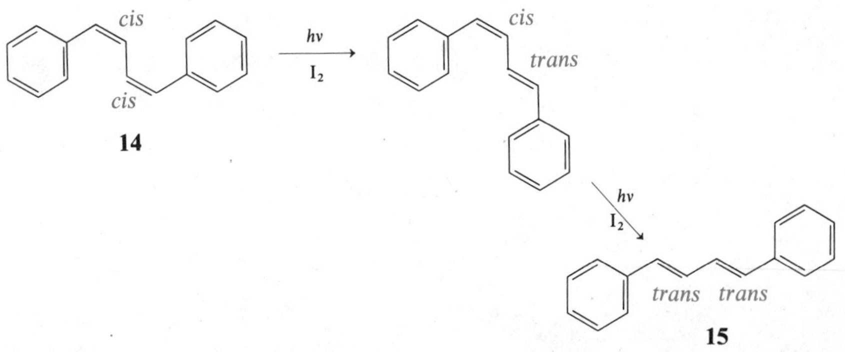

The isomerisation of conjugated dienes and polyenes leads to a number of geometrical isomers, depending on the irradiation conditions. Thus, the sensitised irradiation of *trans,trans*-2,6-dimethylocta-2,4,6-triene (**10**) leads to a mixture of the three geometrical isomers **11**, **12**, and **13**, whereas direct irradiation produces only **11** and **12**. Photoisomerisation of *cis,cis*-1,4-diphenylbuta-1,3-diene (**14**) in the presence of iodine has been shown to proceed in a stepwise manner leading to a photostationary mixture containing 97% of the *trans,trans*-isomer (**15**).

6 Isomerisation in cyclic alkenes

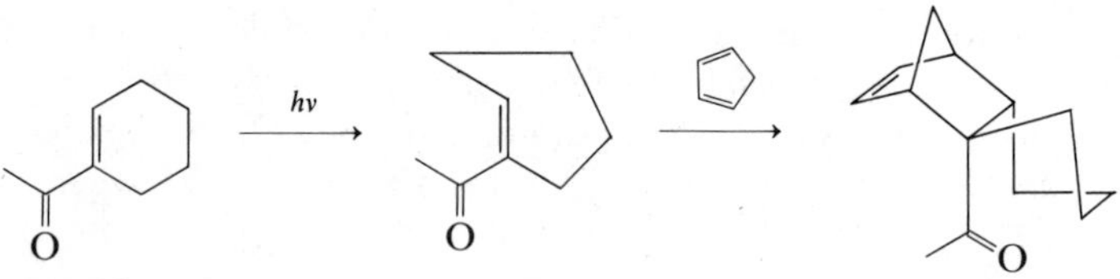

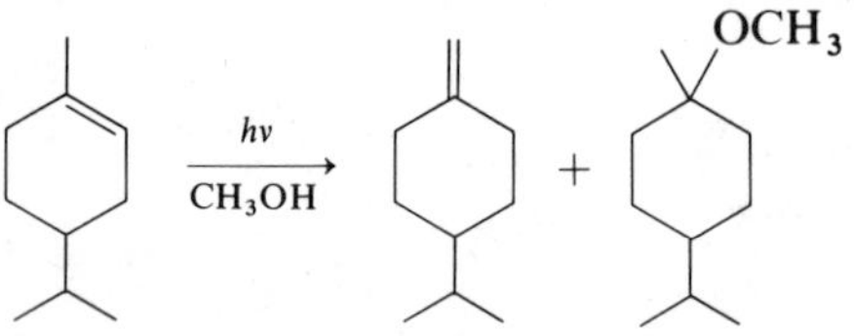

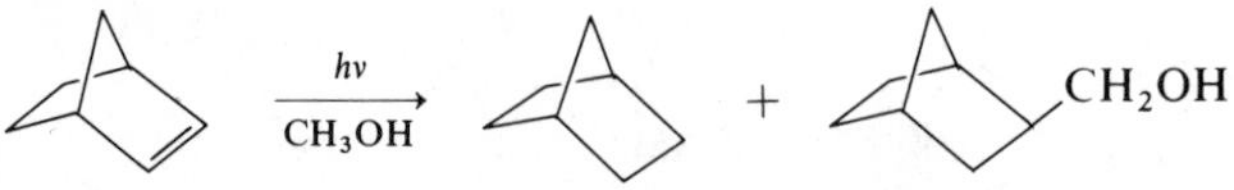

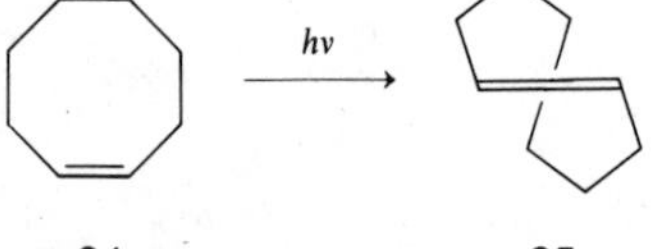

Rotations about double bonds in small rings are sterically impeded, and *cis–trans* interconversions are not normally encountered. Irradiation of the cyclohexene (**16**), however, results in *cis* → *trans* isomerisation about the double bond; this was demonstrated by trapping the transient *trans*-isomer (**17**) with cyclopentadiene and examining the stereochemistry of the resulting cycloadduct. In most irradiations of cycloalkenes, photoprocesses other

16 **17**

18 **19** **20**

21 **22** **23**

24 **25**

than *cis–trans* isomerisation also occur. For example, irradiation of 1-menthene **(18)** in methanol leads to a mixture of the positional isomer **(19)** and the product **(20)** that results from addition of methanol to the double bond. Under similar conditions, norbornene **(21)** gives rise to a mixture of **22** and **23**. On the other hand, irradiation of the larger ring alkene, *cis*-cyclo-octene **(24)**, leads smoothly to the less stable *trans*-cyclo-octene **(25)**, which can be isolated.

7 Synthetic utility

Photochemical *cis–trans* isomerisation plays an important role in a number of syntheses of natural products. For example, the last stage in one of the earliest syntheses of vitamin D_3 **(27)** was the photochemical isomerisation of the isomer **26**. The synthesis of the natural lactone **(30)** from *Anthemis* species requires the *cis*-unsaturated acid **(29)**, which was produced in situ by irradiation of the corresponding *trans*-acid **(28)**. The industrial synthesis of vitamin

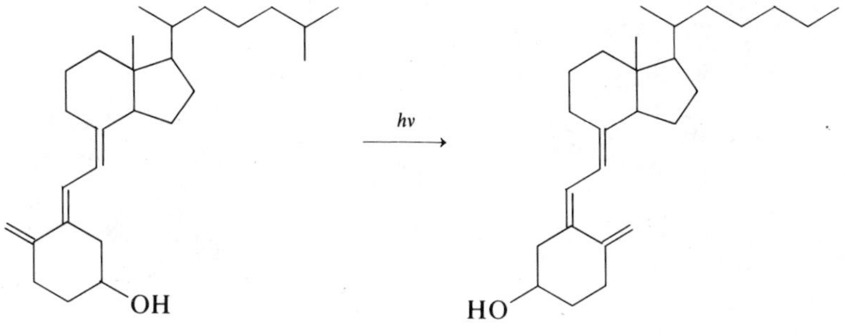

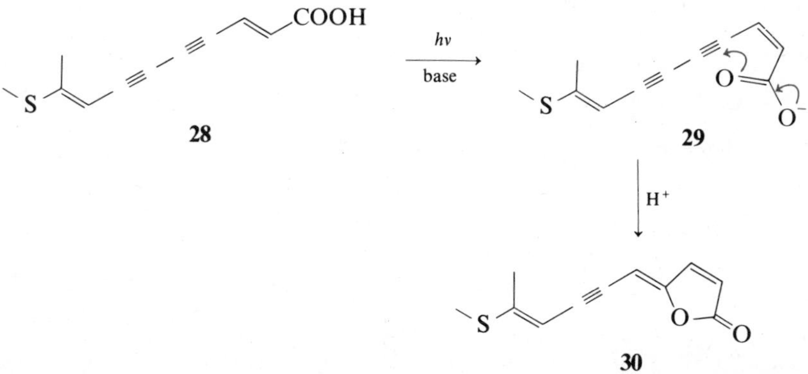

173

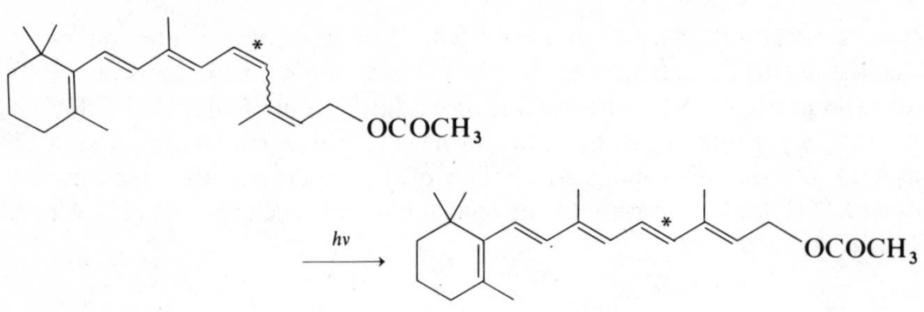

OCOCH3
hν
OCOCH3

31

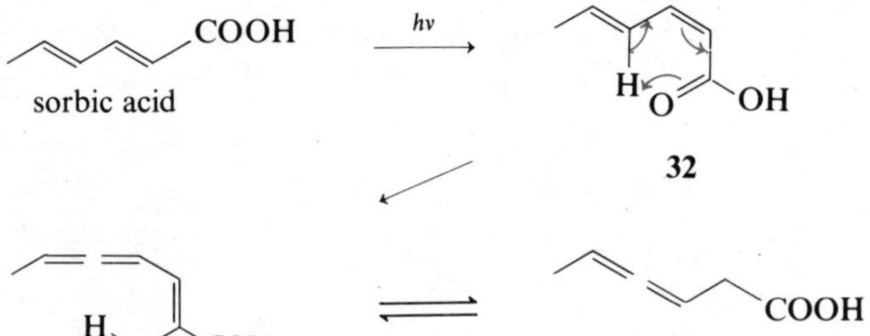

COOH
sorbic acid
hν
H
O
OH
H
O
OH
COOH

32

33

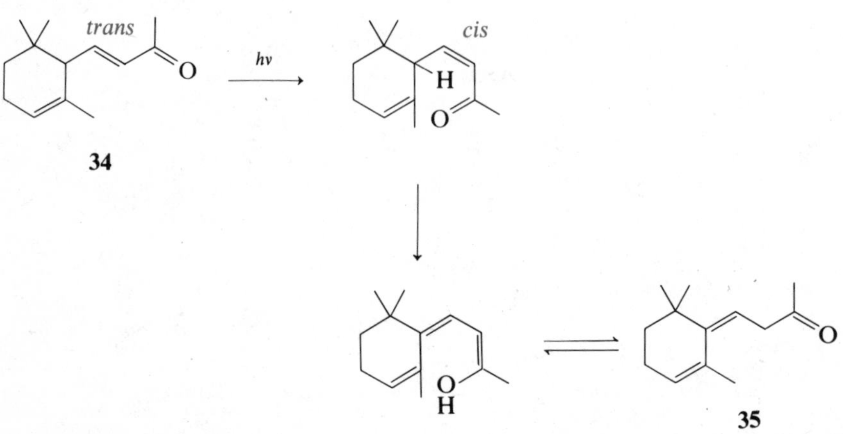

trans
O
hν
cis
H
O
O
H
O

34

35

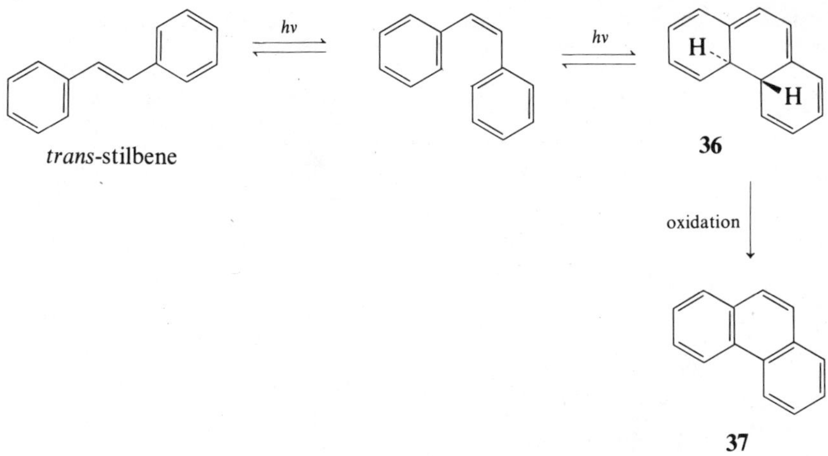

trans-stilbene

36

oxidation

37

A acetate (**31**) employs a reaction which affords a mixture of *cis*- and *trans*-isomers at the disubstituted double bond asterisked. Irradiation of this mixture in the presence of chlorophyll leads to essentially quantitative conversion into the all-*trans* material (**31**), which is used in pharmaceuticals and in animal feeds. Irradiation of sorbic acid (hexa-2,4-dienoic acid) leads to hexa-3,4-dienoic acid (**33**) by intramolecular migration of a hydrogen atom via the *cis*-isomer (**32**). The photochemical isomerisations of α,β-unsaturated ketones and esters to β,γ-unsaturated systems also take place via the corresponding enols, and have been particularly investigated in the rearrangements of ionones (e.g. **34** → **35**).

Some of the most useful applications of photochemical *cis–trans* isomerisations are to be found in those conjugated polyene systems which provide for (electrocyclic) cyclisation via *cis*-isomers. Thus, *trans*-stilbene undergoes a rapid *trans* → *cis* isomerisation on irradiation, and the *cis*-stilbene then cyclises to the *trans*-dihydrophenanthrene (**36**) on further irradiation; subsequent dehydrogenation of the latter with air or iodine then produces phenanthrene (**37**). This type of cyclisation reaction followed by dehydrogenation is a well studied and useful synthetic reaction. It has been used in the synthesis of several types of heterocycles, isoquinoline alkaloids and helicenes (Table 2).

Table 2 Examples of photochemical *cis–trans* isomerisation followed by electro-cyclic ring closure and oxidation

Substrate	Product of electrocyclic ring closure and oxidation

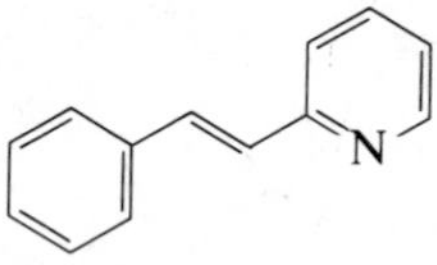

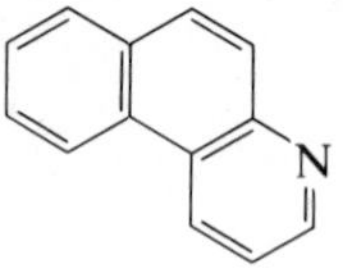

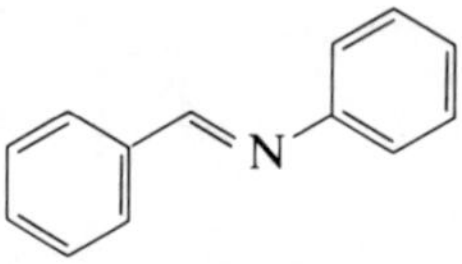

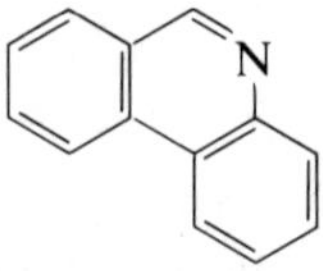

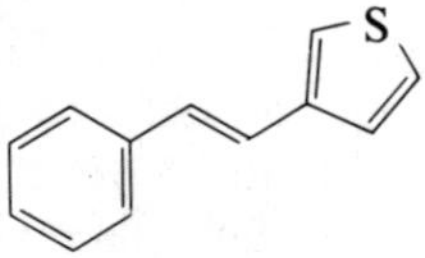

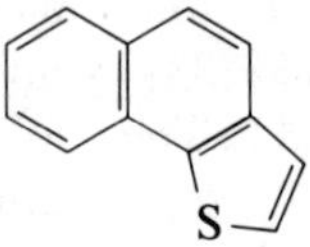

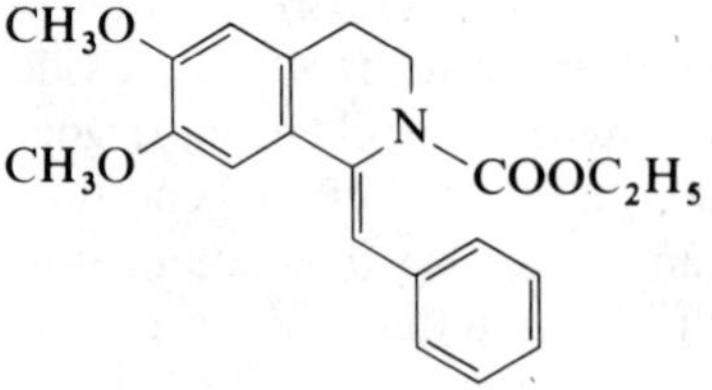

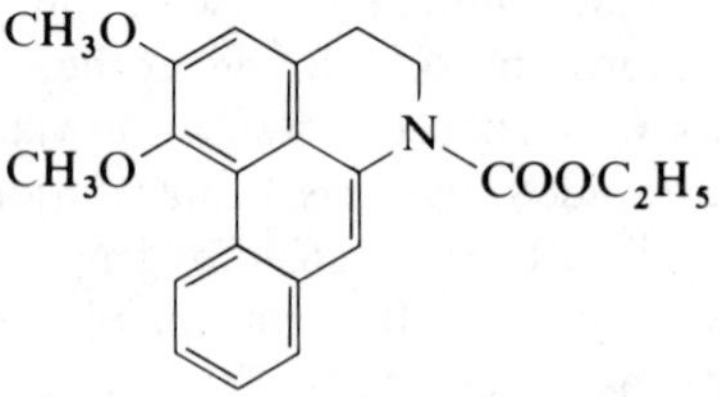

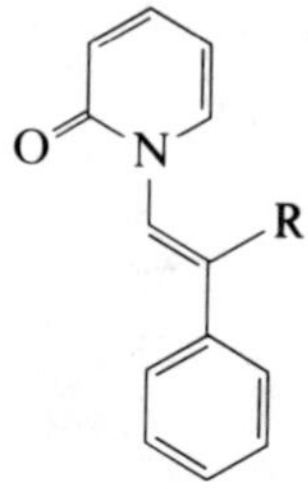

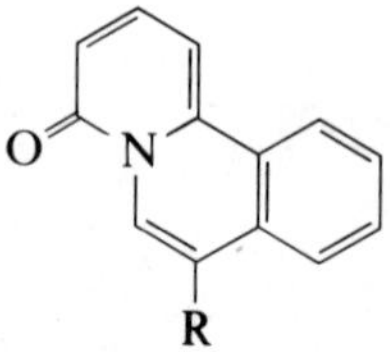

Table 2 (*continued*)

Substrate 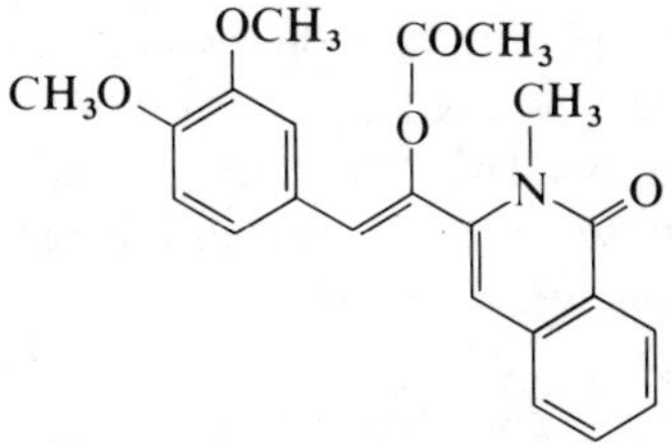	Product of electrocyclic ring closure and oxidation 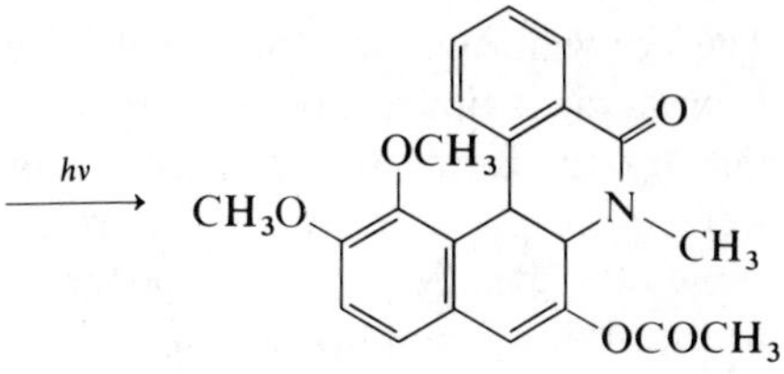

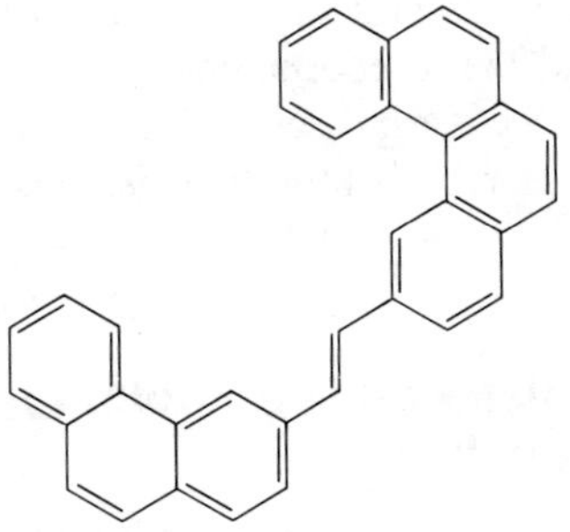

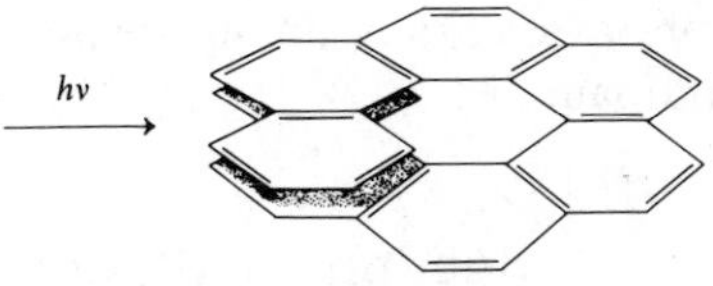

[8]helicene

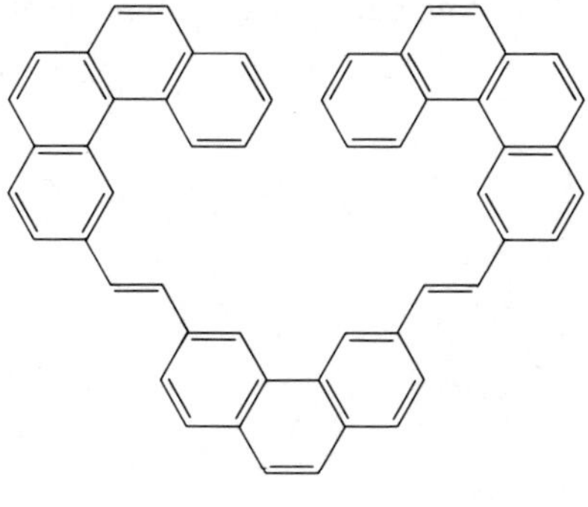

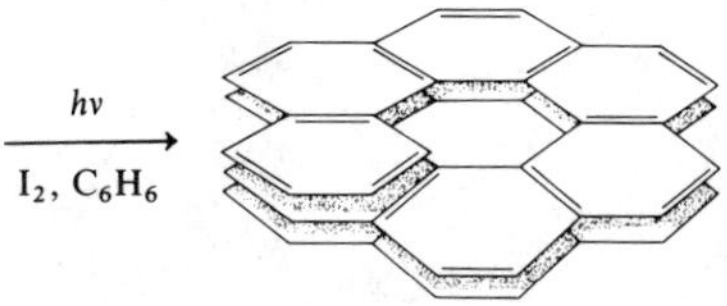

[13]helicene

5·2 Biological effects of ultraviolet radiation

by Godfrey Beddard (The Royal Institution, London)

The conventional wisdom that sunlight cures human illness comes to us from ancient times, and persists to this day. Sunbathing is not a new practice, for the Romans and Greeks had 'patio solaria' open to the sun which were quite popular. While one might consider that a suntan increases, in some non-specific way, one's general well-being, the biological damage done to the skin by sunburn is painfully obvious.

We shall discuss both the damaging and the ameliorating effects of radiation on biological material. The first main section of the chapter deals with the damaging photochemistry of nucleic acids and the repair mechanisms that overcome this damage. In the second main section, photosensitisation reactions, photoallergy, and phototoxic effects are discussed, as well as the use of ultraviolet radiation to treat diseases such as tuberculosis, rickets and neonatal jaundice.

Section A Photochemistry and photobiology of nucleic acids

The discovery that the action spectrum for the killing of cells by ultraviolet light is maximal in the region 260–265 nm implicates DNA (deoxyribonucleic acid) and RNA (ribonucleic acid) as the principal absorbers. If proteins

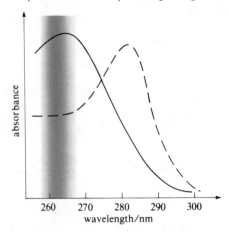

FIGURE 1   The continuous line is the DNA absorption curve, and the dashed line is the protein absorption curve. The shaded region indicates which wavelengths are most effective for the killing of cells.

were involved to any great extent the action spectrum would peak at 280 nm (Figure 1). Because DNA is the basis for storage, transmission, and expression of genetic information, any damage caused to it is likely to have important consequences.

Before describing the photochemistry of nucleic acids, we shall give a brief introduction to the structure and photophysics of DNA.

A1 DNA structure

The essential feature of the gross structure of DNA is that it usually consists of two long polynucleotide chains twisted in an antiparallel manner about the same axis to form a double helix (Figure 2). The internucleotide linkage is via a C-5 hydroxyl group of the pentose part of one unit to a C-3 hydroxyl of the adjacent unit connected via a phosphate group. The nucleic acid bases are located on the inside of the double helix, and intermolecular forces (hydrogen bonds) act between bases on different strands to aid the formation of the double helix (Figure 3). The negatively charged phosphodiester chain faces outwards and so can interact with the water that forms the 'solvent'. The solvent also aids helix formation because of 'hydrophobic forces' between water molecules and the nucleic acid bases, resulting in the inward orientation of the bases. The double helix is also stabilised by stacking forces, which are weak interactions between bases that act parallel to the axis of the helix rather than across it.

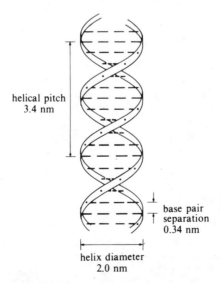

helical pitch
3.4 nm

base pair
separation
0.34 nm

helix diameter
2.0 nm

FIGURE 2   A section of the DNA double helix, showing the gross structure.

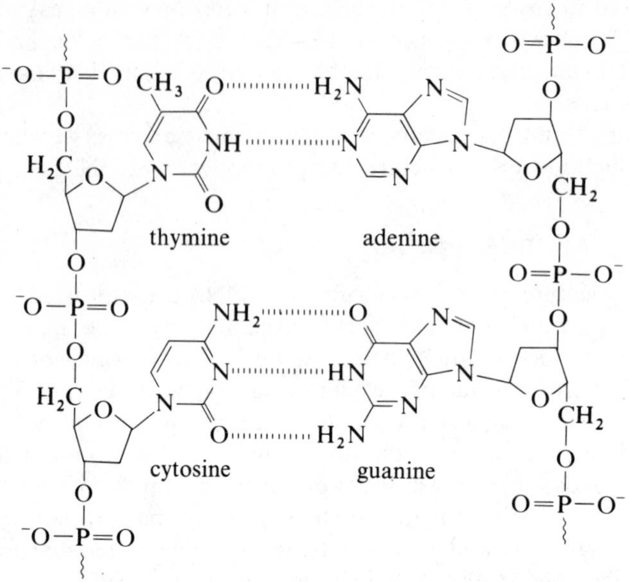

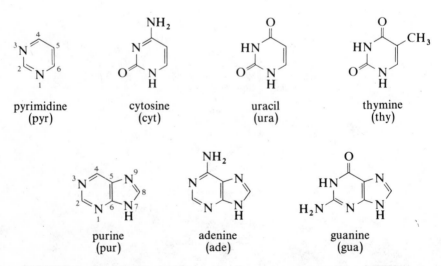

FIGURE 3   A segment of the DNA double helix, showing the hydrogen bonding between base pairs across the axis of the helix.

FIGURE 4   The structures of the pyrimidine and purine nucleic acid bases.

The idea that hydrogen bonding is the stabilising force for the double helix is giving way to the view that hydrophobic and stacking forces are quantitatively as important, if not more important—in fact polynucleotide chains can form single helices when no hydrogen bonding is possible. Hydrogen bonding, however, is the crucial factor in determining biological function, as it is the only way in which the pairing of specific bases (called pair-wise complementarity) can be achieved. In DNA, each guanine (gua) is paired to cytosine (cyt), and every thymine (thy) is paired to adenine (ade); in RNA thymine is replaced by uracil (ura). (Figure 4 shows the structures of the nucleic acid bases.)

A2 DNA photophysics

The intense absorption of DNA at 260 nm is due to $\pi \rightarrow \pi^*$ transitions of the pyrimidine (pyr) and purine (pur) bases; $n \rightarrow \pi^*$ transitions also occur but are much weaker. As the base pairs are 0.34 nm apart, the interactions between base pairs are sufficiently weak that the absorption is qualitatively that of the constituent mononucleotides, but the intensity of the absorption is only about 40% of that expected for the number of absorbers present. The magnitude of this effect is dependent on the solvent (and sample preparations) but reaches a maximum after ten nucleotides in a chain; thus a small polynucleotide has much the same absorption properties as a large one.

Two factors play a role in the intensity effect: a partial (antiparallel) alignment of the transition dipoles by stacking, and an enhancement of this coupling by the hydrophobic effect of the polar solvent. The first effect arises from the electric field of one base altering the absorption intensity of the next, and so on. In the helix the interaction is not strong enough to shift the energy level much, but it has a profound effect on the intensity. Because the coupling drops off with the reciprocal of the distance cubed, only ten bases are needed to give 80% of the effect of an infinite chain.

Energy transfer plays an important role in the photophysics and photochemistry of DNA. Phosphorescence comes from thymine triplets formed after energy transfer from the site of absorption. The order of the triplet energies is cyt > ura > gua > ade > thy, which is why thymine triplets are detected. Photochemistry usually occurs from the thymine triplets, and because of their low energy they can be exclusively sensitised by benzophenone. A sensitiser of higher energy, such as acetone, can excite all five bases.

A3 DNA photochemistry

Pyrimidine dimers of the cyclobutane type are usually the major photoproducts formed on ultraviolet irradiation of DNA. The biological consequences of irradiation are usually ascribed to this type of photoproduct—although it is very difficult to relate the killing of cells to the concentration of dimers. However, a wide range of other products are formed, such as hydrates, photoadducts and the spore products of bacterial DNA; these are described below. Cross-linking of one DNA to another, or of DNA to protein also occurs, as do reactions with exogenous agents that add to the DNA (such as psoralens), or cause oxidative degradation (such as methylene blue). Which one of these reactions is the most important in inducing lethal lesions in the DNA will depend on the particular conditions in which the cell exists while being irradiated.

A4   Pyrimidine photodimers

When thymine is irradiated in frozen aqueous solution, a number of cyclobutane-type dimers (1)–(4) are formed. There is a wavelength dependence of the dimer formation, because at certain wavelengths the dimer dissociates to the monomers. The dimer absorption is due to the grouping $-CO-NH-CO-NH-$ and it peaks at a shorter wavelength than that of the monomer. The absorption spectra for thymine and its dimer are shown in Figure 5. The reason for the wavelength dependence of dimer formation is that the quantum yield for formation of dimers is 0.1 but the quantum yield for dissociation is unity; thus where these two curves cross, at about 245 nm, the rates of dimer formation and dissociation are equal. At longer wavelengths dimer formation predominates, and at shorter wavelengths dissociation predominates.

In natural DNA, two adjacent thymines form a dimer of type 1; a type 2 dimer is formed from denatured DNA. However, both are formed in lower yield than when thymine is irradiated alone, presumably because when the

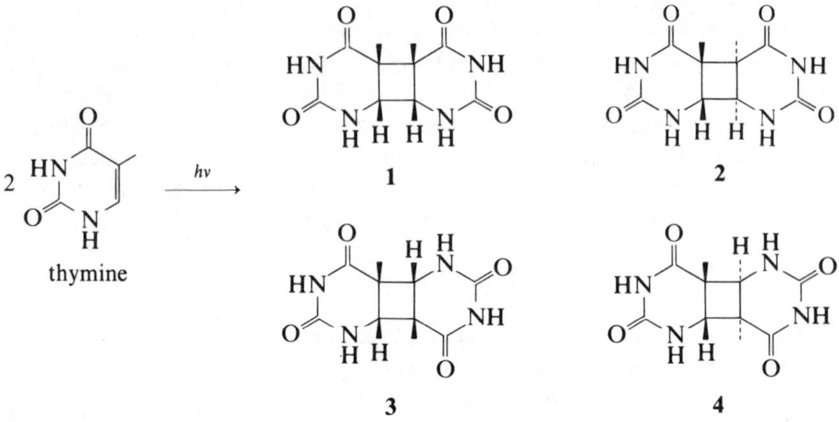

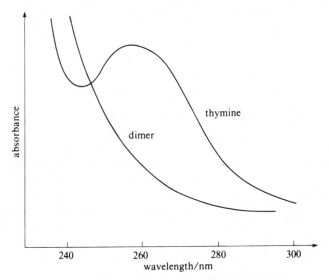

FIGURE 5   The absorption spectra of thymine and its dimer; the dimer absorbance
has been multiplied by 10. (source: Setlow, 1961)

thymines are attached to the sugar phosphate backbone they cannot easily
approach one another closer than 0.34 nm, compared with 0.15 nm in the
frozen solution of thymine. An observation that is not yet fully understood is
that dimers do not occur randomly in the DNA but tend to form in clusters.
Perhaps flexibility of the DNA chain induced by dimer formation allows a
conformation suitable for further reaction to occur more readily than in an
undamaged part of the chain.

Some other cyclobutane-type dimers are known: these are ura-cyt,
ura-thy, cyt-cyt, cyt-thy, and ura-ura. Following such dimer formation cytosine readily loses its amine group because the C-5—C-6 double bond is
saturated; this converts the cytosine into a uracil:

cytosine

(in DNA)

uracil (in DNA)

183

So if such a dimer dissociates (under the influence of an enzyme) a mutation could result because of the presence of a uracil instead of the original cytosine.

A5 Pyrimidine hydrates

Pyrimidine hydrates, e.g. compound **5**, are readily formed when aqueous solutions of pyrimidines are irradiated. Addition occurs across the 5,6 double bond, and the 260 nm absorption is lost. The hydration is reversed if the temperature is raised or if the pH is altered. Although hydrates are readily formed in solution or in single-stranded polynucleotides, their formation is severely restricted in double-stranded polymers: typically, five pyr-pyr dimers are formed for one hydrate. Hydrates decompose with a half-life of 1 hour at room temperature. The low yield and fast decay mean that they are not major lethal lesion sites, but they can have a significant effect if a genome (the total genetic complement of the organism) is single-stranded while it is actively metabolising, allowing hydrate formation to interfere with replication and transcription.

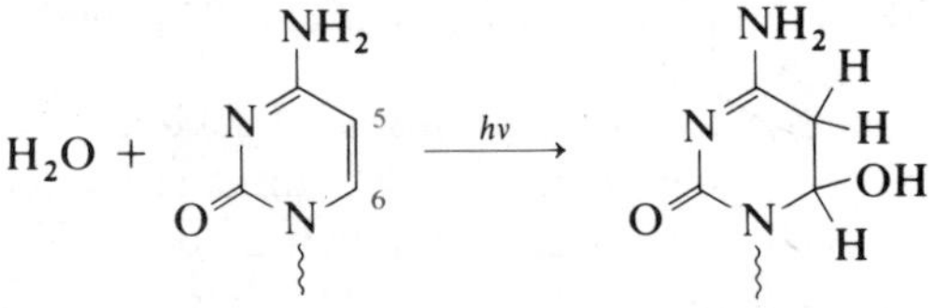

A6 Pyrimidine adducts

As with the cyclobutane-type dimers, pyrimidine adducts, e.g. compound **6**, can be formed in frozen solutions of thymine, and similar adducts are

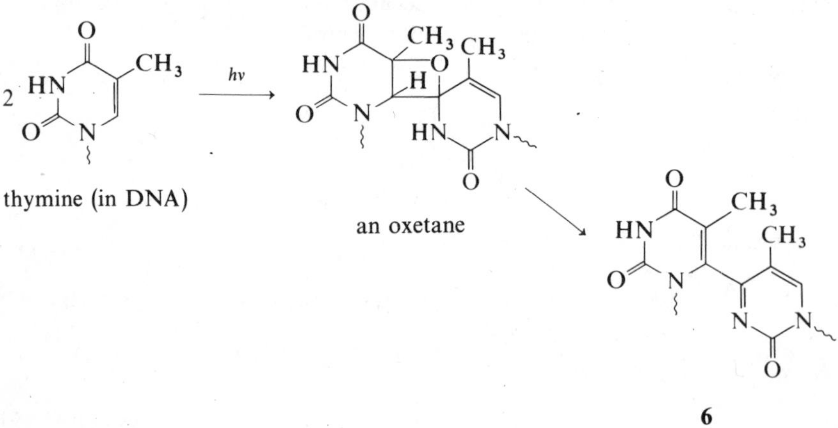

thymine (in DNA)   an oxetane

6

formed from DNA. All pyrimidines and nucleotides form adducts, although only cytosine adducts have been studied in detail. The quantum yield for formation of the thy-thy adduct is less than that for the cyclobutane dimer, but the action spectra are the same. Triplet sensitisers or triplet quenchers have no effect on the rate of formation of adducts, thus they may well be formed by reaction from a singlet state, possibly via isomerisation of the cytosine in the gua-cyt base pair.

When thymine is adjacent to the cytosine in a gua-cyt base pair (as in Figure 3) the reaction is as shown in Scheme 1. The azetidine decomposes to form the thy-cyt adduct (**7**). A thy-thy adduct (cf. compound **6**) would form via an oxetane.

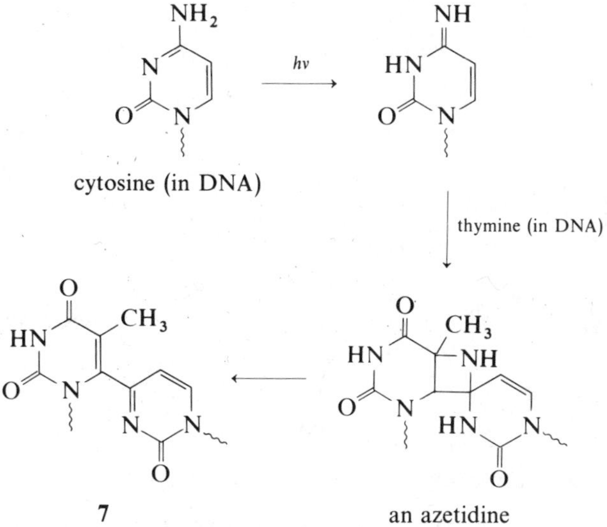

SCHEME 1

The striking feature of this type of adduct is the absorption at 313 nm. Unlike the formation of pyrimidine dimers, the reaction is not photoreversible, although the adduct will decompose to unknown products when irradiated at 310–340 nm. The quantum yield for this decomposition is about 0.003, far less than that for the forward or reverse reaction of the cyclobutane-type dimers.

A7 Spore products

The biological importance of a photoproduct depends on the extent to which it is present under the prevailing growth and radiation conditions. An example of this is found in bacterial spores, where thy-thy dimers play only a small role and the product 5-thyminyl-5,6-dihydrothymine, or 'spore product', is the most important. The same is true of solid DNA. This is the case, however, only in the absence of water, spores being well known for their low water content and also for their high u.v. tolerance and resistance to environmental insult. Spore products are evidently formed from the triplet excited state, because their formation can be inhibited by metal ions that are known triplet quenchers; radical intermediates may be involved (Scheme 2). The formation of a spore product is about ten times less likely to kill the spore than the formation of pyr-pyr dimers is to kill vegetative cells. This may be because the repair mechanism is more efficient in spores, even though the formation of the spore product is not a photoreversible reaction.

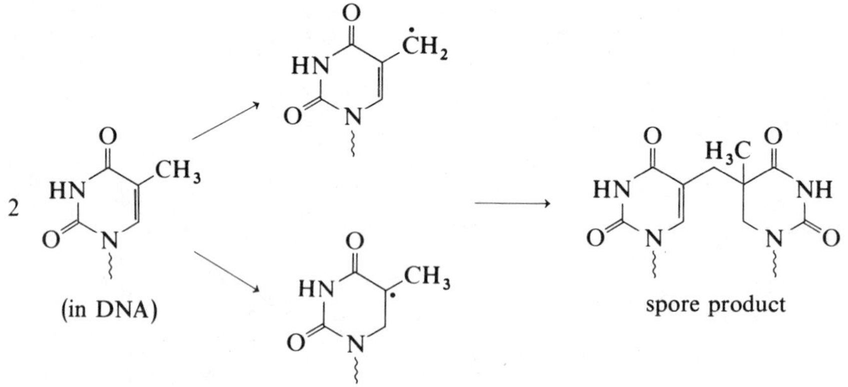

SCHEME 2

A8   Effect of ultraviolet radiation on purines

We have so far emphasised the photochemistry of the pyrimidines rather than that of the purines, and this reflects much of the recent research. Purines are, for instance, about ten times more resistant to radiation than pyrimidines in solution. In living cells, however, not only can energy transfer from purines to pyrimidines induce photochemistry but also purine addition reactions can occur. The biological importance of these reactions has only recently been appreciated, and much work remains to be done before they are understood.

A9   Repair of ultraviolet-induced damage

Many cells contain sunscreens to prevent ultraviolet damage, but others use repair mechanisms to prevent permanent ultraviolet damage to their genetic material and thus reduce the possibility of mutation.

Photoreaction (or enzymatic repair) is used in all cells (except those of mammals) to counter the effects of ultraviolet radiation. The cells must contain a photoenzyme which will become attached to the pyr-pyr cyclobutane dimer in the DNA. Neither the dimer nor the photoenzyme alone absorbs at wavelengths in the near-ultraviolet region, but combined they apparently do and the dimer is split, returning the DNA to its original condition. The action spectrum for repair lies between 300 and 500 nm and is puzzling because no chromophore appears to be present that absorbs in this region; the photorepair mechanism thus remains unknown.

Cells can also repair themselves in the dark, not just from ultraviolet damage but also from other types such as chemical damage, and the dark repair mechanism is possibly responsible for keeping down cancers to a low level. In the rare disease *Xeroderma pigmentosa* the cells of the skin lack this repair, and the skin can become extremely damaged—sunlight-induced malignant tumours generally develop in childhood.

In the process known as excision repair, a patch of damaged DNA about 20 bases long is peeled away from one strand of the double helix by an enzyme, which has recognised the damage. The excised portion is then replicated in undamaged form from information given by the second strand in the double helix. The new piece is then bound to the damaged DNA, which is thus repaired. Although the results of these processes are known, their mechanisms are not.

Section B   Photosensitisation

B1   Electron transfer and photo-oxidation in cells

All cells contain chromophores that can be used to initiate photosensitised reactions. The effects can be either advantageous, as in the photoinduced electron transfer reactions of photosynthetic organisms, or disadvantageous, as with porphyrins in the blood causing porphyria. Most photosensitised reactions studied in biological systems have been photosensitised oxidations, and the sensitiser can be re-used rather like a catalyst. Reactions involving oxygen are called 'photodynamic' reactions.

In photodynamic reactions, triplet states are often responsible for initiating electron transfer reactions: the triplet state, $A(T_1)$, reacts with an electron donor, D, which is subsequently oxidised (equations 1–3).

$$A(T_1) + D \longrightarrow A^{\bar{}} + D^{\ddagger} \tag{1}$$

$$D^{\ddagger} + O_2 \longrightarrow D(\text{oxidised}) \tag{2}$$

$$A^{\bar{}} + O_2 \longrightarrow A + O_2^{\bar{}} \tag{3}$$

The triplet state can be quenched by O_2; alternatively reactions (4)–(6) could take place, in which electron transfer from D to A^{+} occurs or where the superoxide radical ion, O_2^{-}, oxidises species D.

$$A(T_1) + O_2 \longrightarrow A^{+} + O_2^{-} \tag{4}$$

$$A^{+} + D \longrightarrow A + D^{+} \tag{5}$$

$$D + O_2^{-} \longrightarrow D(\text{oxidised}) \tag{6}$$

The net result of all these processes is that compound D is oxidised as a result of triplet sensitisation. The triplet states of a large number of compounds can be involved as photosensitisers; among these are porphyrins, hypericin, and dyes such as riboflavin, Rose Bengal or acridine orange.

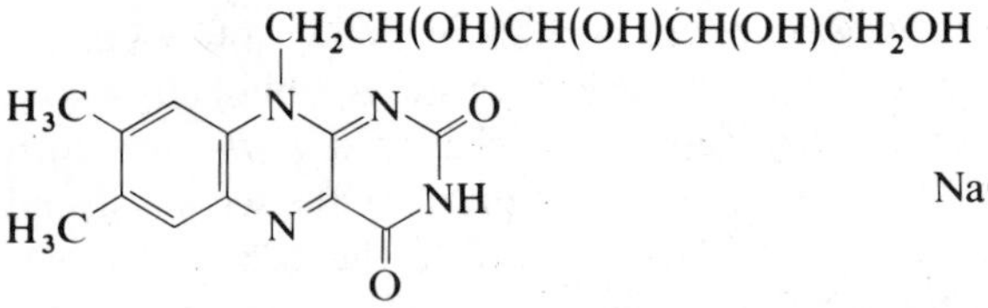

riboflavin

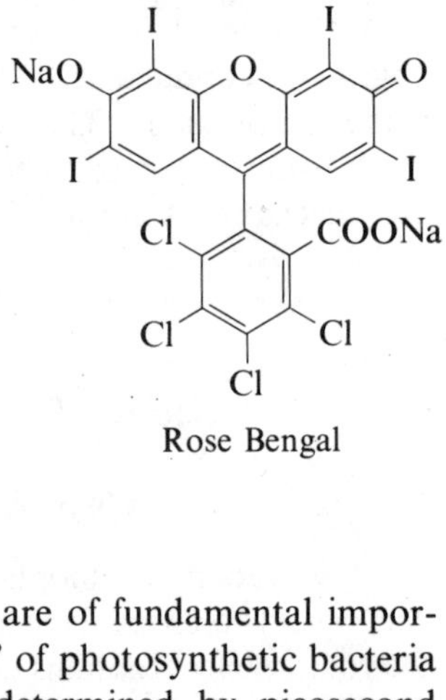

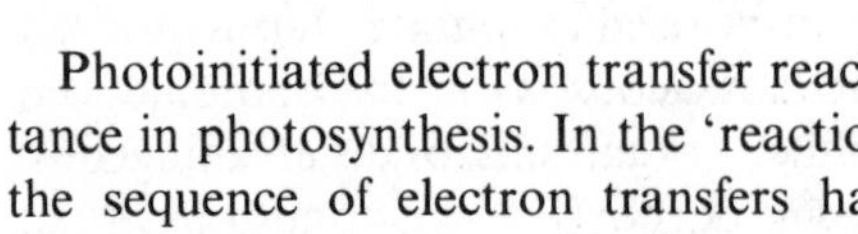

acridine
orange

Rose Bengal

Photoinitiated electron transfer reactions (1) are of fundamental importance in photosynthesis. In the 'reaction centre' of photosynthetic bacteria the sequence of electron transfers has been determined by picosecond spectroscopy. We can write the sequence of electron transfers as:

$$B_2 \, P \, Q \xrightarrow{h\nu} B_2^* \, P \, Q \longrightarrow B_2^{+} \, P^{-} \, Q \longrightarrow B_2^{+} \, P \, Q^{-} \tag{7}$$

where B_2^* is an excited bacteriochlorophyll dimer, P a bacteriopheophytin and Q a quinone. The electron transfer sequence shown above is very rapid—about 250 ps are required to achieve the final charge separation. The reaction does not stop at the third step, but the electrons from Q^{-} travel along an electron transport chain and are used to provide energy for the cell; an electron is then replaced on B_2^{+} by a cytochrome, from an electron source such as H_2S. The starting conditions, $B_2 \, P \, Q$, are thus regenerated.

Before the excitation from the absorbed photon reaches the reaction centre, it travels through an antenna of several hundred chlorophyll molecules. If reaction (8), which is known to occur in solution with many acceptors, were possible in living cells, rapid degradation of the chlorophyll, lipid or proteins would occur.

$$Chl^* + A \longrightarrow Chl^{+}_{\cdot} + A^{-}_{\cdot}$$
$$Chl^{+}_{\cdot} + O_2 \longrightarrow Chl(oxidised)$$

(8)

The reaction is prevented by the presence of carotenes among the chlorophylls. Energy transfer to carotenes occurs at a rate about 1000 times greater than oxidation. Triplet carotenes are presumably produced, which decay rapidly to the ground state because their energy is too low for them to be involved in further reaction. The importance of carotenes is illustrated by comparing a blue-green mutant *Rhodopseudomonas* bacterium with the normal purple bacterium. The blue-green species lacks carotenes and, when it is illuminated in oxygen, growth stops; the normal bacterium is unaffected.

B2   Singlet oxygen reactions

The singlet state of oxygen is also important in oxidation reactions. It can be formed by energy transfer from many triplet states because it is low in energy.

$$A(T_1) + {}^3O_2 \longrightarrow A + {}^1O_2 \tag{9}$$

$${}^1O_2 + D \longrightarrow D(oxidised) \tag{10}$$

Singlet oxygen is far more reactive than the triplet ground state ($^3O_2$), but its lifetime is short (about 2 μs in water) and so it must be produced near to the oxidisable species if it is to react. Methylene blue and Rose Bengal are good singlet oxygen sensitisers, although porphyrins and acridines are also effective.

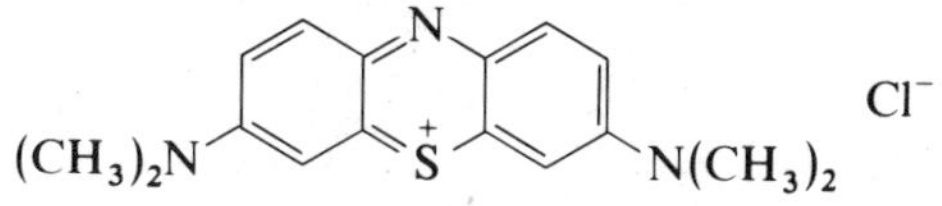

methylene blue

B3   Photo-oxidations of amino acids, proteins and nucleic acids

Of the amino acids, only a few are susceptible to photo-oxidation, whereas essentially all proteins are subject to photo-oxidation. Most frequently the

189

amino acid side-chain is oxidised, and the disulphide and peptide bonds are not often affected. It is suggested that residues undergoing rapid photo-oxidation are those on exposed regions of the protein, while the less affected ones are buried away from the singlet oxygen; thus photo-oxidation could provide structural information about the protein.

Of the purines, pyrimidines, and nucleic acid bases, guanine is oxidised most rapidly, thymine less so and the other bases hardly at all. The chemistry of guanine photo-oxidation is poorly understood, but both singlet oxygen and radical mechanisms are involved. Binding a dye to a nucleic acid base often increases the efficiency of photo-oxidation of that base. Guanine can be selectively destroyed in this way by several dye sensitisers.

B4   Photosensitisation caused by porphyrins

Porphyrins (e.g. haematoporphyrin, **8**) are found in all cells and comprise a family of compounds which vary in their substituents around the same basic skeleton (Chapter 2·3). In human and animal metabolism porphyrins are synthesised as needed, but when the metabolism becomes deranged an excess of some porphyrin can be produced. In humans excess protoporphyrin occurs when the enzyme catalysing the binding of iron to protoporphyrin to form haemoglobin fails to work properly—a disease known as porphyria is caused. Other porphyrias are hereditary, but they can also be induced by drugs, alcohol or poisons.

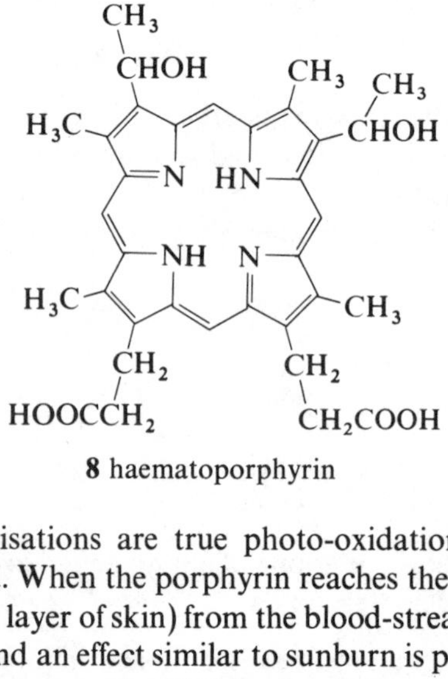

8 haematoporphyrin

Porphyrin sensitisations are true photo-oxidations, as both light and oxygen are required. When the porphyrin reaches the Prickle cells (situated under the top horny layer of skin) from the blood-stream, extreme sensitivity to light can occur and an effect similar to sunburn is produced. This extreme sensitivity was demonstrated in 1912 by the German physician, Meyer Betz, who injected himself intravenously with a solution containing 0.2 grams of haematoporphyrin. He became extremely photosensitive, his face became swollen almost beyond recognition and his breathing laboured. The effect lasted for three months, then gradually lessened and finally disappeared.

The photosensitivity to porphyrins can be alleviated by taking β-carotene orally. Presumably it finds its way to the blood-stream, then to the Prickle cells and quenches the porphyrin triplet state by energy transfer. Curiously, when porphyrins are painted on to the skin, even when the epidermal horny layer is removed, no photosensitised oxidation occurs. Presumably the porphyrin does not enter any cells when applied this way and cannot cause an inflammatory response from the host.

B5   Photosensitisation without oxygen

Furocoumarins (also called psoralens) are effective photosensitisers, but they act directly rather than by photo-oxidation; carotenes do not inhibit their reactions. When psoralens are painted on to the skin, the sensitised region has a response similar to a suntan. The application of psoralens has been used to darken light areas of dark skin in the condition called vitiligo, but there is apparently a risk of skin cancer formation as a result of the use of some psoralen compounds. The psoralens are also effective in killing bacteria when 365 nm radiation is used; this is absorbed by the psoralen alone. Furthermore, these compounds can cause an increase in the frequency of mutations in bacteria and yeasts. As mutation is the result of DNA injury, the psoralen must act on the bases in DNA. The reaction of psoralen with thymine (Scheme 3) produces cyclobutane-type adducts. Psoralens can also form cross-links between two thymines and thus injure the DNA helix; however, the dark repair process can remove this damage. Uracil in RNA is attacked also, but because so much RNA is present compared with DNA, this may not affect the viability of the cell.

Psoralens are also being used to control the disease called psoriasis. This affects 1-3% of the world's population, and causes plaques to be formed on the skin which peel off leaving intense itching. In this disease both DNA synthesis and cell division are accelerated in cells of the epidermis; squamous (scaly) cells are formed in three days instead of twenty days as in normal skin. The cells are not cancerous, and the cause of the loss of control of DNA synthesis is unknown. To control this, 8-methoxypsoralen is given orally and in two hours reaches the skin where the affected area is exposed to intense ultraviolet light (300 to 400 nm). A series of applications leads to remission of symptoms but not a cure of the disease. Possibly the psoralen acts by binding and disrupting the DNA strands, thus preventing successful replication of the cells.

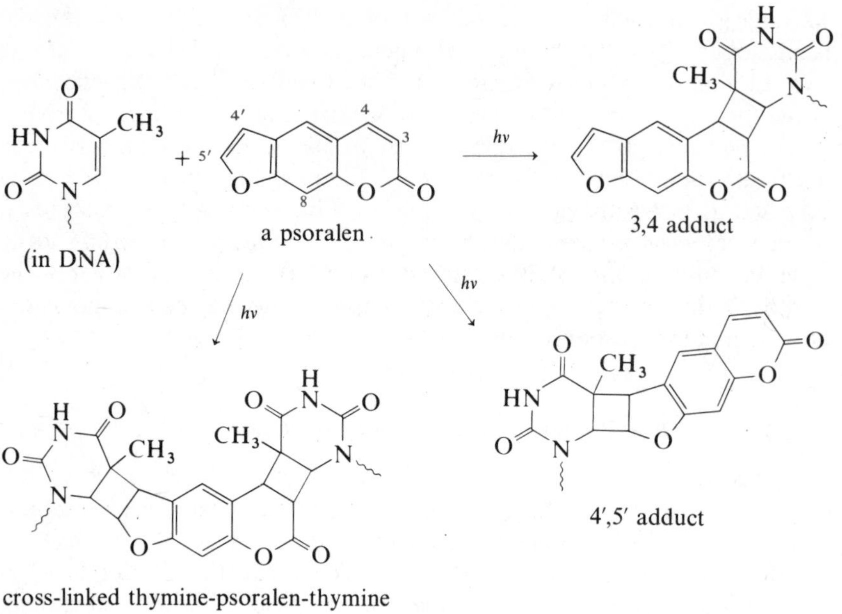

a psoralen

(in DNA)

3,4 adduct

cross-linked thymine-psoralen-thymine

4',5' adduct

SCHEME 3

B6   Photosensitisation by medication

Some medications cause sensitisation to light. Two effects are observed, a phototoxic and a photoallergic effect. The first occurs on exposure to light in the presence of the sensitiser, the latter only after a lapse in time and on a second administration of light and sensitiser. Phototoxic compounds comprise a wide variety of chemicals, for example riboflavin, estrone, methylene blue, barbiturates, some surfactants, and antibacterials in soaps. Not everybody is sensitised by these compounds, but it seems that there is an inverse relationship to the amount of melanin (pigment) in the skin.

In a photoallergic response light converts the photosensitiser into an allergen (i.e., a substance that evokes the formation of an antibody specific to it). After an incubation period and on a second application, an inflammatory antibody–antigen reaction occurs. The major compounds responsible are antibacterials, sulphanilamides, antifungals, antihistamines (e.g. phenergan), cyclamates, diuretics, some sunscreens containing benzoic acid and its derivatives, and tranquilisers, such as chloropromazine. Again, not everybody is sensitive, but those prone to allergies usually are. A phototoxic response in one person may be photoallergic in another. As with porphyrins, carotene taken orally or applied on the affected site protects from sensitisation.

B7   Sunburn and suntan

Normally, human skin begins to redden 10–14 hours after exposure to sunlight and the effect, called erythema, reaches a peak in 24 hours, after a temporary intermediate flushing is observed. Mild sunburn declines shortly afterwards, but even in the minimal dose some cells are killed or rendered abnormal. As the dose is increased, more cells are killed and the symptoms become more pronounced, until the skin becomes very red and blisters. Figure 6 shows the action spectrum for sunburn. UV-B (which is absorbed by window glass) is effectively responsible for sunburn. Even on cloudy days ultraviolet light still reaches the skin because clouds only scatter rather than absorb this radiation.

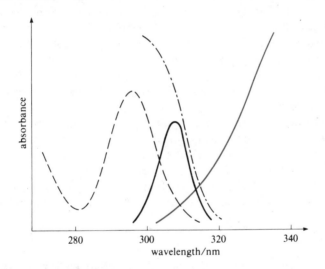

FIGURE 6   The effective sunburn spectrum (*solid black line*) is a combination of the sunburn action spectrum (*dashed line*), and the solar spectrum (*red curve*). An efficient sunscreen has an absorption spectrum (*dashed and dotted line*) that covers almost the entire effective sunburn spectrum.

The horny epidermal layer of skin is composed of clear flattened cells and blocks the short-wavelength ultraviolet light both by absorption and scattering, but considerable light near 300 nm reaches the layer of Prickle cells and even passes to the dermis below. The killing of Prickle cells results in sunburn; other effects can also contribute and are collectively called sunburn. Urocanic acid (**9**) is formed in epidermal cells by the deamination of histidine. The *trans*-isomer appears to offer some protection from ultraviolet radiation, because it isomerises to the *cis*-isomer on absorption of ultraviolet light.

trans-**9** cis-**9**

In addition to reddening of the skin, exposure to sunlight causes two types of tanning to occur, immediate and delayed (10 hours). The immediate tanning is caused by oxidation of melanin precursors in the skin and has a wide action spectrum. For delayed tanning the action spectrum is the same as for sunburn. The latter tan results from the activation of cells called melanocytes, which deposit melanin in body tissue (one melanocyte is present for every 36 Prickle cells). Pigmentation may also follow mechanical or heat injury to the skin. The melanin absorbs over a wide range in the ultraviolet, but also adds protection by forming a cap over the cell nucleus to protect DNA. A good suntan results in 90% of light being absorbed before it reaches the dermis.

Sunburn can be prevented by applying a screen to the skin; this absorbs the ultraviolet light and prevents the development of erythema. Sunscreens such as benzoic acid or menthyl anthranilate absorb just in the region where the atmospheric ozone lets through some ultraviolet light (290–320 nm), as shown in Figure 6. The screens absorb most of the light on the skin surface; zinc oxide and magnesium oxide may also be added to scatter the incident light.

B8 The role of ultraviolet radiation in alleviating disease

The damaging effect that ultraviolet radiation has on living tissue can be put to advantage under certain circumstances. We have already discussed this in the treatment of psoriasis, and light can also be used in the treatment of tuberculosis, rickets, and neonatal jaundice.

It was shown as early as the 1870s that sunlight kills bacteria, and shortly afterwards the ultraviolet component was found to be the cause. Even today, ultraviolet light is sometimes used to sterilise air in a hospital operating room. Because bacteria and viruses are very small, the radiation easily reaches the vital genetic material, whereas in plants and animals the effect takes longer to achieve because of the cytoplasm between the cell surface and the genetic material in the centrally located nucleus. Thus viruses and bacteria on the surface of animals and plants can be killed without much damage to the underlying cells.

Tuberculosis of the skin is a bacterial disease that was once common in Northern European cities where sunlight is weak or absent for long periods during winter months. Ulcers develop on the face and neck, and even when cured they leave ugly scars. The Danish physician Finsen (1860–1904) demonstrated that UV-B is readily absorbed by the cells and a few bacteria can be hit directly; it is now thought that the radiation induces an inflammation that stimulates an immunological response in the tissue, subsequently healing the lesion. Antibiotics are now used to cure this disease, with ultraviolet treatment as a fallback if such chemotherapy fails.

Rickets used to be prevalent in northern industrial towns, particularly among children, and is caused by a disturbance in normal bone formation and hardening. The long bones bend, causing bow legs, and muscular contraction is distorted. The disease is a result of vitamin D deficiency. In skin cells the vitamin D precursor (7-dehydrocholesterol) is converted on irradiation into vitamin D_3 (cholecalciferol). This passes along the blood-stream, first to the liver, then to the kidneys where a water-soluble derivative (1,25-dihydroxycalciferol) is formed. This enters cells in the intestinal lining and reaches the cellular nucleus where association with the chromosomes' genetic material occurs, after which it triggers the formation of a messenger molecule with specific instructions to create a protein that transports calcium. The calcium is transported through the gut cells to the blood-stream and to the bones.

Vitamin D may have influenced the evolution of skin coloration. Fair-skinned people have a selective advantage over dark-skinned people in winter months in northern climates, because with little sunlight and low melanin content in the skin, vitamin D can be synthesised in sufficient amounts. Dark-skinned people in the same latitude have much of the ultraviolet light absorbed by the melanin and, particularly in children, rickets can develop if the diet is not supplemented. Conversely, in lower latitudes, highly pigmented skin prevents sunburn by absorbing much of the ultraviolet but still allows sufficient to penetrate to produce vitamin D. Fair skin in the same conditions is subject to more rapid degradation and cancer induction than dark skin.

Neonatal jaundice may also be treated with light. The haemoglobin in red blood cells is broken down, probably by cells in the liver, to form a compound called bilirubin by opening of the porphyrin ring. In young babies, increased amounts of unconjugated (water-insoluble) bilirubin are present in the blood, caused by the shorter life of the red blood cells and the immaturity of the baby's liver. The bilirubin cannot be converted fast enough into a water-soluble (conjugated) derivative and excreted in the urine, and it thus accumulates in the body. It gives a yellowish colour to the skin, and if untreated it can lead to damage of the central nervous system by deposition

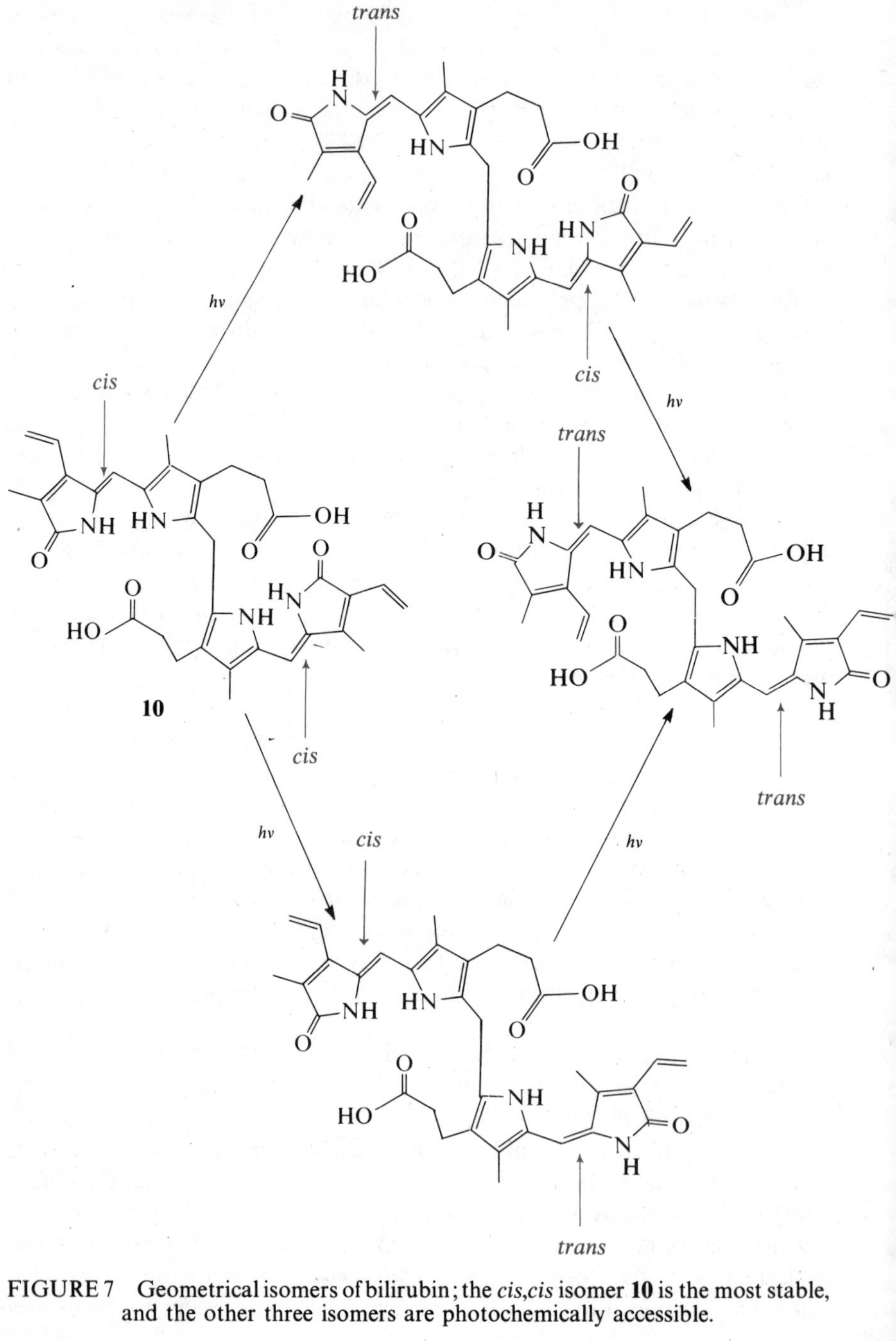

FIGURE 7   Geometrical isomers of bilirubin; the *cis,cis* isomer **10** is the most stable, and the other three isomers are photochemically accessible.

in brain cells. Bilirubin absorbs light in the 450–500 nm region, and it is then oxidised to non-toxic products. The initial effect of phototherapy is not photodegradation of the bilirubin but a simple *cis–trans* isomerisation (Figure 7). Phototherapy enhances the excretion of the neurotoxic bilirubin.

5·3 Photosensitised *cis–trans* isomerisation

by *Godfrey Beddard* (*The Royal Institution, London)*

Sensitised reactions have three major uses: to induce chemistry specifically from the state obtained by sensitisation (such as a triplet); to determine triplet energy levels from observed *cis–trans* isomerisation ratios; and to remove unwanted reactions by deactivating an excited state to an inert acceptor. We shall discuss the first two uses in detail, but we begin by describing the sensitisation process.

1 Sensitised reactions

Reactions from triplet states are often studied by sensitisation because $S_0 \rightarrow T$ absorption coefficients are almost always vanishingly small (and so triplets cannot be produced directly by absorption) and intersystem crossing from S_1 does not always produce a significant population of triplets. Also, reactions from S_1 can compete with those from the triplet state and may lead to different products. The different reactions of the singlet and (sensitised) triplet are shown, for example, by penta-1,3-diene (**1**) and by myrcene (**2**).

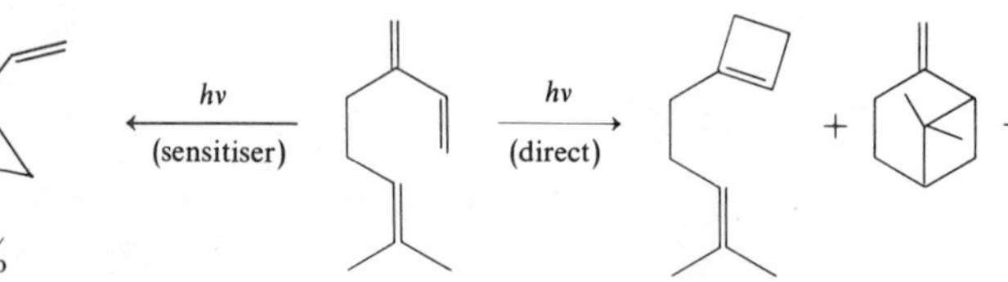

cis-**1** $trans$-**1**

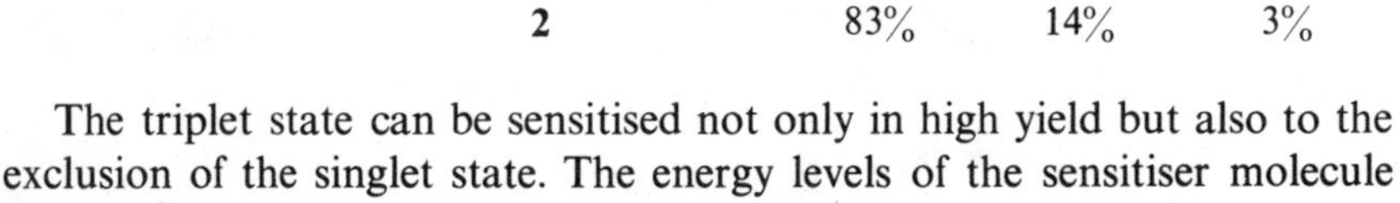

100%

2   83%   14%   3%

The triplet state can be sensitised not only in high yield but also to the exclusion of the singlet state. The energy levels of the sensitiser molecule (donor) and the substrate (acceptor) in Figure 1 show how this can be achieved. Both the S_1 and the T_1 states of the sensitiser lie between the S_1 and T_1 states of the acceptor. Should the triplet energy of the acceptor be unknown, several donors may have to be tried before sensitisation is successful. The energy is transferred from the donor (sensitising) triplet and forms the

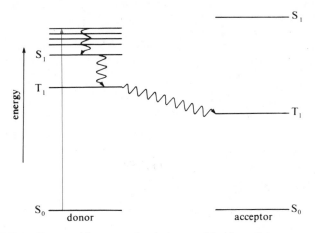

FIGURE 1   Favourable energy levels for sensitisation of the acceptor triplet.

triplet state from which reaction is to occur. This process can be written as

$$D(T_1) + A(S_0) \longrightarrow D(S_0) + A(T_1) \tag{1}$$

Note that this reaction is doubly spin forbidden, but it occurs because exchange interactions between the two excited molecules overcome this restriction and the rate constant can then be very large.

Important considerations when choosing a sensitiser are that its triplet lifetime is long, the triplet yield is high (i.e. the rate of intersystem crossing is fast compared with other processes depleting the singlet state), and the sensitiser singlet absorption is well separated from the acceptor's absorption so that no direct irradiation of the acceptor occurs. Additionally, sensitisers should have good solubility, be inert towards the excited state of the acceptor or subsequent products, and be easily separated from the reaction mixture.

These conditions are easily met by a sufficiently large number of compounds, and Table 1 lists a number of sensitisers and their triplet energies. Ketones such as biacetyl and benzophenone are commonly used because their singlet states are low in energy and their singlet–triplet energy gap is small (so that intersystem crossing is fast). Benzophenone can undergo its own photochemistry, however, often by hydrogen abstraction from the solvent (such as propan-2-ol), which competes with the preferred process of energy transfer by virtue of the high concentration of solvent:

$$(C_6H_5)_2CO(T_1) + A(S_0) \longrightarrow (C_6H_5)_2CO + A(T_1) \tag{2}$$

$$(C_6H_5)_2CO(T_1) + (CH_3)_2CHOH \longrightarrow (C_6H_5)_2\dot{C}OH + (CH_3)_2\dot{C}OH \tag{3}$$

199

Table 1 Some sensitisers and their triplet energies

Compound	E_T/kJ mol^{-1}	Compound	E_T/kJ mol^{-1}
benzene	351	thioxanthone	272
acetone	326	phenanthrene	259
acetophenone	308	naphthalene	255
benzaldehyde	301	biacetyl	234
benzophenone	288	fluorenone	222
triphenylene	284		

Reaction (2) has a rate constant of 5×10^9 l mol^{-1} s^{-1}, and reaction (3) has a rate constant of about 10^6 l mol^{-1} s^{-1}. (In these two reactions, $(C_6H_5)_2CO(T_1)$ is triplet benzophenone and A is an acceptor with a triplet energy lower than that of benzophenone.)

A few other energy transfer reactions besides those shown in equation (1) can also occur, as shown in equations (4)–(6). In these reactions the mechanism is dipole–dipole energy transfer which, like the exchange mechanism (equation 1), requires the overlap of the donor emission and the acceptor absorption spectra.

$$D(S_1) + A(S_0) \longrightarrow D(S_0) + A(S_1) \qquad (4)$$

$$D(S_1) + A(S_0) \longrightarrow D(S_0) + A(T_1) \qquad (5)$$

$$D(T_1) + A(S_0) \longrightarrow D(S_0) + A(S_1) \qquad (6)$$

By suitable positioning of the donor and acceptor energy levels, these unwanted reactions can be avoided (see Figure 1).

Only if the triplet energy of the donor (E_D) is lower than that of the acceptor (E_A) is the rate constant for transfer related to the energy difference, ΔE, between the two triplet states; the relationship is

$$k_{\Delta E} = k_0 \exp(\Delta E/RT)$$

$$\text{when } \Delta E < 0$$

where k_0 is the rate constant when the donor is higher than the acceptor in energy, R the gas constant, and T the temperature in kelvins; RT represents the thermal activation of the process. Table 2 shows the rate constants for various pairs of molecules with different values of ΔE.

Note that when ΔE is small (as between phenanthrene and naphthalene in Table 2) the rate constant for energy transfer is about 1000 times lower

Table 2 Calculated rate constants for energy transfer

Donor	Acceptor	ΔE/kJ mol^{-1}	Rate constant/l mol^{-1} s^{-1}
biacetyl	1,2-benzanthracene	38	3×10^9
triphenylene	naphthalene	26	1.3×10^9
phenanthrene	naphthalene	4	3×10^6
naphthalene	triphenylene	-26	5×10^4

than when ΔE is 20–40 kJ mol^{-1}. The reason for this is that energy transfer back to the sensitiser can occur:

$$D(T_1) + A(S_0) \rightleftharpoons D(S_0) + A(T_1)$$

and the apparent (measured) rate constant for the forward reaction is reduced. Other molecules that show this reversible transfer are biacetyl with 1,1′-binaphthyl.

When ΔE is large, the rate of transfer is approximately one-half of the diffusion-controlled rate as calculated from the Debye formulae ($k_D = 8RT/3000\eta$, where η is the solvent viscosity). The reason for this lower rate constant is that energy transfer only occurs once every few collisions of the reactive partners. Note that the rate constant is nearly independent of the sensitiser triplet energy when ΔE is large.

An alternative sensitisation mechanism to the one just outlined has been proposed. This is called the Schenck mechanism, and it postulates that either a σ-bond is formed between the sensitiser triplet state and, for example, a diene acceptor, or that a loose charge-transfer complex (or exciplex) is formed. The σ-bonded intermediate (**3**) decomposes to form the isomers or cycloaddition products.

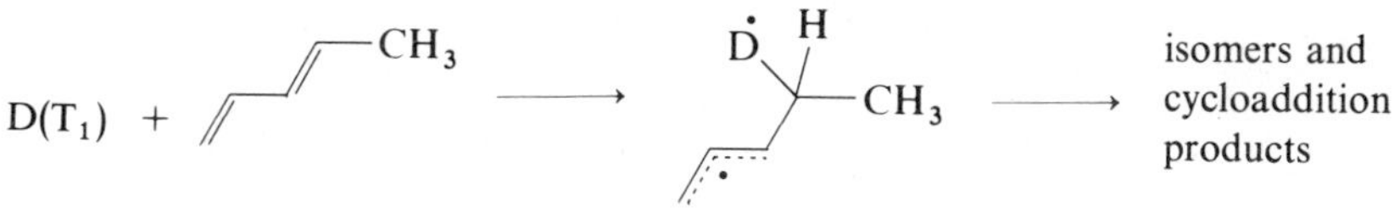

3

We now illustrate the uses of sensitised reactions in the study of the *cis–trans* isomerisation of stilbene and in the determination of triplet energy levels by the sensitisation of penta-1,3-diene.

2 *Cis–trans* isomerisation of stilbene

One of the most extensively studied sensitised reactions has been the isomerisation of *cis*- and *trans*-stilbene:

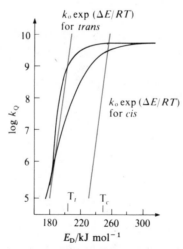

cis-stilbene

trans-stilbene

Starting with either pure *cis*- or pure *trans*-isomer, a photostationary mixture of the two isomers is formed after irradiation in the presence of a sensitiser, because either isomer can be sensitised to the other. (If in practice, other reactions occur that slowly remove the stilbene and prevent a true steady state from being reached, this will not affect our arguments.) The two stilbene isomers have different triplet energy levels, 247 kJ mol^{-1} for the *cis* and 205 kJ mol^{-1} for the *trans*, thus the rate constant for transfer from a sensitiser to the *cis*-isomer will be different from that for transfer to the *trans*-isomer, unless the energy of the sensitiser is greater than the triplet energy of the *cis*-isomer.

Figure 2 indicates how the rate constants, k_Q, for energy transfer to the two stilbene isomers vary with the energy of the sensitiser (E_D). Note that the rate

FIGURE 2   Rate constants for the quenching of sensitisers by stilbenes. T_t and T_c mark the triplet energies for *trans*-stilbene and *cis*-stilbene, respectively. (source: Herkstroeter and Hammond, 1966)

constant for the interaction of the *cis*-isomer with low-energy sensitisers is much greater than would be predicted from the expression

$$k_Q = k_0 \exp(\Delta E/RT)$$

where ΔE is the difference between the triplet energies of the sensitiser and the stilbene. The red lines in Figure 2 are calculated from the above expression. The right-hand line is that predicted for *cis*-stilbene, and the one on the left is for *trans*-stilbene. The latter follows the experimental curve closely, but the former does not.

The percentage of the *cis*-isomer in the photostationary state varies with the energy of the sensitiser, as shown in Figure 3. When the triplet energy of

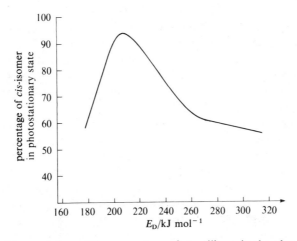

FIGURE 3   The variation of the percentage of *cis*-stilbene in the photostationary mixture with the triplet energy of the sensitiser. (source: Herkstroeter and Hammond, 1966)

the sensitiser (E_D) is greater than the triplet energy of *cis*-stilbene, the rates for *cis* → *trans* and *trans* → *cis* conversion are similar and constant, so the percentage of the *cis*-isomer is almost constant. As E_D decreases, the rate for *cis* → *trans* becomes less than that for *trans* → *cis*, because E_D is less than the triplet energy of *cis*-stilbene. So more *trans* molecules are converted into *cis* and the percentage of the *cis*-isomer increases. If the *cis* triplet behaved 'classically', as does the *trans* triplet, the percentage of the *cis*-isomer would increase towards 100% as E_D continued to decrease. However, as Figure 2 shows, the rate constants for the *cis* → *trans* and *trans* → *cis* reactions are almost equal when E_D falls to about 205 kJ mol^{-1} or less. This means that the percentage of the *cis*-isomer falls to a value similar to that obtained with high-energy sensitisers (Figure 3).

The data of Figures 2 and 3 suggest that there exists an intermediate triplet state, T_p, which has an energy lower than those of both the *cis* triplet (T_c) and the *trans* triplet (T_t) and from which isomerisation occurs. A kinetic scheme to rationalise these data is set out in reactions (7)–(12).

$$D(S_0) \xrightarrow{hv} D(S_1) \longrightarrow D(T_1) \tag{7}$$

$$D(T_1) + (S_0)_t \longrightarrow D(S_0) + T_t \tag{8}$$

$$D(T_1) + (S_0)_c \longrightarrow D(S_0) + T_c \tag{9}$$

$$T_t \rightleftharpoons T_p \tag{10}$$

$$T_c \longrightarrow T_p \tag{11}$$

$$T_p \longrightarrow \gamma(S_0)_t + (1 - \gamma)(S_0)_c \tag{12}$$

In this scheme, γ is the fraction of *trans*-isomer produced by the decay of the intermediate triplet state T_p, and as γ is found to be about 0.4 this explains why, in Figure 3, the percentage of *cis*-isomer in the photostationary mixture with high energy sensitisers is nearer to 60% than 50%. Furthermore, the ratio of *trans/cis* isomers predicted by the scheme closely follows the experimental curve in Figure 3.

As both the *cis* → *trans* and *trans* → *cis* reactions pass through a common triplet state, it has been proposed that this has a geometry twisted about the stilbene C=C bond. Figure 4 shows the variation of the energies of the triplet state and the ground state on twisting about this bond. The ground state reaches maximum energy at 90° twist where the triplet reaches a minimum, as occurs also in ethene. Additionally, the 90° twisted triplet is close in energy to the *trans* triplet, which is indicated by the reversibility of equation (10). The experimental evidence for the closeness in energy of these two states

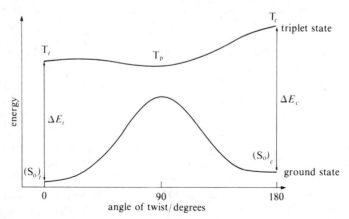

FIGURE 4   Energy diagram for twisting about the central C=C bond in stilbene.

comes from the similarity of the observed rate constants (for sensitisation of the *trans*-isomer) with the predicted line for the *trans* triplet (Figure 2), and also from results obtained with an added low energy acceptor, such as azulene.

The proposed twisted intermediate triplet state (sometimes called the 'non-spectroscopic' triplet) has not yet been detected spectroscopically, and its twisted geometry is thus only a hypothesis. The reason for not detecting this intermediate may be due not only to the rapid rate of intersystem crossing to the ground state because of the small energy gap between this state and the ground state with the same geometry (Figure 4), but also to the large change in geometry expected to occur as the double bond twists, making Franck–Condon factors for absorption from the ground state vanishingly small. A recent examination of the exchange mechanism for energy transfer from the sensitiser to stilbene has shown that the rate constant for transfer follows closely the $S_0 \rightarrow T$ absorption spectrum for both *trans*- and *cis*-stilbene. This means that the transfer obeys the Franck–Condon rule as expected; the twisted triplet is populated in the normal manner, but because of the small Franck–Condon factors (due to the large geometrical change) its absorption has not yet been detected.

Stilbene derivatives such as 1,2-diphenylpropene (**4**) also undergo isomerisation by a similar mechanism, but both *cis* and *trans* triplets behave non-classically.

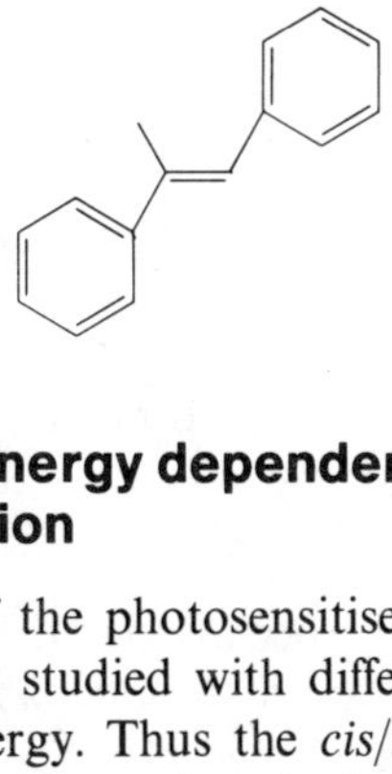

4 *trans*-1,2-diphenylpropene

3 Triplet energy dependence of product distribution

The product distribution of the photosensitised reactions of alkenes and dienes has been extensively studied with different sensitisers and can be related to the sensitiser energy. Thus the *cis/trans* ratio of an irradiated mixture can now be used to determine the (unknown) triplet energy of a sensitiser.

trans-Penta-1,3-diene (**5**) and its *cis*-isomer (**6**) are often used to determine the triplet energy of a sensitiser, provided it is greater than 219 kJ mol^{-1}.

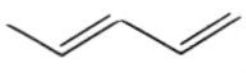

5 *trans*-penta-1,3-diene

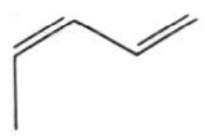

6 *cis*-penta-1,3-diene

The percentage of the *cis*-isomer present in the photostationary mixture is 45% for a high energy sensitiser. This percentage falls to 20% when E_D is between 260 and 246 kJ mol^{-1} and rises to 50% when E_D is less than 230 kJ mol^{-1}. This behaviour is opposite to that of the stilbenes (Figure 3). The two penta-1,3-dienes also behave non-classically, although not for the same reason as the stilbenes. The *trans* and *cis* triplet energies are almost the same, being 246 kJ mol^{-1} and about 238 kJ mol^{-1}, respectively.

The difference between the dienes and alkenes (such as stilbene) is that the diene excited triplet (**7**) cannot rotate about the central bond, i.e. the *cis* and *trans* triplets cannot interconvert, as shown in Scheme 1. In this scheme the different conformations of the *trans* (**5**) and *cis* (**6**) ground states caused by rotations about the central (single) bond between the double bonds are included.

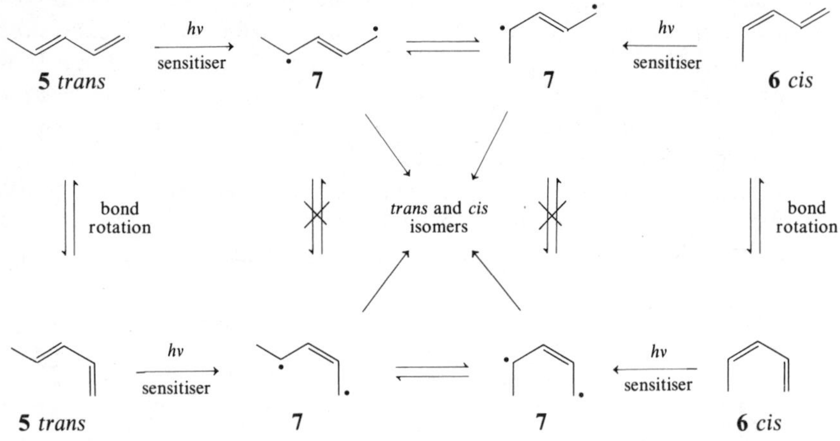

SCHEME 1

It is these conformations that lead to different (non-interconvertible) excited triplet states, and, as shown in Scheme 1, there are two twisted triplet states, each of which can decay to ground state *cis*- or *trans*-diene.

Triplet states of dienes can also give rise to cyclic dimers, and irradiation of cyclic dienes leads largely to such dimers, because *cis–trans* isomerisation is prevented by the molecular geometry. This is shown below for cyclopenta-1,3-diene (**8**).

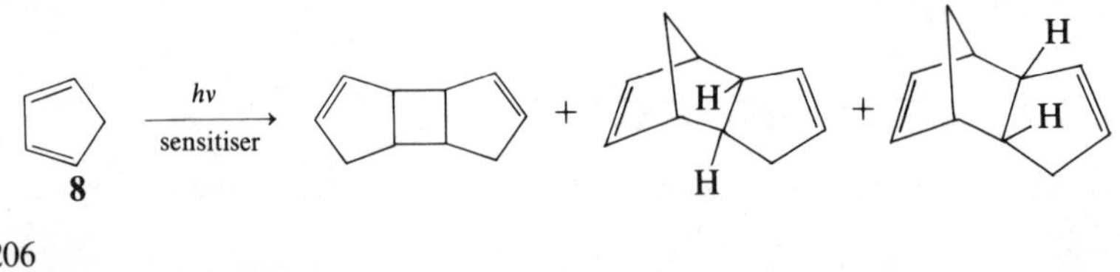

5·4 Applications of flash photolysis

by *Godfrey Beddard (The Royal Institution, London)*

The excited state lifetimes of polyatomic molecules span an enormous time range—from picoseconds (10^{-12} seconds) to tens of seconds; the rates of their reactions also cover a wide range of values. These properties can be probed if the absorption of the excited molecule can be measured, and flash photolysis techniques enable this to be done.

To illustrate the electronic transitions involved in a typical organic molecule, Figure 1 shows the singlet–singlet ($S_1 \rightarrow S_n$) and triplet–triplet ($T_1 \rightarrow T_n$) transitions that can be measured in absorption. The universal applicability of flash photolysis arises from the fact that not only do all excited states absorb (very many in the 200–1 000 nm range), thus making every type of molecule amenable to study, but also the time resolution of the technique now extends to times as short as a few picoseconds, short enough for the most transient of species to be observed.

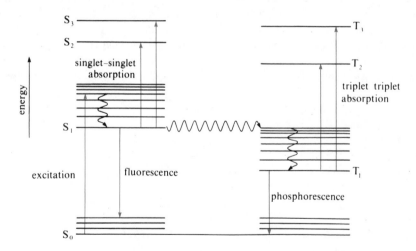

FIGURE 1   Energy level diagram illustrating $S_1 \rightarrow S_n$ and $T_1 \rightarrow T_n$ absorption.

We begin with a brief study of the principles involved in making measurements by this technique, then show how first-order and second-order rate constants and excited state absorption coefficients can be measured, and conclude with an example of an electron transfer reaction studied with picosecond time resolution.

1 Principles of flash photolysis

For the absorption of an excited state to be measured, two basic conditions have to be met. First, the measuring instrument must have a time resolution fast enough to observe the excited molecule before it decays, and second, the exciting flash of light must produce a significant population of molecules in this excited state to enable their absorption to be detected. These conditions have led to two variants of the flash photolysis technique, the kinetic and spectrographic methods.

The kinetic method measures primarily the decay of the excited state absorption as a function of time (using a photomultiplier and an oscilloscope) at one wavelength. The information obtained is the rate of decay of the excited molecule. If this measurement is repeated at different monitoring wavelengths, spectra can be constructed by plotting the absorbance at any fixed time after excitation with different wavelengths.

In the spectrographic method the whole absorption spectrum is recorded, for instance with a spectrograph and photographic plate, at a fixed time after excitation. The decay of the excited molecule can then be observed by recording spectra at different time intervals after excitation. Usually in an investigation of the behaviour of a molecule in its excited state, both kinetic and spectroscopic information will be measured, although in principle all the information can be obtained from one of the techniques alone.

It should be remembered that in the flash photolysis method the total absorbance of the solution is measured, i.e. the combined spectra of the

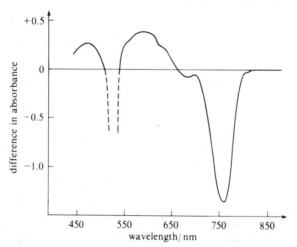

FIGURE 2   Difference spectrum for the formation of the excited state of bacteriopheophytin following excitation at 530 nm. Scattered exciting light interferes with measurements of the ground state absorption band near 530 nm. (source: Gouterman, Hollen, Windsor and Rockley, 1976)

ground state and excited state. The ground state spectrum can then be subtracted and the 'difference spectrum' is obtained. Figure 2 shows such a spectrum of the bacteriopheophytin singlet state, measured point by point from the transient absorbance traces. Note that this spectrum has positive and negative values of the absorbance difference. This means that when the absorbance is negative the ground state absorbs more than the excited state, and when it is positive the excited state absorbs more. When both states absorb equally there is no change in absorbance. The decay of the excited state is thus best measured when there is a large change in absorbance in the difference spectrum, such as at 610 or 760 nm in Figure 2.

2 Absorption of excited singlet and triplet states

We shall now consider some applications of flash photolysis to the study of the lifetimes and reactions of excited states. The most straightforward measurement is that of the lifetime of a singlet or triplet state. As the S_1 or T_1 state decays so does the intensity of the $S_1 \to S_n$ or $T_1 \to T_n$ absorption; thus if this decrease in absorption is measured, the decay time of the excited state can be determined. This is an alternative approach to measuring the decay time of fluorescence or phosphorescence. Figure 3 shows spectra taken only a few nanoseconds after excitation of an aromatic hydrocarbon (phenanth-

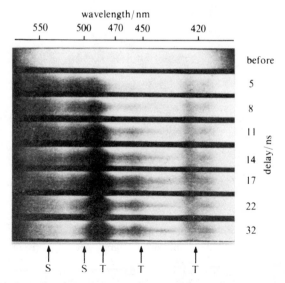

FIGURE 3   Absorption of phenanthrene at different time intervals after excitation with 347 nm radiation. (source: Porter and Topp, 1970)

rene) by a *Q*-switched ruby laser (at 347 nm) having a pulse duration of a few nanoseconds. The monitoring (interrogating) pulse used to measure the spectra has also to be of short duration. To make this measurement, part of the laser pulse can be split off to excite a scintillator, which fluoresces with a broad spectrum and which is then used to interrogate the sample. The variable time interval between excitation and interrogation is achieved by delaying the laser pulse down a long optical path after it has excited the sample and before it has excited the scintillator.

The scintillator method is not used much today, and instead a broad band emission can be obtained using a pulse of picosecond duration by focusing part of this laser pulse into a cell containing one of many liquids such as CCl_4, H_2O or D_2O. Figure 4 shows an outline of an instrument for measuring absorbances of picosecond duration. (An instrument of this type was used to obtain the spectrum in Figure 2.) The time interval between excitation and measurement is also achieved in this instrument by an optical delay line.

Figure 3 shows the singlet–singlet absorption decaying in the 500–550 nm region and the triplet–triplet absorption appearing at 480, 450 and 420 nm. The increase in absorbance of the triplet state is particularly noticeable at

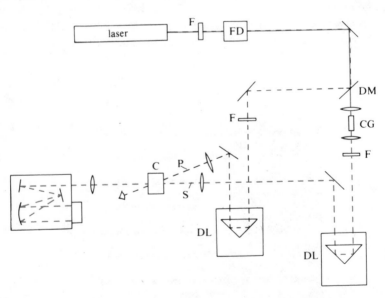

FIGURE 4 Picosecond flash photolysis and spectroscopy apparatus. FD, frequency doubler; DM, dichroic beam splitter; CG, fundamental laser focused into cell containing CCl_4 generates white-light continuum; DL, variable optical delay line; C, sample cell; P, pump pulse path (*black*); S, probe pulse path (*red*); F, coloured glass filters. (source: Magde and Windsor, 1974)

420 nm, and a plot of the change of absorbance with time would enable the appearance of the triplet to be measured. A more direct way of doing this would be to use an instrument such as the one sketched in Figure 5. This is used for kinetic spectroscopy, and the absorbance induced in the sample is monitored on a photomultiplier by the change in transmittance of the sample to a continuous light source such as a xenon arc lamp.

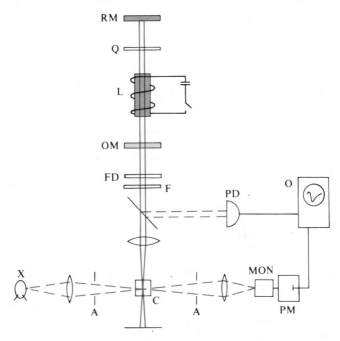

FIGURE 5   Kinetic flash photolysis apparatus. RM, 100% reflecting mirror; Q, Q-switch; OM, output mirror; L, laser rod; FD, frequency doubler; F, filter; PD, photodiode; O, oscilloscope; MON, monochromator; PM, photomultiplier; X, xenon arc lamp; C, cell; A, aperture.

In all experiments we must remember that the Beer–Lambert law should be obeyed, i.e. if I_t is the transmitted intensity at time t, and I_0 the initial intensity of the incident light (at $t = 0$), then

$$I_t = I_0 \exp(-\epsilon_\lambda l[M]_t)$$

where $[M]_t$ is the concentration of molecules in the light path at time t, ϵ_λ the absorption coefficient at the monitoring wavelength, λ, and l the path length of the excited region of the sample. Additionally the detector (a photomultiplier) must respond linearly to light intensity. In the spectroscopic method the Beer–Lambert law must also apply, and calibration plates of known optical density are inserted in front of the photographic plate.

3 Kinetics of first-order and second-order processes

In the measurement of the excited state absorption, the following scheme forms the basis for determining rate constants:

$$S_0 \xrightarrow{h\nu} S_1$$

$$S_1 \xrightarrow{k_S} S_0$$

$$S_1 \xrightarrow{k_{isc}} T$$

$$T \xrightarrow{k_T} S_0$$

$$T + T \xrightarrow{k_b} S_0 + S_1$$

$$T + O_2 \longrightarrow S_0 + O_2$$

$$S_1 + O_2 \longrightarrow S_0 + O_2$$

From this we can write the time dependences of the concentrations of the S_1 and T states (ignoring for the moment the reactions with oxygen):

$$\frac{d[S_1]}{dt} = \epsilon_g I_t - (k_S + k_{isc})[S_1] + k_b[T]^2 \tag{1}$$

$$\frac{d[T]}{dt} = k_{isc}[S_1] - k_T[T] - k_b[T]^2 \tag{2}$$

In equation (1) the term $\epsilon_g I_t$ represents the rate at which the S_1 state is populated from the ground state by a light pulse of intensity I_t at time t. Let us assume that this pulse is so short compared with the lifetime of S_1 that the term can be neglected, and also sufficiently weak that the triplet concentration is low enough for us to ignore the term $k_b[T]^2$. This greatly simplifies equation (1) and we can integrate it to give:

$$[S_1]_t = [S_1]_0 \exp[-t(k_S + k_{isc})] \tag{3}$$

where the subscripts on $[S_1]$ refer to the time of measurement. The absorbance, D, of the species S_1 is related to the measured transmitted light by the Beer–Lambert law:

$$D = \epsilon_\lambda l[S_1] \equiv \ln \frac{I_0}{I_t}$$

Figure 6 shows how I_0 and I_t are measured on a kinetic absorption trace. The equation that has to be used to extract the kinetic information using equation (3) is:

$$\ln (\ln(I_0/I_t)) = \ln (\ln(I_0/I_i)) - t(k_S + k_{isc})$$

where I_i is from Figure 6 the initial intensity of the transmitted light i.e. at

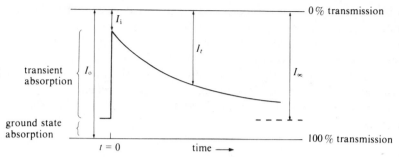

FIGURE 6   Excited-state absorption decay as seen on an oscilloscope. When there is no ground state absorption, $I_0 = I_\infty$.

the peak of the absorption. In the general case where some ground state absorption is present, I_∞ is used instead of I_0 (Figure 6).

This is the method used to determine all first-order rate constants, whether from the singlet, as in the example given here, or from triplets or radicals.

We have remarked in connection with Figure 3 how the absorbance of the triplet 'grows-in' with time. Except with nanosecond and picosecond spectroscopy this is not generally observable, because it occurs relatively quickly (less than 50 ns for most molecules). Equation (2) shows that the appearance of the triplet is governed by the rate $k_{isc}[S_1]$, because the triplet lifetime is much longer than the singlet: $k_T^{-1} \gg (k_S + k_{isc})^{-1}$ (k_T^{-1} is 10 μs for phenanthrene, whereas $(k_S + k_{isc})^{-1}$ is 42 ns). If we now turn our attention to the microsecond or millisecond time domain, long after the singlet state has decayed, we can measure the triplet decay. The term $k_{isc}[S_1]$ is now zero and the two remaining terms in equation (2) become important. The term $k_b[T]^2$ represents the bimolecular annihilation of triplet states brought together by molecular diffusion, and this term is important at times longer than the singlet lifetime but less than the triplet lifetime, i.e. it can be observed in the initial part of the triplet decay. The rate constant k_b is dependent on the solvent viscosity and the term can also be drastically reduced by lowering the intensity of the exciting flash so that [T] is reduced. A typical value for k_b in cyclohexane is $7 \times 10^9 \, \text{l mol}^{-1} \, \text{s}^{-1}$ (measured for anthracene triplets). Besides this annihilation process, quenching of the triplets by paramagnetic molecular oxygen is often faster than the inherent triplet decay. This reaction is written as

$$T + {}^3O_2 \xrightarrow{k_Q} S_0 + {}^1O_2$$

with a rate, $k_Q[T][{}^3O_2]$, which must be included (as a negative term) in the right-hand side of equation (2) with oxygen present. As $k_Q \sim 10^9 \, \text{l mol}^{-1} \, \text{s}^{-1}$ this is often the dominant decay path for triplets, and for this reason triplet measurements are usually undertaken in degassed rather than in aerated solution; in cyclohexane, for instance, $[^3O_2] = 3 \times 10^{-3}$ mol l^{-1}. A similar reaction occurs for singlets but, because the singlet lifetime is shorter, diffusion is less likely to bring the two species together in time to react.

To illustrate further the applications of flash photolysis we shall look briefly at the reactions of duroquinone. The kinetic scheme derived from these measurements with quinone (Q) and solvent (RH, such as ethanol in water) is:

$$Q \xrightarrow{h\nu} Q_S \longrightarrow Q_T$$

$$Q_T + RH \xrightarrow{k_4} QH\cdot + R\cdot \tag{4}$$

$$2QH\cdot \xrightarrow{k_5} Q + QH_2 \tag{5}$$

$$QH\cdot \underset{k_6}{\rightleftharpoons} Q^- + H^+ \tag{6}$$

$$2Q^{-} \xrightarrow{k_7} Q + Q^{2-} \tag{7}$$

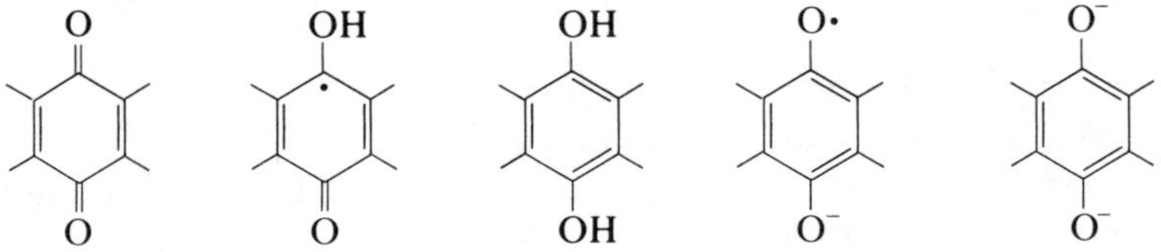

QH$\cdot$ is the semiquinone radical, Q^{-} the semiquinone radical ion, QH$_2$ the reduced quinone, and Q^{2-} the dianion. Using the spectroscopic technique an absorption at 490 nm has been attributed to the triplet state, Q$_T$. The semiquinone radical, QH$\cdot$, has also been identified by its characteristic absorption at 410 nm, and Figure 7 shows the decay of the triplet and semiquinone radical. Notice that for the triplet, the log of the absorbance is plotted for the pseudo-first-order decay, but that reciprocal absorbance is plotted for the semiquinone radical, which decays by the bimolecular reaction (5). The reasons for this can be seen as follows. The second-order decay of QH$\cdot$ is written as

$$\frac{d[QH\cdot]}{dt} = -k_5[QH\cdot]^2 \tag{8}$$

If we substitute in the absorbance, $D^Q = \epsilon_\lambda l[QH\cdot]$ and integrate this equation, then the absorbance at time t, D_t^Q, is given by:

$$\frac{1}{D_t^Q} - \frac{1}{D_{t=0}^Q} = \frac{k_5 t}{\epsilon_\lambda l} \tag{9}$$

where ϵ_λ is the absorption coefficient of the species and l the path length

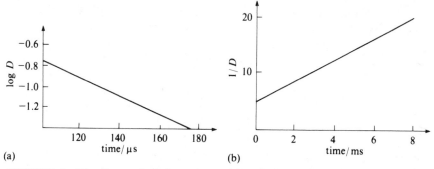

FIGURE 7   The decay of triplet quinone (a) and of the semiquinone radical (b). (source: Bridge and Porter, 1958)

of the sample. Thus the rate constant k_5 can be obtained from the measured rate only if ϵ_λ and l are known. In this example $k_5 = 7.9 \times 10^4\ \epsilon_{410}$ $l\ mol^{-1}\ s^{-1}$ in acid solution (pH 2.7 to 5.7), and as no radical ion ($Q^{\bar{}}$) is observed, the equilibrium (reaction 6) lies well on the $QH\cdot$ side. In alkaline solution the radical ion is observed, by its absorption at 435 nm, and decays by reaction (7). This reaction is also bimolecular but with a lower rate: $k_7 = 4.6 \times 10^2\epsilon_{435}\ l\ mol^{-1}\ s^{-1}$. In both these bimolecular decay processes the rate constant contains an unknown quantity (ϵ_{410} or ϵ_{435}) referring to the absorption coefficient of the relevant species at that wavelength.

The question of whether the initial reaction of the quinone with solvent (reaction 4) is electron transfer or hydrogen abstraction is answered by studying the reactions in ethanol solution rather than ethanol–water mixtures. Here the equilibrium (reaction 6) is slowly achieved. Because $QH\cdot$ is formed in excess, the absorbance at 435 nm (i.e. the wavelength at which $Q^{\bar{}}$ absorbs) can be monitored to show a gradual appearance of $Q^{\bar{}}$ and a rate constant of $7.4 \times 10^3\ s^{-1}$ has been measured. Thus the initial reaction with the solvent is via hydrogen abstraction from the solvent by the (n,π^*) triplet state of the quinone rather than by electron transfer to give $Q^{\bar{}}$ directly.

4   Measuring absorption coefficients

We shall now consider two of the various methods of obtaining excited-state absorption coefficients, because these are required for obtaining second-order rate constants. Remember, however, that first-order rate constants can be obtained directly from the transient decay.

The most direct method is by 'bleaching' the ground state. If the molecule has a ground-state absorption band which is narrow and in a region where triplet–triplet absorption is weak (e.g. chlorophyll), excitation with a pulse of sufficient intensity will excite a large fraction of (i.e. bleach)

215

the ground state, and a corresponding absorption of the triplet state appears. The change in absorbance of the ground state singlet, ΔD_S, is caused by the same concentration of molecules that produces the triplet absorbance, ΔD_T, so the ratio of these changes in absorbance is equal to the ratio of the absorption coefficients:

$$\frac{\Delta D_T}{\Delta D_S} = \frac{\epsilon_T}{\epsilon_S}$$

The ground-state absorption coefficient is known, and the two ΔD values can be measured, hence ϵ_T can be determined. The bleaching can be seen for bacteriopheophytin in Figure 2 at about 750 nm.

If there is a large overlap of the singlet and triplet absorption bands and the spectra are broad, then the bleaching method cannot be used. Also, in highly fluorescent compounds, relatively few triplets are formed and the small singlet depletion and triplet absorption lead to considerable inaccuracies in the estimated absorption coefficients. In these cases the triplet state can be populated by energy transfer from another triplet state of higher energy whose absorption coefficient is known; naphthalene is often used for this purpose. If this reaction is very slow then an energy acceptor, such as anthracene, can be added instead, to which energy transfer occurs. If D is the donor, and A the acceptor, the reaction is

$$D(T_1) + A(S_0) \longrightarrow D(S_0) + A(T_1)$$

When the energy levels of the triplet donor are well above those of the acceptor the rate is diffusion-controlled, with a rate constant of about 10^{10} l mol^{-1} s^{-1}. Typical acceptors are rhodamines or coumarins (both used as laser dyes) or perylene, naphthacene or anthracene.

If the donor is in 1 000-fold excess and an excitation flash of low energy (say 2 J) is used, the donor reacts with an acceptor at a rate that is much faster than competing singlet–triplet or triplet–triplet annihilation reactions. The number of donor triplets deactivated is equal to the number of acceptor triplets produced, and the ratio of the decrease in absorbance of the donor (say naphthalene at 10^{-3} mol l^{-1}) to the increase in triplet acceptor (say anthracene at 10^{-6} mol l^{-1}) equals the ratio of their absorption coefficients. Under these conditions the rate of decay of the donor absorbance is matched by the rate of formation of the acceptor. Benzophenone triplets are also often used as donors and they can abstract a hydrogen from solvents such as cyclohexane to form a ketyl radical, $(C_6H_5)_2\dot{C}OH$, both in the presence and absence of acceptors. The absorption coefficient of the ketyl radical can be estimated independently and so provide a calibration when using the method outlined above for determining unknown absorption coefficients (and hence second-order rate constants).

5 Picosecond flash photolysis

We have already briefly met the type of instrument used in picosecond flash photolysis (Figure 4). We shall now consider it in more detail and give an example of its use in studying the reactions of benzoquinone (Q) with bacteriopheophytin (P).

The excellent time resolution of this instrument comes from the picosecond pulses produced by a mode-locked neodymium laser. These are produced as a short train of a few hundred pulses each separated by the round trip time of the laser cavity. One pulse at 1064 nm is selected and frequency-doubled to 532 nm. This is used to excite the sample. The remaining 1064 nm light (because frequency-doubling is not 100% efficient) is focused into a cell containing carbon tetrachloride, and a white-light continuum is produced. This is used to interrogate the sample at a time after excitation as determined by the distance taken by light travelling down the optical delay line (Figure 4).

The triplet states of porphyrins such as chlorophyll or pheophytins (chlorophylls without the central magnesium atom) readily undergo electron transfer reactions; in our example this is:

$$P \xrightarrow{h\nu} P(S) \longrightarrow P(T)$$
$$P(T) + Q \longrightarrow P^{\cdot +} + Q^{\cdot -}$$

The two ions are able to diffuse apart and can be readily detected. At higher quinone concentrations (10^{-2} to 10^{-1} mol l^{-1}) the singlet P(S) can react as follows:

$$P(S) + Q \longrightarrow P + Q$$

No ions could be detected in this case, even at times as short as 30 ps, although the singlet state of the pheophytin is quenched as shown by monitoring the absorbance decay at 610 nm in Figure 2. The difference between the reactions of the two excited states, P(S) and P(T), is probably due to the spin properties of the complex, $[P^{\cdot +} Q^{\cdot -}]$, formed before complete electron transfer occurs. This is formed as either a triplet or a singlet complex. The spin forbiddenness in the triplet allows the ions to separate before charge recombination can occur, but in the singlet complex the opposite happens and charge recombination occurs before the ions separate, and so no ions are detected. Electron transfer processes of this type are important in primary charge separation in photosynthesis, where charge separation from an excited bacteriochlorophyll singlet state is known to occur (see Section B1 in Chapter 5·2).

5·5 Photoinitiation of polymerisation

by Robert Cundall (University of Salford)
and
M. Sharif Salim (Crown Decorative Products Ltd)

1 The nature of polymerisation

Polymers are substances of high relative molecular mass, formed by the covalent linking of small molecules known as monomers. In the process of addition polymerisation, the linking occurs through the breaking of bonds and formation of new single bonds with other similar units. The monomer generally contains a double bond (e.g. reactions 1–3) or a strained ring (e.g. reaction 4).

$$n\ CH_2{=}CH_2 \longrightarrow -\!(CH_2{-}CH_2)\!_n \qquad (1)$$

ethylene (ethene)　　　　poly(ethene)

$$n\ C_6H_5CH{=}CH_2 \longrightarrow -\!(CH{-}CH_2)\!_n \qquad (2)$$
$$\underset{C_6H_5}{|}$$

styrene (phenylethene)　　　polystyrene

$$n\ H_2C{=}O \longrightarrow -\!(CH_2{-}O)\!_n \qquad (3)$$

formaldehyde (methanal)　　　paraformaldehyde

$$n\ \overset{O}{\overset{\displaystyle\triangle}{CH_2{-}CH_2}} \longrightarrow -\!(O{-}CH_2{-}CH_2)\!_n \qquad (4)$$

ethylene oxide (oxirane)　　　poly(ethylene oxide)

Polymers formed in this way need not be simple linear chains of monomer units joined end to end. Branched polymers may be formed, in which monomer units become attached in such a way that side-chains are formed. Diacrylates and triacrylates are examples of monomers used commercially which exploit this to produce tough and durable films. A particular example is the polymerisation of ethylene glycol diacrylate. Materials of this type are used in lacquers and varnishes, which are formed by the effects of light (u.v. curing). They are used for coating tin plate, paper (for record sleeves) and wood (for furniture).

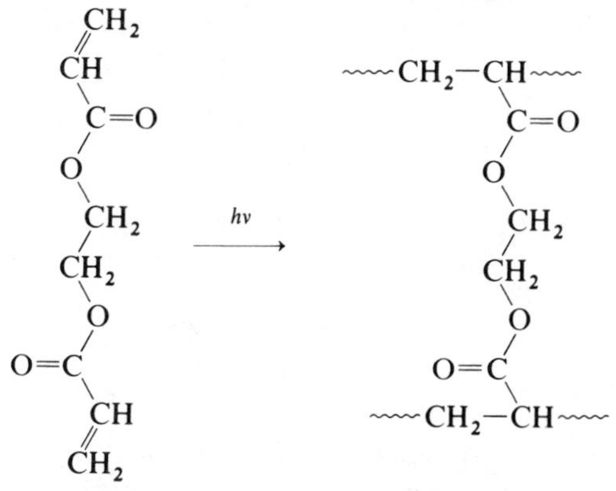

ethylene glycol
diacrylate

poly(ethylene glycol
diacrylate)

The general mechanism of polymerisation involves three types of reaction:

1 the formation of reactive intermediates (initiation),
2 the reaction of monomers to form larger assemblies (propagation),
3 the disappearance of reactive intermediates (termination).

Such a sequence, which constitutes a chain reaction, can be brought about by a radical mechanism. An alternative mechanism for coupling double-bonded or cyclic monomers involves the formation of ions, which can grow or terminate in a similar manner to radicals.

Photochemical excitation is an important method of initiation. It has the advantage of operating only whilst the system is exposed to the appropriate radiation. Also it is effective at room temperature, and solvents are generally not necessary: both these factors are of considerable economic and environmental advantage.

2 Polymerisation kinetics

A proper understanding of the photoinitiation of polymerisation can be achieved only through some formalisation of the kinetics. The first stage of addition polymerisation requires the generation of reactive intermediates

$$\text{initiator} \longrightarrow X^*$$

Heat or light generates the reactive species, X^*, which then reacts with a monomer and begins the sequence of monomer-consuming reactions to form polymer:

$$X^* + M \longrightarrow XM^*$$

$$XM^* + M \longrightarrow XM_2^* \text{ etc.}$$

The sequence can be stopped by one of a number of termination steps. In radical systems, combination and disproportionation are important:

$$XM_m^* + XM_n^* \longrightarrow XM_{m+n}X \qquad \text{(combination)}$$

$$XM_m^* + XM_n^* \longrightarrow XM_m H + XM_n(-H) \qquad \text{(disproportionation)}$$

In ionic systems other termination processes operate.

Rarely does each sequence of reactions from an individual initiating centre form only one polymer molecule, because growing chains have the tendency to transfer 'activity' by reaction with another molecule known as a chain-transfer agent, represented here as S:

$$XM_n^* + S \longrightarrow XM_n + S^*$$

A chain-transfer agent may be added specifically to the system or it may be solvent, monomer, adventitious impurity, or another polymer molecule. This is followed by reaction of S^* with a monomer molecule

$$S^* + M \longrightarrow SM^*$$

and hence no chain-propagating centres are lost. Clearly the average relative molecular mass of polymer formed will depend on the transfer efficiencies, as well as on the relative probabilities of propagation and termination.

The chemical structure of the monomer determines the nature of the reactive site, which may be a radical, an anion or a cation. The cationic mechanism is favoured by monomers with electron-repelling substituents, such as alkyl groups, whereas radical and anionic reactions are favoured by electron-withdrawing groups, such as CN and COOR.

Photolytic decomposition of an initiator to form radicals is particularly important. The full polymerisation sequence is:

$$\text{initiator} \xrightarrow{h\nu} 2R\cdot$$

$$R\cdot + M \longrightarrow RM\cdot$$

$$RM\cdot + M \longrightarrow RM_2\cdot$$

$$RM_n\cdot + M \longrightarrow RM_{n+1}\cdot$$

$$RM_m\cdot + RM_n\cdot \longrightarrow RM_{m+n}R$$

$$RM_m\cdot + RM_n\cdot \longrightarrow RM_m H + RM_n(-H)$$

The rate of polymerisation is given by

$$\text{rate} = \sum k_p[\text{RM}_i\cdot][\text{M}]$$

where k_p is the rate constant for reaction of a polymer radical with monomer (i.e. propagation), and $\sum[\text{RM}_i\cdot]$ is the total concentration of polymer radicals. For simplicity, it is assumed that k_p is the same for all propagation steps. The conditions of polymerisation are such that, in reactions of this type, polymer formation proceeds steadily at a rate that decreases because of the fall in the concentration of the reactive monomer, and the concentration of chain-propagating centres is effectively invariant during irradiation:

$$d(\sum[\text{RM}_i\cdot])/dt = \text{initiation rate} - \text{termination rate} = 0$$

So we can now write

$$\phi_R I_{abs} - k_t(\sum[\text{RM}_i\cdot])^2 = 0$$

and hence

$$\sum[\text{RM}_i\cdot] = (\phi_R I_{abs}/k_t)^{1/2}$$

where I_{abs} is the intensity of light absorbed by the initiator, ϕ_R is the quantum yield of radicals produced by its decomposition, and k_t is the rate constant for radical termination. Hence the rate of polymerisation is given by

$$\text{rate} = k_p[\text{M}](\phi_R I_{abs}/k_t)^{1/2}$$

It is important to note that the dependence of the rate on the square root of the intensity of absorbed light is a consequence of the bimolecular termination reactions that occur in radical systems.

If the intensity of light absorbed is increased, the concentration of propagating radicals is greater and consequently the rate of termination is enhanced. This has the effect of reducing the average relative molecular mass of the polymer molecules produced.

Although the most usual consequence of photoactivation of a molecule in the 250–400 nm region is the generation of neutral radical centres by bond homolysis, reactive ions can be generated either directly or indirectly in many systems. This allows a wider variety of monomers to be selectively polymerised. An additional advantage of ionic systems is that the troublesome effects of oxygen, which interferes with (inhibits) radical polymerisation, can be avoided.

In ionic polymerisation, termination is not due to interaction between two growing polymer molecules, owing in part to the strong electrostatic repulsion between like charges, and the rate is usually dependent on I_{abs} rather than $(I_{abs})^{1/2}$. This means that more effective polymerisation can be achieved with intense light sources when ionic initiators are used.

In ionic polymerisation systems the termination processes are inefficient, and polymerisation may continue for a considerable time after irradiation has ceased. This is very useful in pigmented systems used in lacquers and inks, where opaque particles, such as those of titanium dioxide, which may be present in commercial preparations, prevent illumination of the whole volume of the system. Diffusion of the reaction centres through the system can overcome this problem if they are sufficiently long-lived.

3 Properties of photoinitiators

The most important properties of a compound that is to be used as a photoinitiator are as follows.

1 The initiator should be stable under all reasonable conditions, except the irradiation conditions to be used.

2 The absorption spectrum of the initiator should be such that: the photochemical reaction arising from normal room lighting conditions is insignificant; the maximum absorption coincides as nearly as possible with the most intense emissions from available light sources; the colour of the initiator or products derived therefrom does not interfere with the appearance and other properties of the polymer product; the absorption overlaps as little as possible with those of the monomer and added pigments.

3 The quantum yield of formation of reactive intermediates from the initiator should be as high as possible. This yield can be limited by processes such as internal conversion, fluorescence and excited-state quenching. (The chain length of the polymerisation can also be modified by reaction with oxygen or other adventitious impurities.)

There are other criteria to be considered which are not based on photochemistry but are nevertheless very important. These include toxicity, expense, and solubility.

4 Radical-initiated photopolymerisation

Ultraviolet and visible light dissociate simple diatomic molecules, such as halogens, to form atoms; for example:

$$Cl_2 \xrightarrow{\ h\nu\ } 2Cl\cdot$$

These atoms can react with a variety of molecules. In particular, they can add to double bonds and so, in principle if not in practice, can be used to initiate polymerisation by the scheme of reactions outlined earlier.

More complex molecules can be used with advantage. Examples are provided by aliphatic azo compounds, and a widely used compound of this group is 2,2'-azo-bis-isobutyronitrile, which forms two radicals and a molecule of nitrogen:

$$
\underset{\substack{|\\CH_3}}{\overset{\substack{CH_3\\|}}{NC-C-N}}=N-\underset{\substack{|\\CH_3}}{\overset{\substack{CH_3\\|}}{C-CN}} \xrightarrow{h\nu} 2NC-\underset{\substack{|\\CH_3}}{\overset{\substack{CH_3\\|}}{C\cdot}} + N_2
$$

Other molecules surrounding these radicals prevent them from diffusing apart rapidly, and so they may recombine rather than react with monomer molecules. This so-called 'cage effect' results in the quantum yield of the radical being much below the value expected. The actual value of ϕ_R depends on solvent viscosity as well as on the wavelength of the radiation.

Benzoin ethers, another useful group of compounds, undergo photocleavage to produce benzoyl and alkoxybenzyl radicals:

$$
\underset{\substack{|\\H}}{\overset{\substack{O\;\;OR\\\|\;\;|}}{C_6H_5-C-C-C_6H_5}} \xrightarrow{h\nu} \overset{\substack{O\\\|}}{C_6H_5-C\cdot} + \underset{\substack{|\\H}}{\overset{\substack{OR\\|}}{C_6H_5-C\cdot}}
$$

The radicals that give rise to polymerisation are formed from excited states that are often not properly characterised. The failure of triplet quenching agents to reduce the photocleavage suggests, but does not prove, that reaction occurs from the excited singlet state. On the other hand, the observation that the decomposition of benzoin isopropyl ether can be brought about by a triplet sensitiser shows that decomposition can occur from what is probably a triplet (n, π^*) state. This is consistent with very rapid dissociation of a triplet state of energy about 305 kJ mol^{-1}. This energy is more than sufficient for dissociation of the bond in question (263 kJ mol^{-1}).

1 benzophenone   2 thioxanthone   3 2-chlorothioxanthone

Benzoin ethers are used particularly as photoinitiators in the ultraviolet curing of lacquers for application to paper (for record sleeves and book covers). Other types of carbonyl compound, for example 1–3, have also found wide application as photoinitiators. They all produce initiator radicals through hydrogen abstraction from a suitable donor. The reactions that occur between the photoinitiator (P) and hydrogen donor (RH) are as follows:

$$P \xrightarrow{hv} {}^1P* \qquad \text{absorption}$$

$${}^1P* \longrightarrow {}^3P* \qquad \text{intersystem crossing}$$

$${}^1P* \longrightarrow P \qquad \text{singlet decay}$$

$${}^3P* + RH \longrightarrow PH\cdot + R\cdot \qquad \text{hydrogen abstraction}$$

$${}^3P* \xrightarrow{Q} P \qquad \text{quenching}$$

$${}^3P* \longrightarrow P \qquad \text{triplet decay}$$

Hydrogen abstraction is envisaged as occurring from the triplet state, because its radical character is more developed than that of the excited singlet state, and it also has a longer lifetime during which reaction can take place. The efficiency of the reaction depends on (i) the intersystem crossing efficiency, (ii) the type of triplet formed, $(n,\pi*)$ or $(\pi,\pi*)$, and (iii) the polarity of the solvent.

Particularly reactive hydrogen-atom donors are those in which (i) the active hydrogen atom is directly attached to sulphur, as in thiols (RSH), or (ii) a hydrogen atom is in a position alpha to an oxygen atom, as in alcohols (R_2CHOH) or ethers (R_2CHOR'), or alpha to a nitrogen atom, as in tertiary amines ($R_2CHNR'_2$). In the case of alcohols and ethers, hydrogen abstraction occurs by reaction with $(n,\pi*)$ triplets, which have more strongly developed radical character than the $(\pi,\pi*)$ states. It is important in practice to recognise that quenching of the triplet state by atmospheric oxygen can be more efficient than the initiating process (hydrogen abstraction).

The mechanism and efficiency of a photoinitiator can be changed and improved by the addition of other molecules, which interact with the excited state of the light-absorbing molecule. In the case of carbonyl–amine systems, hydrogen abstraction is preceded by the rapid formation of an excited state complex (an exciplex) between the amine and triplet ketone (Scheme 1). The exciplex is stabilised by charge transfer, because of the low ionisation potential of the amine donor, but the efficiency of such complex formation also

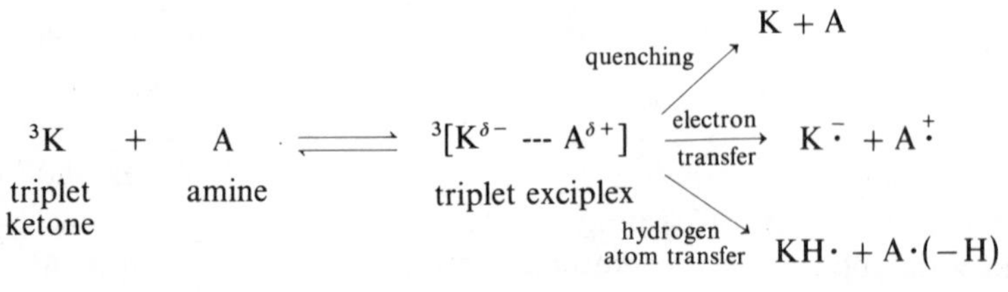

$$
\begin{array}{ccc}
 & & K + A \\
 & & \nearrow \text{quenching} \\
{}^3K \;+\; A \;\rightleftharpoons\; {}^3[K^{\delta-} \text{---} A^{\delta+}] & \xrightarrow[\text{transfer}]{\text{electron}} & K^{\bar{\cdot}} + A^{\cdot+} \\
\text{triplet} \quad \text{amine} \qquad \text{triplet exciplex} & & \\
\text{ketone} & \searrow \text{hydrogen} & \\
 & \text{atom transfer} & KH\cdot + A\cdot(-H)
\end{array}
$$

SCHEME 1

depends on the electron affinity of the ketone. The effectiveness of any particular amine–ketone combination as a photoinitiator depends on the relative extents of the various processes for decomposition of the exciplex.

The use of amines as co-initiators is also convenient for ketones, such as thioxanthone or 2-chlorothioxanthone, which have high absorption coefficients and possess low hydrogen abstraction reactivity because the lowest triplet states are (π,π^*) in character. In commercial practice, an amine such as ethyl *p*-dimethylaminobenzoate (4) proves useful and convenient. Michler's ketone (5) and its derivatives possess both diaryl ketone and

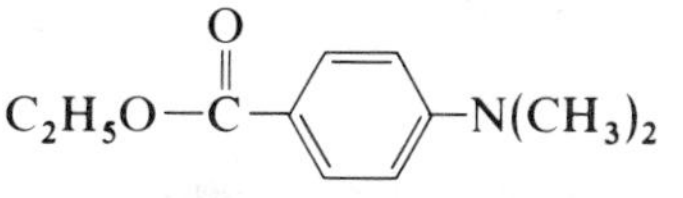

4

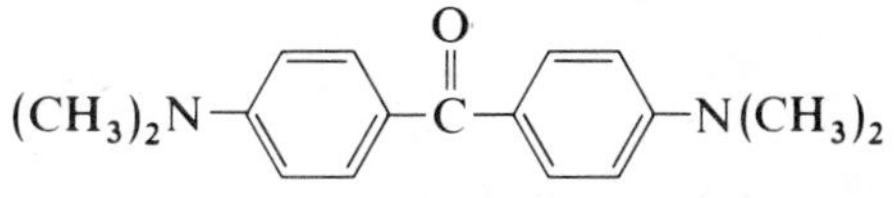

5

tertiary amino groups, and so combine both features in one molecule and are widely used as photoinitiators. In the case of 4,4′-bis(diethylamino)-benzophenone (DEABP), electron transfer occurs to form a complex, which can then dissociate to two radicals (Scheme 2). An excited triplet state of this and similar molecules will also interact with benzophenone to form complexes that can give rise to radicals.

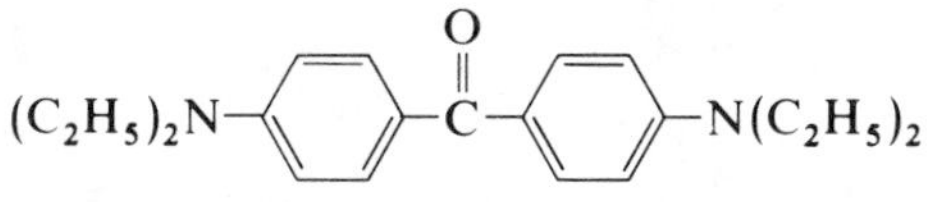

DEABP

$$^{3}\text{DEABP} + \text{DEABP} \rightleftharpoons {}^{3}(\text{complex})$$

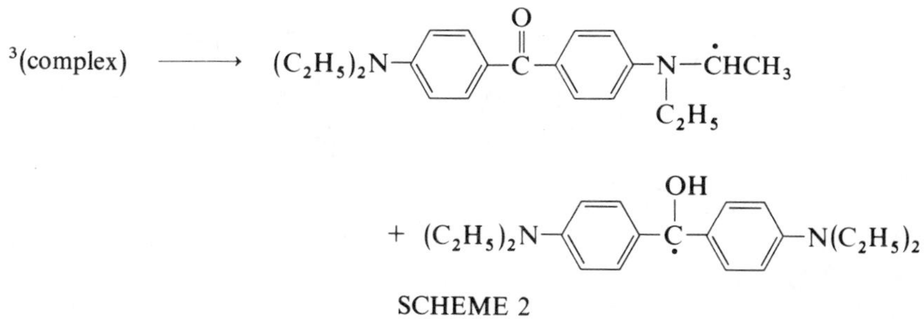

SCHEME 2

Photosensitisation is conveniently applied in many photoinitiating systems. The photosensitiser (D) absorbs the light and undergoes rapid intersystem crossing

$$\text{D} + h\nu \longrightarrow {}^{1}\text{D} \longrightarrow {}^{3}\text{D}$$

The triplet state transfers energy to the photoinitiator, which undergoes cleavage or participates in a hydrogen abstraction reaction. For example, dyes such as benzoflavin can be used to excite diaryliodonium salts, which do not absorb light in the range 400–800 nm. Diaryliodonium salts, e.g. $(CH_3C_6H_4)_2I^+ AsF_6^-$, have been used with dye sensitisers to carry out the

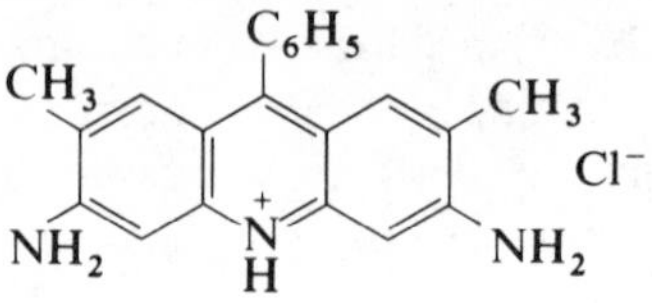

benzoflavin

photoinitiated cationic polymerisation of epichlorohydrin and 2-chloroethyl vinyl ether $(ClCH_2CH_2OCH=CH_2)$ with visible light. Triaryl sulphonium salts (6) bearing non-nucleophilic complex metal halide anions of the type

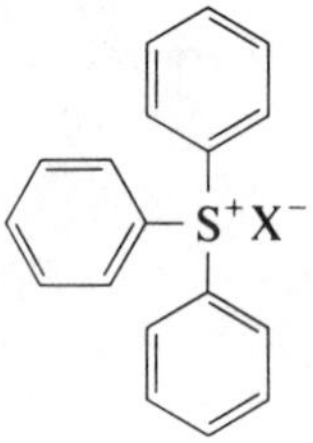

6 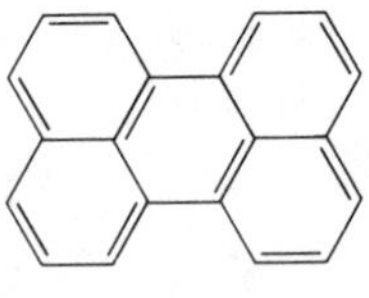   7

BF_4^-, AsF_6^-, PF_6^- or SbF_6^- are also highly efficient photoinitiators for cationic polymerisation. These salts, like their diaryliodonium salt

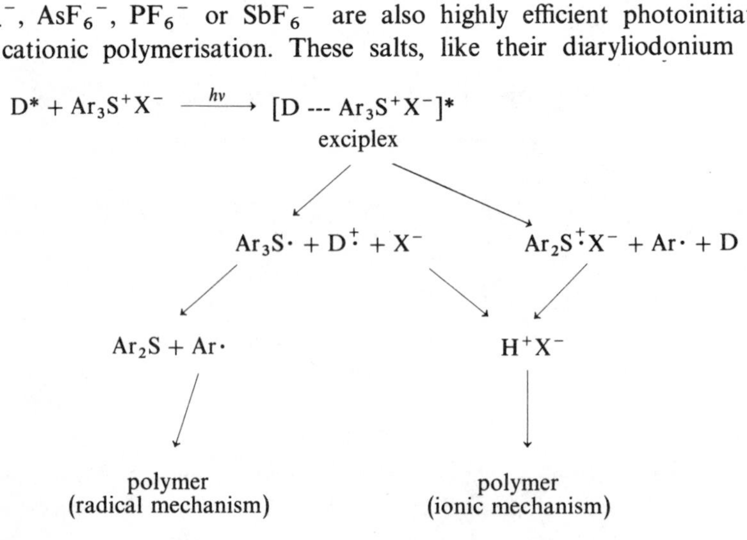

SCHEME 3

counterparts, do not absorb visible light. Except for perylene (**7**), dyes that sensitise diaryliodonium salts are completely inactive when applied to triarylsulphonium salts. Note that this type of system can initiate both radical and ionic polymerisation; one possible mechanism is shown in Scheme 3.

5 Photoinitiation of cationic polymerisation

The ring-opening of cyclic ethers (particularly epoxides), through the generation of Lewis acids by photochemically induced electron transfer, has proved useful because of the availability of cationic photoinitiators, for example the aryldiazonium salts:

$$[Ar-\overset{+}{N}{\equiv}N] BF_4^- \xrightarrow{h\nu} ArF + N_2 + BF_3$$

The Lewis acid (BF_3) which is generated can initiate cationic polymerisation.

In technological applications diazonium salts are sensitive to visible as well as ultraviolet light, and are also sensitive to thermal decomposition. For these reasons, cationic photoinitiators such as diaryliodonium salts (e.g. diphenyliodonium hexafluorophosphate $(C_6H_5)_2I^+ PF_6^-$) are preferred. The mechanism by which diaryliodonium salts are thought to act is:

$$Ar_2 I^+ X^- \xrightarrow[SH]{h\nu} ArI + Ar\cdot + S\cdot + HX \tag{5}$$

$$M + HX \longrightarrow HM^+ + X^- \tag{6}$$

$$HM^+ + M \longrightarrow HM_2^+ \tag{7}$$

$$HM_n^+ + M \longrightarrow HM_{n+1}^+ \tag{8}$$

The reaction is terminated by nucleophilic impurities in the system. The radicals generated by reaction (5) can initiate radical polymerisation. Whether this is significant depends on the relative susceptibilities of the monomers to radical and ionic propagation. A related group of cationic photoinitiators are the triarylsulphonium salts (Scheme 3).

Charge-transfer complexes are also important in photoinitiated ionic polymerisation. Irradiation of charge-transfer complexes of electron-donating monomers (M) and electron acceptors (A) can lead to polymerisation by radical cations through the mechanism shown in Scheme 4.

Similar in principle, but anionic in nature, is the polymerisation of nitroethene in tetrahydrofuran. Nitroethene $(CH_2{=}CHNO_2)$ has a high

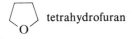 tetrahydrofuran

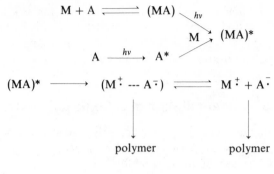

SCHEME 4

electron affinity, while tetrahydrofuran acts as an electron donor and is also, conveniently, a suitable solvent. The development of a weak absorption at around 450 nm indicates that a ground state complex is formed.

A monomer (A) that is a poor electron acceptor, such as acrylonitrile, CH_2=CHCN, can interact with a Lewis acid, such as triethylaluminium, $(C_2H_5)_3Al$. A ground state complex is formed, which is a strong electron acceptor. This can form a ground state complex with a donating monomer such as styrene, C_6H_5CH=CH_2. Absorption of light by this complex forms an initiating species (Scheme 5). Note that in this type of system the donor and acceptor monomers enter the chain together as a single repeating unit.

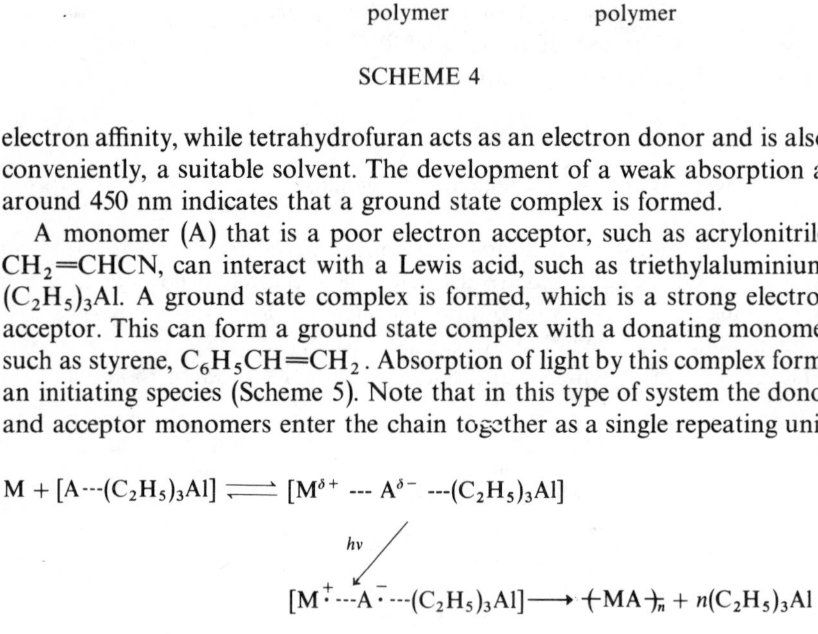

$$M + [A\text{---}(C_2H_5)_3Al] \rightleftharpoons [M^{\delta+}\text{ --- }A^{\delta-}\text{ ---}(C_2H_5)_3Al]$$

$$\overset{h\nu}{\diagup}$$

$$[M^+\text{---}A^-\text{---}(C_2H_5)_3Al] \longrightarrow \text{+MA+}_n + n(C_2H_5)_3Al$$

SCHEME 5

5·6 Photochemical cross-linking of polymers

by Anthony Ledwith (University of Liverpool)

The oldest recorded example of photochemically induced cross-linking in a polymer-based system goes back to pre-Biblical times when, for the preparation of Egyptian mummies, linen cloths were dipped into a solution of lavender oil containing Syrian asphalt. The latter is a bituminous material, which hardens under the influence of sunlight, and it is now known to contain a variety of unsaturated aromatic, heterocyclic and other compounds. A similar photohardening of asphalt was used in the first imaging material for permanent photographs as early as 1822. Later in the nineteenth century, a second photochemical cross-linking system was discovered, involving insolubilisation of gelatin when exposed to sunlight in the presence of potassium dichromate. It is now known that gelatin may be replaced by poly(vinyl alcohol) or other natural or synthetic polymers with hydroxyl, amino, amide, and/or carboxyl groups. Although the detailed chemistry of these systems is still not fully understood, this type of photochemical cross-linking formed the basis of the earliest types of photoresist. Photoresists are materials that undergo changes in physical properties (e.g. solubility) when exposed to light, and hence afford convenient ways of distinguishing between exposed and unexposed areas.

1 The nature and properties of cross-linked polymers

Macromolecules are formed by two main processes; for mechanistic reasons these are called step-growth polymerisation and chain-growth polymerisation. In the former the polymer chain grows from monomer molecules by a succession of repetitive reactions yielding stable molecules after each step, in which the number and types of reactive functional group remain the same. In contrast, chain-growth polymerisation of alkenes or strained cyclic compounds must be catalysed or initiated by a reactive species independent of the monomer molecules. Similarly, the formation of cross-linked polymers may be induced by a number of step-growth processes or by chain-growth processes. For the special case of photochemically induced cross-linking, it should be noted that whereas chain reactions would be expected to show a very high quantum efficiency for the number of growth steps induced, step-growth processes are limited to a maximum of one chemical transformation (cross-link or growth step) for each photon absorbed.

229

During any polymerisation process there exists the possibility that side reactions will create sequences of monomer units pendant to the main chain. This branching can occur in many different ways, and may involve very short or very long branches which may be frequent or infrequent in relation to the important macromolecular backbone. The formation of cross-links is essentially a special (i.e. extended) case of branching which may, similarly, involve short or long cross-links with a high or low frequency of occurrence along the main polymer backbone. A schematic representation of branching and cross-linking is given in Figure 1. Although the nature and length of the cross-links are not necessarily determined by whether the process is a step reaction or a chain reaction, it is usually much easier to produce longer cross-links by chain-growth polymerisation of alkenes or epoxides (oxiranes). In either case, as the degree of cross-linking reaches the extent of approximately one cross-link per macromolecule, on average, the result will be an infinite, three-dimensional network. The point at which branching and cross-linking form a network is known as the gel point for the system.

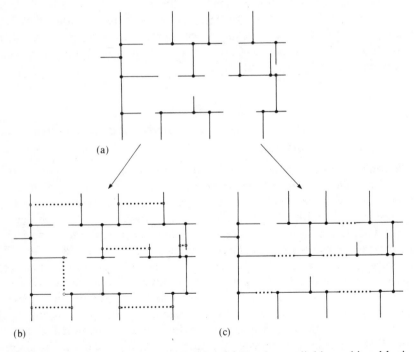

(a)

(b)   (c)

FIGURE 1   (a) Branched macromolecules. (b) Total cross-linking achieved by increasing the number of cross-linking points. (c) Total cross-linking achieved by increasing the degree of polymerisation of the linear chains.

In Figure 1 straight lines are used to depict polymer chains which, in reality, adopt a variety of coiled conformations according to their structures and environments. If the branch chain is made of monomers different from those in the main chain, the product macromolecule is more correctly referred to as a *graft copolymer*. Except for some which decompose below their melting temperatures, most macromolecular materials are *thermoplastic*. This means that there is a temperature range in which they show a reversible transition from a hard glassy material into a soft plastic one. This transition occurs through a more or less definite stage of rubber-like elasticity. Thermoplasticity is lost through cross-linking. At low degrees of cross-linking (i.e. large separations between the cross-links), the cross-linked material remains elastic above the softening point without being able to flow, whereas increased degrees of cross-linking make the material increasingly hard and brittle. An example of a commercially important lightly cross-linked polymer is vulcanised rubber. Very tightly cross-linked polymers are represented by phenol–formaldehyde, melamine–formaldehyde, and phthalic anhydride–glycerol resins. Such resins are infusible and are therefore called *thermosetting resins*, in contrast to thermoplastic materials.

Another important difference in physical properties between linear (or branched) and cross-linked polymers lies in their solubility. When non-cross-linked polymers are treated with solvents, the random coils gradually adopt conformations that reflect the balance between polymer–polymer and polymer–solvent interactions and gradually pass through solvent-swollen states into true solutions. Cross-linked polymers are insoluble in all solvents but, according to the degree of cross-linking, they can be swollen to a smaller or larger extent. The degree of swelling may be taken as a direct measure of the degree of cross-linking, and it is the insolubility of cross-linked polymers that forms the main basis for the development and applications of polymeric photoresists.

Other properties of a polymeric system that are affected by cross-linking include adhesion and cohesion (to surfaces and to applied liquid inks), permeability to gases and liquids, and refractive index. Several of these are also utilised in photoimaging and in the manufacture of relief plates.

2 Photochemical cross-linking by step growth

Photochemical cross-linking of polymers is one of the competing processes involved in the degradation of polymers in both the solid state and in solution. Frequently, precise details of the chemical transformations are not fully understood. For low degrees of cross-linking, increased mechanical strength and weather resistance are observed, whereas for higher degrees of cross-linking, there may be excessive brittleness and loss of mechanical strength. These processes are best exemplified by the case of poly(ethene): it is quite feasible to improve mechanical and thermal properties by inducing limited cross-linking in the presence of a sensitiser, such as benzophenone. The probable mechanism is outlined in Scheme 1, where P_n —H represents any carbon–hydrogen bond in poly(ethene).

$$(C_6H_5)_2C{=}O \xrightarrow{hv} (C_6H_5)_2C{=}O\,(S_1) \longrightarrow (C_6H_5)_2C{=}O\,(T_1)$$

$$(C_6H_5)_2C{=}O\,(T_1) + P_n{-}H \longrightarrow (C_6H_5)_2\dot{C}{-}OH + P_n\cdot$$

$$P_n\cdot + P_n\cdot \longrightarrow P_n{-}P_n \text{ (cross-linked polymer)}$$

SCHEME 1

This process can be made more efficient by use of a polymerisable aromatic ketone, such as *p*-propenoyloxybenzophenone (**1**), as sensitiser. The 'acrylic' alkene unit reacts with a radical site in the polymer backbone to form a short side-chain. The new radical site is in a position less sterically hindered than the original site, and cross-linking is more efficient.

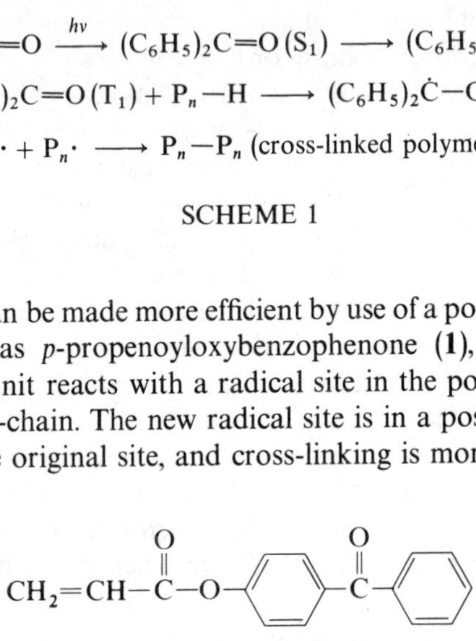

CH$_2$=CH—C—O— ... —C—

1

Radical sites formed on the polymer backbone by hydrogen abstraction may initiate polymerisation of the sensitiser, with ultimate formation of longer cross-links between the poly(ethene) chains. (This is a rather special case of cross-linking by chain growth, which is discussed later.) In principle these types of cross-linking can be applied to any preformed polymer having C—H bonds in either the backbone or side groups and branches. More usually, however, where cross-links are an essential part of a technologically important material, such as a photoresist, it is preferable to employ one of the two following methods of stepwise cross-linking.

Organic azides (RN_3) afford a convenient source of the highly reactive, electron-deficient nitrogen species known as nitrenes ($R{-}\ddot{N}{:}$). Formation of nitrenes may be accomplished by both thermal and photochemical activation of azido compounds and, for practical reasons, the most important precursors are aromatic azides (ArN_3), arylsulphonyl azides ($ArSO_2N_3$), and azidoformates ($ROCON_3$). In all cases, the azido compound yields (initially) a singlet nitrene, which may then undergo intersystem crossing to the corresponding triplet state. It is however, possible to generate triplet nitrenes directly by the usual expedient of using triplet sensitisers for the photolysis.

$$RN_3 \xrightarrow[\text{or heat}]{hv} R\ddot{N}: + N_2 \longrightarrow R\ddot{N}:$$

singlet   triplet

Nitrenes can react in two ways. The first is by electrophilic attack on bonding electron pairs. This involves insertion into a C—H bond by singlet nitrene, or hydrogen abstraction by triplet nitrene:

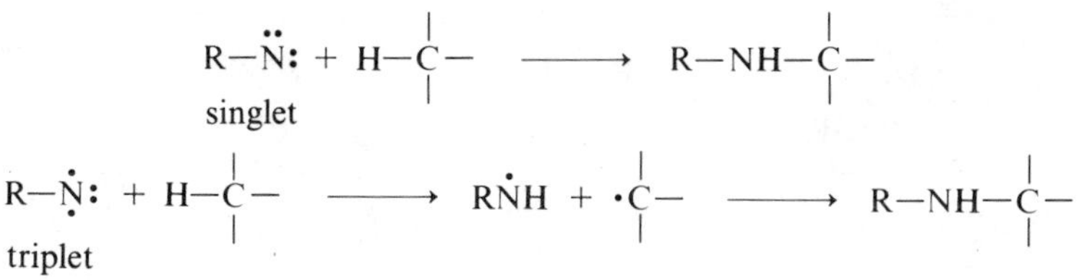

$$R-\ddot{N}: + H-\overset{|}{\underset{|}{C}}- \longrightarrow R-NH-\overset{|}{\underset{|}{C}}-$$

singlet

$$R-\overset{.}{\underset{}{N}}: + H-\overset{|}{\underset{|}{C}}- \longrightarrow R\overset{.}{N}H + \cdot\overset{|}{\underset{|}{C}}- \longrightarrow R-NH-\overset{|}{\underset{|}{C}}-$$

triplet

The second way is by addition to double bonds:

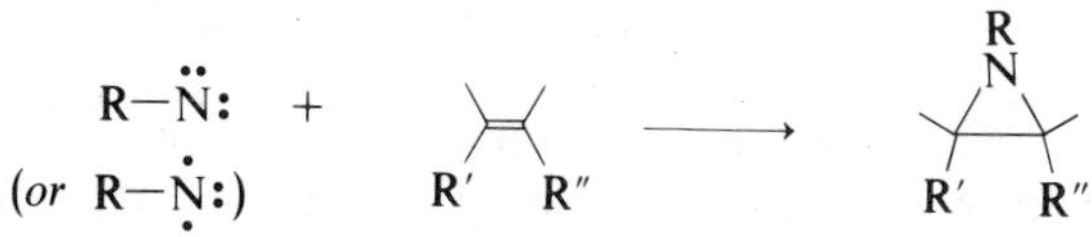

$$R-\ddot{N}: +$$

(*or* R—$\overset{.}{\underset{.}{N}}$:)

The very high and relatively unselective reactivity of nitrenes, coupled with the convenience of synthesis of appropriate azido compounds, affords a very large number of ways in which polymers may be cross-linked. The two most important are (i) the use of bis-azido compounds $(N_3—R—N_3)$, which will induce cross-linking in preformed polymers containing saturated and/or unsaturated hydrocarbon groupings by the various C—H insertion and C=C addition mechanisms, and (ii) the use of polymers functionalised with pendant azido groups which may then undergo a variety of photoinduced self-condensation processes. Representative examples of difunctional azido compounds are **2** and **3**.

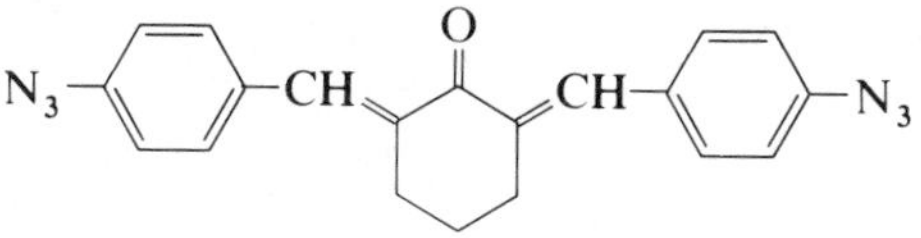

2 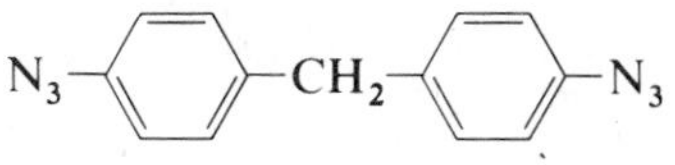   3

A second, even more widely employed method of photochemical cross-linking via step growth utilises the well known propensity of cinnamic acid

(3-phenylpropenoic acid; **4, R = H**) and its derivatives to undergo photoinduced cyclodimerisation. The reaction is efficient, in a photochemical sense, especially when sensitised with one of a very wide range of aromatic carbonyl and organic dye compounds. Triplet–triplet energy transfer is presumed to be the most important type of sensitisation, but in some cases, because of the relative triplet energy levels, other mechanisms (e.g. exciplex intermediates) must prevail. In common with many other α,β-unsaturated carbonyl compounds, cinnamate esters may also undergo cyclodimerisation on direct excitation.

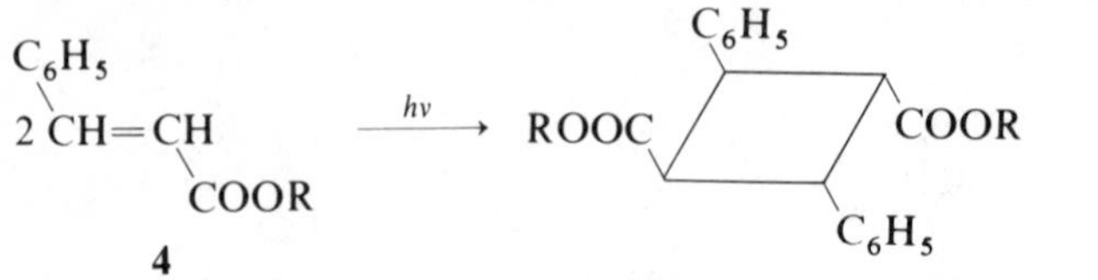

Cinnamic acid moieties are readily introduced into polymers by reactions of side-chain hydroxy groups in, for example, poly(vinyl alcohol) with cinnamoyl chloride, and the generalised cross-linking mechanism may be represented as shown in Scheme 2. Increased reactivity in cross-linking is observed for polymers substituted by conjugated homologues of cinnamic acid, such as may be obtained from appropriate reactions of 5-phenylpenta-2,4-dienoyl chloride, $C_6H_5(CH=CH)_2COCl$.

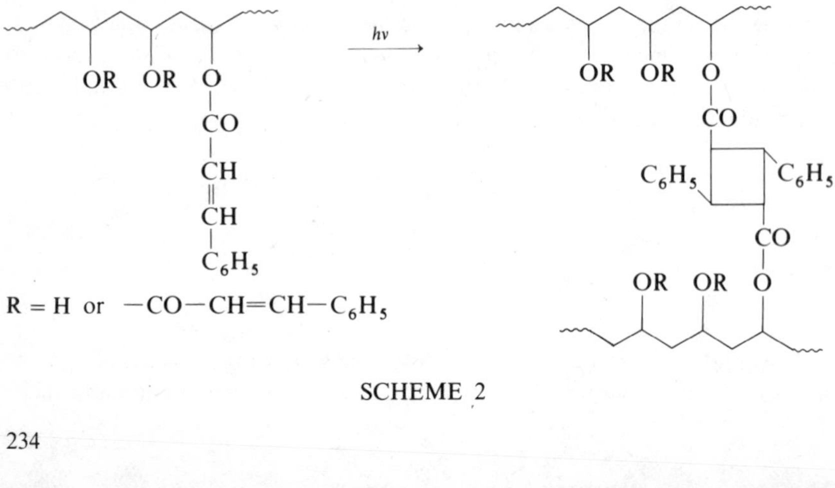

R = H or $-CO-CH=CH-C_6H_5$

SCHEME 2

Cyclodimerisation of other types of unsaturated molecule may also be utilised to effect cross-linking of preformed polymers, and here also all methods of polymer synthesis are applicable to formation of photochemically active polymers. In addition to the cinnamates already mentioned, other groups useful in photodimerisation include chalcones (RCH=CHCOAr), stilbenes (ArCH=CHAr'), coumarins (a special class of α,β-unsaturated esters), anthracenes, maleimides, and strained cycloalkenes (**5**). Such polymers find wide application as photoresists for the manufacture of printed circuit boards, microelectronic components, and a variety of printing plates used in the newspaper and magazine industries.

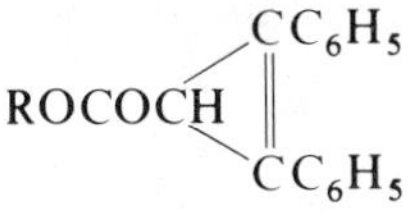

$$\text{ROCOCH} \underset{\diagdown C\,C_6H_5}{\overset{\diagup C\,C_6H_5}{\big\|}}$$

5

3 Photochemical cross-linking by radical chain growth

Cross-linking by chain processes is very easily accomplished in polymer systems, and most commonly involves radical intermediates. The presence of a vinyl group is necessary, and this can be incorporated into the polymer in a number of ways.

1 Polymers derived from conjugated 1,3-dienes and from maleic and fumaric acids (*cis*- and *trans*-butenedioic acid) contain vinyl groups in the polymer backbone:

$$\underset{\substack{| \\ \text{R}}}{\sim\text{CH}_2-\text{C}=\text{CH}-\text{CH}_2\sim} \qquad\qquad \sim\text{O}-\overset{\overset{\text{O}}{\|}}{\text{C}}-\text{CH}=\text{CH}-\overset{\overset{\text{O}}{\|}}{\text{C}}-\text{O}\sim$$

cis and trans   cis and trans

2 Unsaturated units can be introduced as side-chains, either during polymerisation by using a monomer containing two different vinyl groups, one of which does not polymerise readily, for example:

$$\text{CH}_2=\text{CH}-\text{A}-\text{R}-\text{B}-\text{CH}=\text{CH}_2 \longrightarrow \underset{\substack{| \\ \text{A}-\text{R}-\text{B}-\text{CH}=\text{CH}_2}}{\sim\text{CH}_2-\text{CH}\sim}$$

or by treatment with a suitable reagent after the polymer has been made, for example:

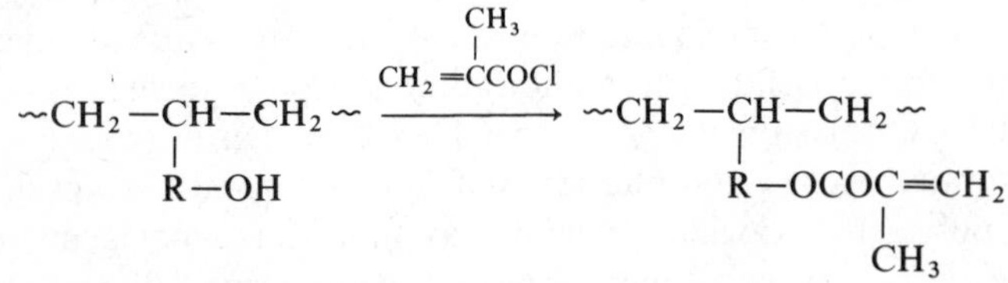

$$\sim CH_2-CH-CH_2\sim \xrightarrow{\underset{\overset{|}{CH_2=CCOCl}}{CH_3}} \sim CH_2-CH-CH_2\sim$$

with the left structure bearing $R-OH$ and the right structure bearing $R-OCOC=CH_2$ with CH_3.

3 If the monomer contains two (or more) groups that polymerise equally readily, for example monomers **6** and **7**, then polymerisation will yield cross-linked polymers directly. Most practical applications are based on this principle.

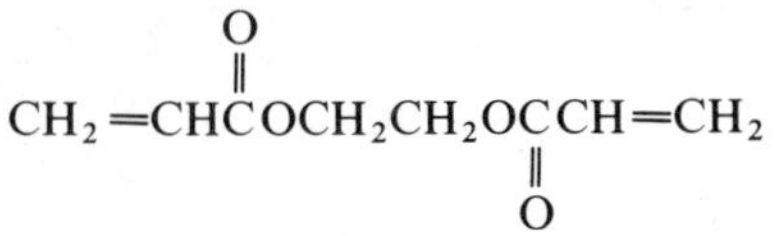

$$CH_2=CHCOCH_2CH_2OCCH=CH_2$$

with carbonyl oxygens shown above and below.

6

$$CH_2=CHCNHCH_2NHCCH=CH_2$$

with carbonyl oxygens shown above and below.

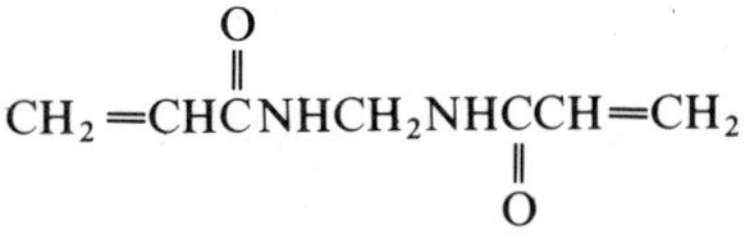

7

Any of the reagents normally used to accomplish photochemical initiation of radical polymerisation may, in principle, be used to initiate cross-linking reactions, but practical considerations restrict the choice to two types of photoinitiation.

(a) Photochemical fragmentation (α-cleavage) of benzoin or acetophenone derivatives, for example:

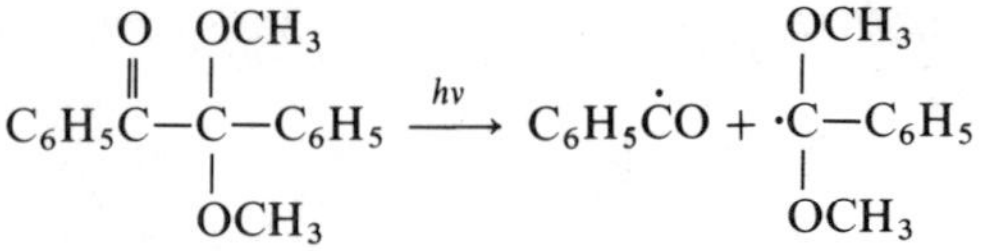

$$C_6H_5C-C-C_6H_5 \xrightarrow{h\nu} C_6H_5\dot{C}O + \cdot C-C_6H_5$$

with O and OCH$_3$ substituents as shown.

(b) Formation of radicals via exciplex interactions of aromatic carbonyl compounds with a wide range of amino compounds, especially tertiary amines; for example:

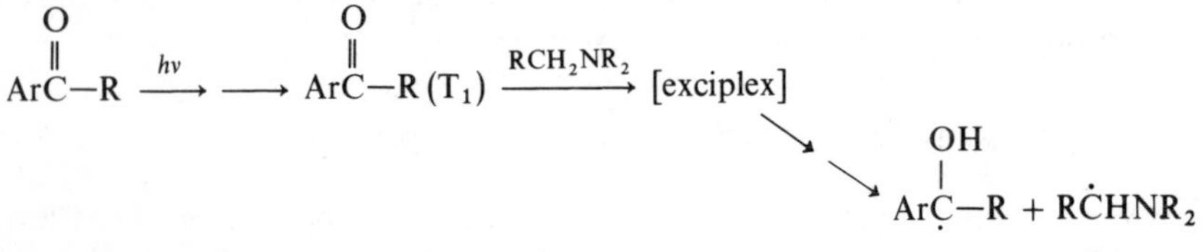

$$ArC-R \xrightarrow{h\nu} \longrightarrow ArC-R\,(T_1) \xrightarrow{RCH_2NR_2} [\text{exciplex}]$$

$$\searrow \searrow \underset{Ar\dot{C}-R + \dot{R}CHNR_2}{\overset{OH}{|}}$$

In this case it is the radical derived from the amine that is the initiator; the

$$OH$$

ketyl radicals $(Ar-\overset{|}{C}-R)$ derived from the carbonyl compounds are known to form dimers very readily.

Benzoin-type initiators are most useful in clear polymerising systems, such as transparent surface coatings. In contrast, ketone/amine combinations are especially advantageous in pigmented polymerising systems, such as are found in inks and many decorative coatings. This is mainly because some ketones are sensitive to radiation of longer wavelength (>400 nm), which does not affect titanium dioxide pigments. The latter are perhaps the most common ingredient of all pigmented coatings, and absorb ultraviolet light up to approximately 390 nm. Ketones active in photoinitiation (benzil, thioxanthone, fluorenone) have long-wavelength absorption tails extending beyond 400 nm.

A very special component of ketone/amine initiation systems is 4,4'-bis(dimethylamino)benzophenone (Michler's ketone) which can serve as both carbonyl compound and amine activator, and hence may be used by itself or (more efficiently) in conjunction with benzophenone.

In all cases of photoinduced cross-linking by chain growth it is preferable to utilise mixtures of preformed polymers, with in-chain or pendant polymerisable groups, derived from monofunctional and polyfunctional alkenes.

A further influence on the degree of cross-linking is the termination mechanism. Radical polymerisation may terminate in a bimolecular manner by either combination or disproportionation; only the former mechanism yields cross-links.

4 Photochemical cross-linking by ionic chain growth

In contrast to radical systems, only a small number of alkenes and strained heterocyclic molecules are susceptible to ionic polymerisation.

Anionic reactions have not so far found any application in photoinitiated cross-linking, but cationic polymerisations have become increasingly important in recent years. Alkenes containing electron-releasing substituents, such as $ROCH=CH_2$ and $C_6H_5CH=CH_2$, and strained cyclic ethers, such as epoxides, can undergo cationic polymerisation. Of these, only epoxides have found significant application in cross-linkable systems–especially as utilised in surface coatings–but this may reflect the wide availability of multifunctional epoxides from the epoxy resin industry.

Polymerisation of an epoxide by a cationic process may be represented as shown in Scheme 3 (the methods employed to generate initiating species X^+

by photochemical means are described later). In the absence of deliberately added nucleophilic agents, the polymerisation could continue almost indefinitely, and the propagating oxonium ion is uninfluenced by atmospheric oxygen. This is one of the reasons why cationic cross-linking of epoxides is considered to be potentially better than radical systems where atmospheric oxygen may exhibit a marked retarding effect because it reacts with radicals.

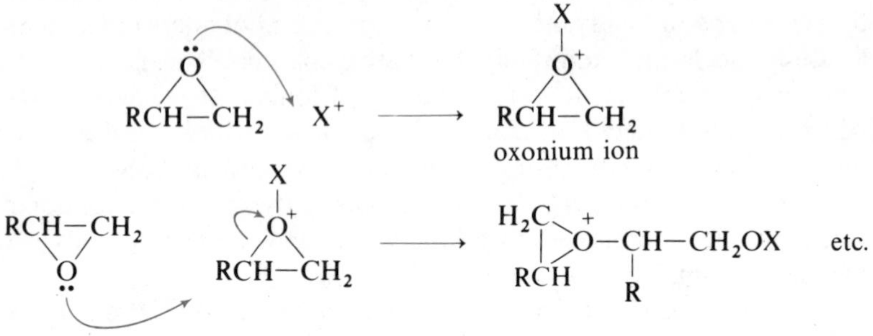

SCHEME 3

Epoxide polymerisations are, however, subject to a variety of chain-transfer reactions of which transfer to an added proton acid is the most likely, for example:

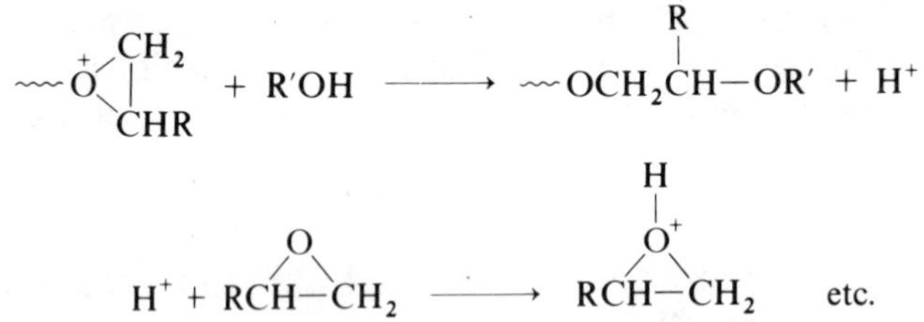

Transfer processes are not particularly disadvantageous when cross-linking is required, and hence the use of difunctional epoxides (e.g. **8** and **9**) and epoxide-substituted polymers affords the opportunity for efficient cross-linking.

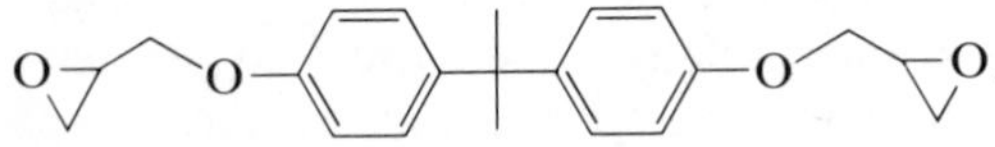

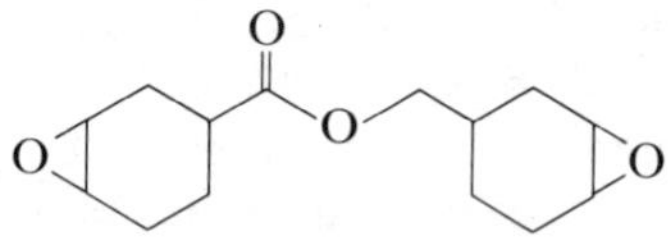

It is also highly convenient to synthesise polymers having pendant epoxide groups by radical copolymerisation of glycidyl methacrylate (**10**).

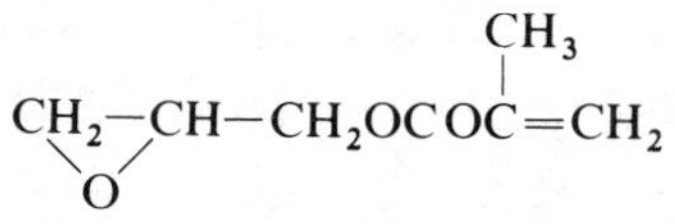

$$CH_2-CH-CH_2OCOC=CH_2$$
$$\underset{O}{\diagdown\diagup} \qquad \overset{CH_3}{\mid}$$

10

Initiation requires the formation of X^+, which may be a proton acid, a carbonium ion, or a Lewis acid species, and is accomplished by photochemical decomposition of aryldiazonium (ArN_2^+), diaryliodonium (Ar_2I^+), or triarylsulphonium (Ar_3S^+) salts. Each salt must have an appropriate anion (e.g. PF_6^-, AsF_6^-, SbF_6^-, BF_4^-), and the detailed chemistry of the photofragmentation is complicated and different for the three types of salt. The best known case (aryldiazonium salts) appears to give free Lewis acid on photolysis, which then initiates the epoxide polymerisation:

$$ArN_2^+BF_4^- \xrightarrow{\ hv\ } ArF + N_2 + BF_3$$

(a Lewis acid)

For the other types of salt, acid fragments derived in part from monomer, solvents, etc., may be the important intermediates, but detailed mechanistic information is lacking.

5·7 Chemistry of the photodegradation of polymers

by John Mellor (University of Southampton)

Most organic polymers undergo chemical change when exposed to ultraviolet radiation (or even visible radiation in some cases). These changes are often called *photodegradation* and result in a deterioration of the mechanical properties of the bulk polymer; for example, drastic loss of elasticity, or conversion of a polymer film into a fine powder. The great importance of organic polymers in exterior constructions and in a variety of manufactured goods exposed to weathering has stimulated much research into the controlled photodegradation of polymers. This research has been directed to two separate areas. First, the retardation of photodegradation, leading to the concept of the *photostabilisation of polymers*, which by prevention of the loss of mechanical properties increases the useful lifetime of the polymer. Second, the deliberate acceleration of photodegradation, leading to the concept of *photodegradable plastics*, which by rapid change of the bulk polymer to a fine powder may avoid environmental pollution.

The photodegradation process may arise from changes in the structure of the polymer involving cleavage of the polymer backbone. This process of *chain scission* leads to a reduction of the average relative molecular mass. Loss of properties can also occur, however, if the relative molecular mass increases. This process of *cross-linking* is quite common.

We will see that only a limited number of manufactured polymers (e.g. polysulphones) and natural polymers (e.g. wool) absorb light to a significant extent above 270 nm. The hydrocarbon polymers, which we will examine in detail, do not significantly absorb light above 270 nm, and yet they can undergo rapid photodegradation by sunlight. This photodegradation is initiated by small amounts of impurities present in the polymer. These impurities initiating photodegradation are called *photosensitisers*.

Generally, a photosensitiser absorbs light and undergoes either bond homolysis or a bimolecular reaction with polymer. In either case a radical intermediate is formed. These intermediates are capable of participating in chain reactions that lead to photodegradation of polymer. Photosensitisers can also act by light absorption and transfer of energy from an excited state of the photosensitiser to populate an excited state of the polymer. The latter excited state then undergoes a chemical change, often leading to radical intermediates.

As photodegradation usually follows chain reaction kinetics, the photostationary concentration of radical intermediates in the chain critically determines the overall rate of photodegradation. Addition of photosensitisers indirectly increases the concentration of radicals and hence accelerates degradation. Conversely, any method of decreasing radical concentrations will retard photodegradation. A number of approaches to stabilisation are possible, including:

1 Addition of *quenchers*, which retard degradation by quenching the excited states responsible for the initiating processes;

2 Addition of *screens* or *absorbents*, which prevent light absorption by potential sensitisers;

3 Addition of *antioxidants* which, by reaction with radical intermediates, reduce the concentration of those species in the photodegradation chain.

These different types of additive are often referred to by the single term *photostabiliser*.

1 Saturated hydrocarbon polymers

Hydrocarbon polymers, such as poly(ethene) and poly(propene), might be expected to have a high stability to photodegradation because of the low density of chromophores capable of light absorption in the ultraviolet and visible regions. The observed instability of such polymers originates in the photoprocesses initiated by impurities that result from the manufacturing process and from initiator residues. The commonest such impurities are hydroperoxides $(R-O-O-H)$ and peroxides $(R-O-O-R)$ or aldehydes and ketones. In the absence of oxygen, high purity poly(ethene) is a relatively stable material, and prolonged exposure to ultraviolet light (254 nm) leads to cross-linking, hydrogen abstraction and other processes, with only very low quantum yield. It is the presence of oxygen in thermal processing or on exposure to radiation that leads to a build-up of hydroperoxide and carbonyl impurities in the material. The stages of initiation, chain propagation and termination can be distinguished in the auto-oxidation of hydrocarbons (Scheme 1).

Auto-oxidation overall converts a hydrocarbon, RH, into a hydroperoxide, ROOH. In poly(ethene), residual double bonds favour formation of allylic hydroperoxides because of the greater stability of the intermediate allylic radicals. A route for their decomposition is shown in Scheme 2.

Possible initiators of this radical auto-oxidation are radicals from hydroperoxide decomposition (HO·, H·, R· and RO·) or carbonyl compounds. The excited states of both saturated and unsaturated carbonyl compounds can produce, via for example a Norrish type 1 process, radical initiation   initiator $\longrightarrow$ X·

$\qquad\qquad$ X· + RH $\longrightarrow$ R· + HX

propagation   R· + O_2 $\longrightarrow$ ROO·

$\qquad\qquad$ ROO· + RH $\longrightarrow$ ROOH + R·

termination   ROO· + ROO· $\longrightarrow$ non-radical products

$\qquad\qquad$ ROO· + R· $\longrightarrow$ non-radical products

$\qquad\qquad$ R· + R· $\longrightarrow$ non-radical products

SCHEME 1

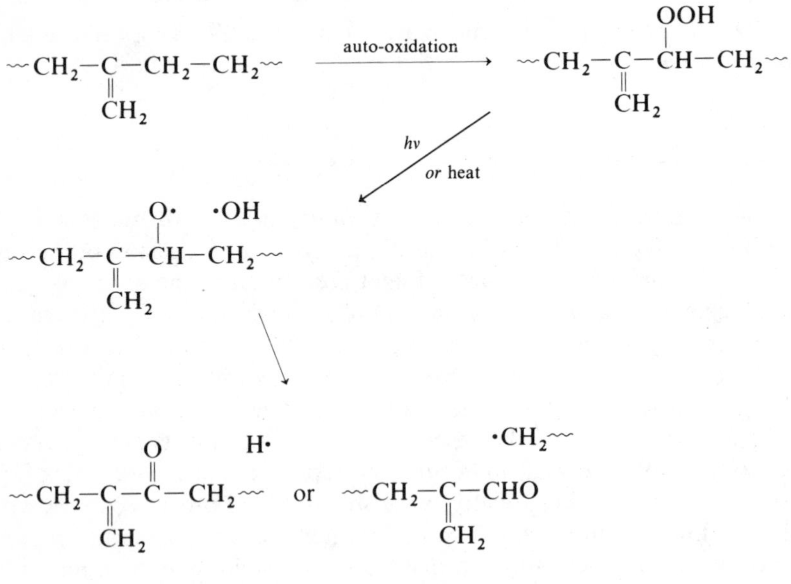

SCHEME 2

intermediates capable of chain initiation. Such processes are shown in Scheme 3 for the typical products of poly(propene) degradation. The relative dissociation energies of the C—H bonds determine the predominant site of attack in the initial auto-oxidation.

The processes outlined in Schemes 1–3 for poly(ethene) and poly(propene) lead to a build-up of impurities. These impurities absorb more strongly than the bulk polymer and can initiate further oxidative processes. Such processes of chain scission lead to a reduction of relative

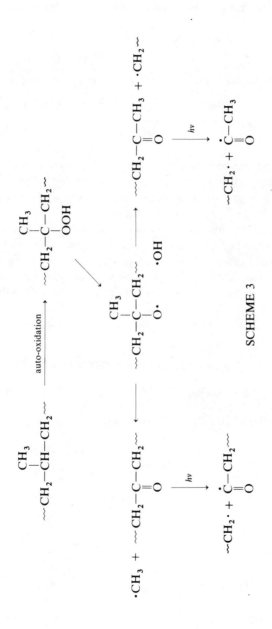

SCHEME 3

molecular mass of the polymer. However, competitive cross-linking (Scheme 4), leading to an increase in relative molecular mass, can also occur.

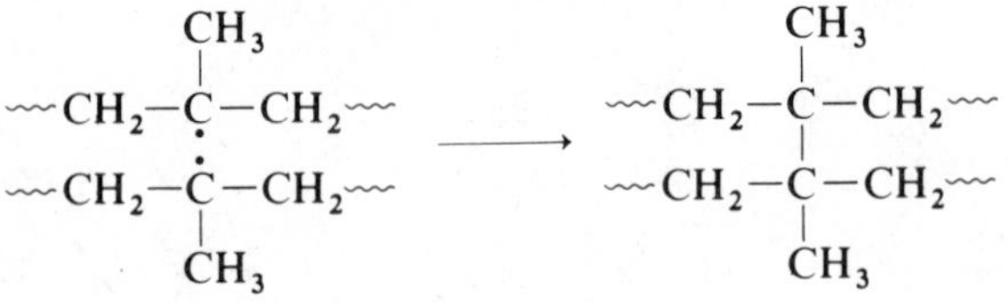

$$
\begin{array}{ccc}
& CH_3 & & & CH_3 \\
& | & & & | \\
\sim CH_2-\overset{\cdot}{C}-CH_2\sim & & & \sim CH_2-\overset{|}{C}-CH_2\sim \\
\sim CH_2-\overset{\cdot}{C}-CH_2\sim & \longrightarrow & & \sim CH_2-\overset{|}{C}-CH_2\sim \\
& | & & & | \\
& CH_3 & & & CH_3 \\
\end{array}
$$

SCHEME 4

The balance between chain scission and cross-linking depends on a number of factors. For example, it may be controlled by the diffusion rate of oxygen, which is greater in amorphous regions of a hydrocarbon polymer than in crystalline regions. Typically for a hydrocarbon polymer, poly(propene) films undergo maximum photodegradation at the surface where there is the highest concentration of oxygen and of photoinitiators. In spite of possible cross-linking, photodegradation following absorption of light by hydroperoxide (<280 nm) and by aldehydes and ketones (~ 300 nm) rapidly leads to loss of mechanical properties in both poly(ethene) and poly(propene). Poly(2-methylpropene) has no tertiary C—H bond in the repeating unit and is less readily photodegraded than poly(propene).

2 Unsaturated hydrocarbon polymers

In the absence of oxygen, high purity poly(styrene) is photochemically stable. In the presence of oxygen, however, commercial samples are readily photodegraded (Scheme 5). Hydrogen abstraction gives the stabilised benz-

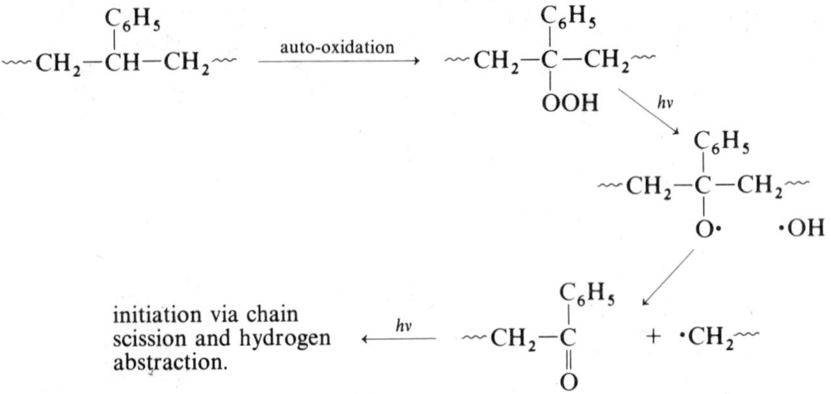

$$
\begin{array}{ccc}
C_6H_5 & & C_6H_5 \\
| & \xrightarrow{\text{auto-oxidation}} & | \\
\sim CH_2-CH-CH_2\sim & & \sim CH_2-C-CH_2\sim \\
& & | \\
& & OOH \quad \searrow hv
\end{array}
$$

$$
\begin{array}{c}
C_6H_5 \\
| \\
\sim CH_2-C-CH_2\sim \\
| \\
O\cdot \qquad \cdot OH
\end{array}
$$

initiation via chain scission and hydrogen abstraction. $\xleftarrow{\ hv\ }$ $\sim CH_2-\overset{C_6H_5}{\underset{\overset{\|}{O}}{C}}$ $+$ $\cdot CH_2\sim$

SCHEME 5

ylic radical, hence initiation of radical chains is easy. In the subsequent hydroperoxide decomposition, aryl ketones are produced which absorb at longer wavelengths than saturated ketones and with a greater absorption coefficient. Such aromatic ketones are efficient initiators of further photodegradation.

Natural rubber (*cis*-1,4-polyisoprene) is very susceptible to photodegradation. At room temperature, hydroperoxide and peroxide formation is very easy. Consequently, rubber is normally heavily contaminated with peroxide impurities capable of initiating photodegradation (Scheme 6). A rapid but complex degradation results.

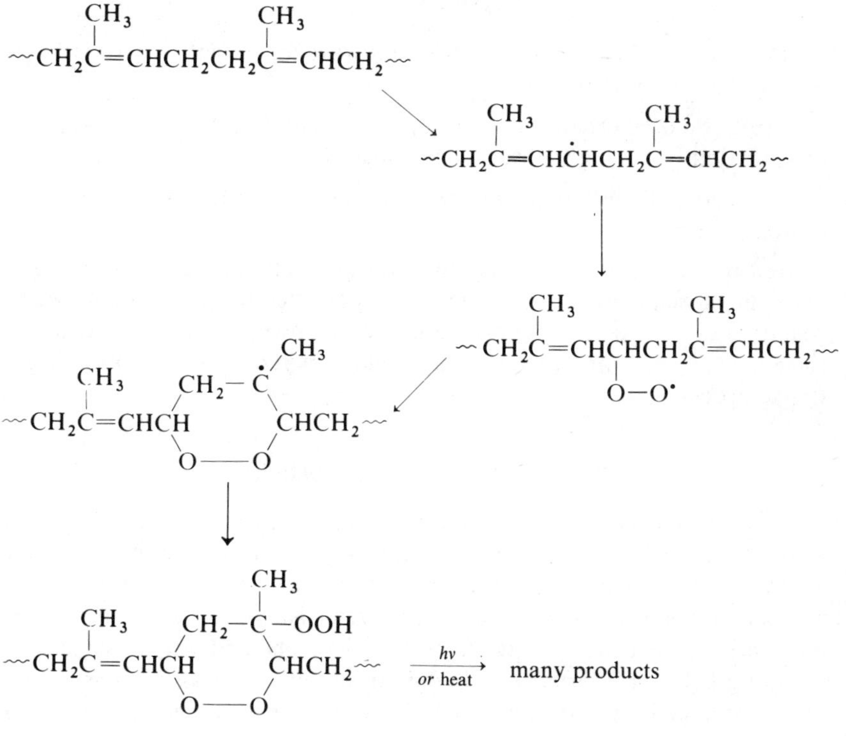

SCHEME 6

Copolymers of acrylonitrile (propenenitrile), butadiene and styrene (ABS) are commercially important. However, the incorporation of butadiene into the copolymer leads to easy photodegradation.

245

3   Photostabilisation of hydrocarbon polymers

Photodegradation may be retarded by interference at several points in the oxidation mechanism shown in Scheme 1. Progress in achieving satisfactory levels of photostabilisation has been largely by an empirical approach, and normally protection is achieved by a combination of factors. Protection from photo-oxidative processes might be achieved by:

1   Purification of polymers to avoid incorporation of impurities (reducing the rate of initiation);

2   Protection from oxygen (reducing the rate of propagation);

3   Prevention of light absorption (reducing the rate of initiation);

4   Deactivation of excited states of possible photosensitisers (reducing the rate of initiation);

5   Provision of alternative chemical pathways for potential sensitisers (reducing the rate of initiation);

6   Provision of alternative chemical pathways for intermediates involved in propagation (reducing the rate of propagation);

7   Provision of additional modes of termination (enhancing the rate of termination).

Neither the use of purified polymers nor protection from oxygen is practical in most cases. Hence the main effort is directed towards minimising the role of photosensitisers by prevention of light absorption and by quenching their excited states, and towards chemical interference with the photodegradative process.

3.1   Prevention of absorption of light

The key impurities, hydroperoxides and peroxides, absorb light of wavelengths less than 300 nm, and carbonyl impurities absorb at about 300 nm. In the simpler methods of protection the extent to which light of all wavelengths penetrates into the bulk polymer is reduced. Pigments can be introduced which are opaque to ultraviolet light and act as screens by reflecting light, or alternatively highly absorbent materials such as carbon black are added. In both cases the bulk polymer is protected, and photodegradation is confined to surface areas.

Zinc oxide is a white photostabiliser, which reflects efficiently in the region 240–380 nm. Titanium oxides are used similarly. Disadvantages in the use of these and other (coloured) pigments arise because of loss of desirable mechanical properties and the introduction of undesirable colouring. This limits the incorporation of pigments, and both inorganic and organic pigments can initiate undesirable photoprocesses.

Incorporation of a carbon black gives excellent photostabilisation and is limited chiefly by the resultant black colouring. The efficiency of carbon black is determined by the particle size and the degree of dispersion in the polymer phase. In addition to acting as a screen for the harmful radiation, carbon black offers a secondary protective role by interfering with the chemical processes of photodegradation.

An alternative strategy of protection is to incorporate a highly absorbent material, which efficiently and harmlessly dissipates the critical radiation, but unlike carbon black does not markedly colour the polymer. Very many compounds have been examined as potential screens. An ideal compound would absorb intensely in the ultraviolet region, and have a high quantum yield of fluorescence. Such a compound remains to be discovered, and the screens currently used dissipate the absorbed energy by a chemical process. The photoexcited states of three important classes of screens, phenyl salicylates, hydroxybenzophenones, and hydroxyphenylbenzotriazoles dissipate excess energy via the processes shown in Scheme 7.

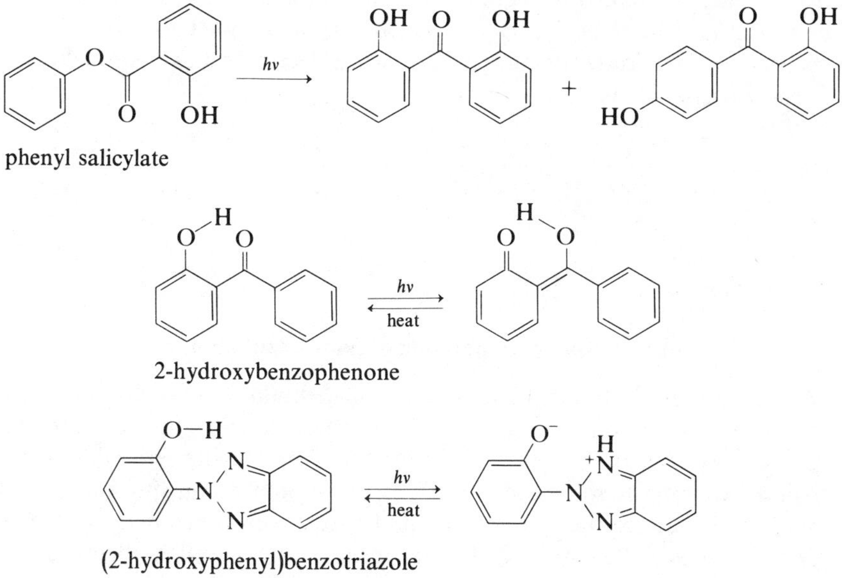

phenyl salicylate

2-hydroxybenzophenone

(2-hydroxyphenyl)benzotriazole

SCHEME 7

The use of such screens is limited by a number of factors. A yellow colouration results, which if it is not acceptable, must be masked. More critically the screen must be adequately soluble in the polymer, must not affect the mechanical properties unduly, and must not be easily lost by migration, leaching or other processes. These are very severe constraints. For example, in low density poly(ethene), benzophenones require a long alkyl side-chain to be retained in the polymer. In spite of their limitations, however, these screens are very widely used.

3.2 Quenching of excited states responsible for photoinitiation

The use of quenchers is directed mainly at preventing relatively long-lived triplet states of ketones and aldehydes from initiating further photodegradation. Quenching of short-lived excited states of hydroperoxides or of singlet excited states of carbonyl compounds is impractical.

At 77 K the phosphorescence attributable to ketonic impurities in thermally oxidised poly(butadiene) is quenched by moderate concentrations of additives, for example compound **1**, which has a low triplet energy. At room temperature, addition of **1** endows poly(butadiene) with additional photostability but results in discolouration. It is probable that other additives, which act mainly through a chemical mode (Section 3.3), confer some photostability by their ability to quench carbonyl triplet states by energy transfer to their lowest lying triplet states. Screens such as hydroxybenzophenones can act similarly.

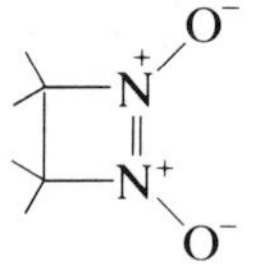

1

3.3 Chemical methods of photostabilisation

Early stages of photodegradation concern the build-up of hydroperoxides, which act as photoinitiators by decomposition to radicals and carbonyl compounds. Harmless chemical destruction of such hydroperoxides is thus required to prevent auto-oxidation. The role of photostabilising additives is often poorly understood. Recently, the hydroxybenzophenones have been shown to react chemically with hydroperoxides, as well as being useful screens. Effective decomposition of hydroperoxides is also achieved by metal dithiocarbamates (**2**), metal dithiophosphates (**3**), and cyclic phosphate esters (**4**).

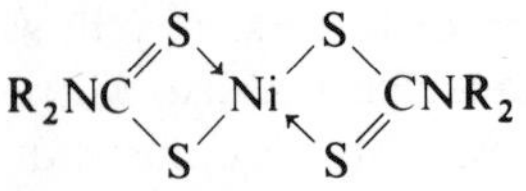

2 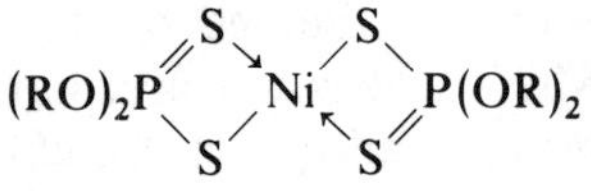   3 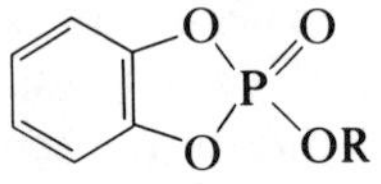   4

Various additives called *radical scavengers* act by chemical reaction with intermediate radicals of the degradation process. By reduction of the total radical concentration, antioxidants such as phenols, hydroquinones and thiols retard photodegradation (Scheme 8).

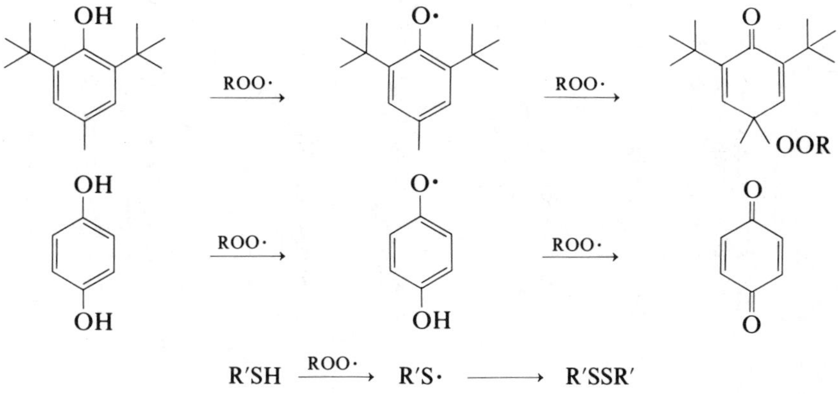

R'SH $\xrightarrow{\text{ROO}\cdot}$ R'S· $\longrightarrow$ R'SSR'

SCHEME 8

4 Accelerated photodegradation

Concern over the unacceptable environmental pollution by plastic waste has stimulated the production of polymers that undergo complete photodegradation in sunlight to give a biodegradable fine powder. An efficiently photodegradable polymer can be produced by copolymerisation of styrene with a vinyl-substituted benzophenone. Such a polymer has carbonyl groups–initiators of photo-oxidation–incorporated in the backbone. By variation of the ratio of the two different monomer units, the lifetime of the copolymer can be controlled. Similarly, photodegradable poly(ethene) (Ecolyte PE) and poly(propene) (Ecolyte PP) contain a vinyl ketone comonomer. Other commercial products rely simply on addition of a photosensitive additive, for example benzophenone to poly(styrene). An alternative system relies on addition of metal salts capable of accelerating photodegradation.

5 Non-hydrocarbon polymers

Characteristics of the photodegradation of a number of important commercial and natural polymers are shown in Table 1. Incorporation of aromatic residues generally leads to greatly decreased photostability. The least stable

249

Table 1 Characteristics of the photodegradation of non-hydrocarbon polymers

Polymer	Repeating unit	Absorptivity to solar spectrum	Comments	Overall photostability
poly(vinyl chloride)	Cl $-CH-CH_2-$	low	loss of HCl to give alkene initiated by hydroperoxides, ketones and catalyst residues	low
poly(methyl acrylate)	$COOCH_3$ $-CH-CH_2-$	low	degradation initiated by impurities	high
poly(ethylene terephthalate)	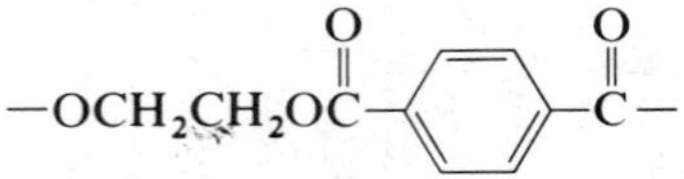 $-OCH_2CH_2OC(=O)\!-\!C_6H_4\!-\!C(=O)-$	high	absorption by chromophore leads directly to chain scission	low
nylon-6,6	$-C(CH_2)_4CNH(CH_2)_6NH-$ (with $=O$ groups)	low	catalyst impurities initiate degradation	moderate
phenol–formaldehyde	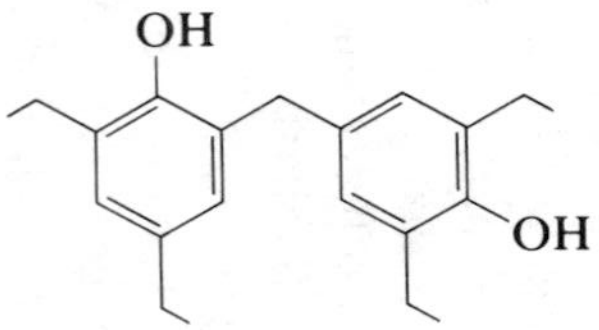 (structure)	high	absorption by chromophore leads directly to chain scission	low
polysulphones	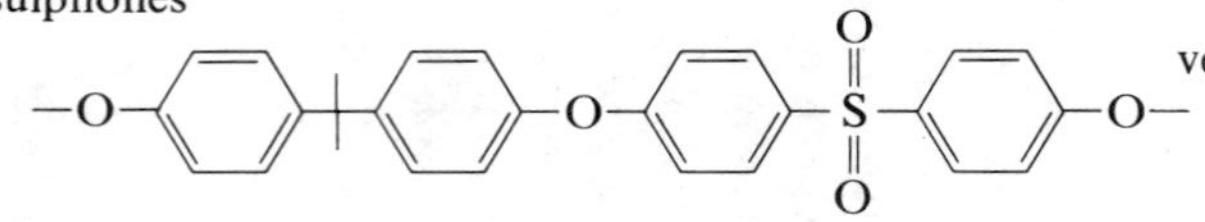 (structure)	very high	absorption by chromophores leads to chain scission and loss of SO_2	very low
wool	irregular polyamide structure	high	absorption mainly by tryptophan residue leads to rapid yellowing	moderate

polysulphones colour very rapidly, and this coloration has been used as a form of actinometry to provide quantitative information on levels of solar radiation (in the ultraviolet region). Polysulphone film in the form of badges has been used to monitor ultraviolet radiation therapy.

Cellulose materials (cotton and paper) and wool rapidly turn yellow on exposure to light. With wool, the effect may be partially masked by addition of optical brighteners (Chapter 3·3, Section 4).

5·8 Photohalogenation and related processes

by Alan Cox (University of Warwick)

Photohalogenation reactions offer a number of advantages over corresponding thermal processes. Relatively low working temperatures are possible, and because of the high quantum yields, the cost of the light energy does not normally play a decisive role in industrial radical chain reactions. Photoprocesses are easily initiated and interrupted, and are particularly useful where radical chains are short.

1 Photochlorination

Irradiation of mixtures of chlorine and hydrocarbons at wavelengths shorter than 478.5 nm (the onset of the absorption continuum) can lead to chlorination of the organic molecule. These reactions occur through a radical chain process:

$$
\begin{array}{lrcl}
\text{initiation} & \text{Cl}_2 & \xrightarrow{h\nu} & 2\text{Cl}\cdot \\
\text{propagation} & \text{Cl}\cdot + \text{RH} & \longrightarrow & \text{HCl} + \text{R}\cdot \\
& \text{R}\cdot + \text{Cl}_2 & \longrightarrow & \text{RCl} + \text{Cl}\cdot \\
\text{termination} & \text{Cl}\cdot + \text{Cl}\cdot & \longrightarrow & \text{Cl}_2 \\
& \text{R}\cdot + \text{R}\cdot & \longrightarrow & \text{R}_2 \\
& \text{R}\cdot + \text{Cl}\cdot & \longrightarrow & \text{RCl}
\end{array}
$$

The overall quantum yields are usually very high and suggest chain lengths which often exceed 10^6 (i.e. more than 10^6 propagation cycles for each termination step). Although the chain length is adversely affected by many impurities, such as oxygen, phenols or amines, photochemical chlorination can be a good way of introducing a reactive centre into a molecule. Compared with the thermal process, however, photochemical monochlorination of alkanes is generally less widely used commercially. Simple alkanes yield every possible monochloro compound, in proportions that reflect the relative stabilities of hydrocarbon radicals, which are tertiary > secondary > primary. This sequence, which is the reverse of the order of C—H bond dissociation energies, is the same as for carbonium ions, although the differences are smaller for radicals.

In general, the relative selectivities of hydrogen abstraction processes (i.e. the relative rates of hydrogen abstraction per hydrogen atom), also depend on the halogens themselves, the more reactive halogens being the less selective. Thus the highly reactive fluorine atom shows very little discrimination between various types of hydrogen atom, whereas the iodine atom reacts almost exclusively with tertiary hydrogens. The overall order of selectivities is $I\cdot > Br\cdot > Cl\cdot > F\cdot$ and is a consequence of the way the position of the activated complex on the reaction co-ordinate is influenced by the halogen. For a less reactive atom such as $Br\cdot$ the activated complex occurs sufficiently late on the reaction co-ordinate for the stability of the product radical to be reflected in the energy of the activated complex. Consequently, the relative magnitudes of the activation energies for hydrogen abstraction are tertiary < secondary < primary. For the more reactive chlorine atom, the activated complex occurs earlier, with the result that the differences between the activation energies are smaller and the degree of discrimination is correspondingly less (cf. Table 1).

Table 1   Relative reactivities of hydrogen atoms towards abstraction by halogen atoms

Type of hydrogen atom	Example	Halogen atom used	
		$Br\cdot$ at 100 °C	$Cl\cdot$ at 25 °C
primary	C_2H_5—H	1	1.0
secondary	$(CH_3)_2CH$—H	160	4.4
tertiary	$(CH_3)_3C$—H	4713	6.7

1.1   Photochlorination of alkylaromatics

Photochemical chlorination of alkylaromatics, such as toluene and xylenes, gives the corresponding side-chain chloro derivatives, though some ring chlorination and other side reactions may occur. Exhaustive chlorination gives benzotrichloride ($C_6H_5CCl_3$; (trichloromethyl)benzene) in the case of toluene, and 1-dichloromethyl-2-trichloromethylbenzene (**1**) in the case of *o*-xylene. Side-chain chlorination can also be initiated by heat or peroxides or sulphuryl chloride (SO_2Cl_2). The chlorination of alkylaromatics is especially interesting, because the substrate itself may form a complex with the chlorine atom. Thus at 40 °C, chlorination of ethylbenzene in the absence of a solvent leads to a mixture of (1-chloroethyl)benzene (**2**) and (2-chloroethyl)benzene (**3**) in the ratio 14.5 to 1. If this reaction is carried out in a solvent

$$\underset{\textbf{1}}{\text{CHCl}_2 / \text{CCl}_3 \text{ benzene}} \qquad \underset{\textbf{2}}{\text{CH}_3 / \text{CHCl benzene}} \qquad \underset{\textbf{3}}{\text{CH}_2\text{Cl} / \text{CH}_2 \text{ benzene}}$$

that cannot effectively complex the chlorine atoms, the selectivity is decreased (the ratio is 5.65 at 40 °C and at a concentration of 4.98 mol l^{-1} in cyclohexane).

Exhaustive side-chain photochlorination of toluene is a stepwise process which can be controlled so that intermediate chlorination products are isolable. By use of 1.1 moles of chlorine to 1 mole of toluene, benzyl chloride (C$_6$H$_5$CH$_2$Cl; (chloromethyl)benzene) may be obtained in yields of up to 80% in gas phase reactions, whereas benzal chloride (C$_6$H$_5$CHCl$_2$; (dichloromethyl)benzene) is the major product if 2.0–2.2 moles of chlorine are used per mole of toluene. Further photochlorination at temperatures between 100 and 140 °C can give benzotrichloride in yields of 95%. Both batch and continuous processes are used in the commercial production of these compounds. Because the cost of chlorine is high, the by-product HCl is often converted back into chlorine, which is then recycled. Benzyl chloride is used in the manufacture of benzyl butyl phthalate, a vinyl resin plasticiser, and benzal chloride and benzotrichloride are converted into benzaldehyde and benzoyl chloride, respectively.

The photochlorination of substituted toluenes is only partially dependent on the strength of the bond being broken. Of particular interest in this connection is the observation that, despite the much greater resonance stabilisation in the benzyl radical as opposed to the cyclohexyl radical, the hydrogen atoms in cyclohexane are 1.85 times as reactive as those in toluene in the liquid phase at 40 °C. In the gas phase at 70 °C this ratio rises to 2.1. This testifies to the lack of any significant contribution of the resonance stabilisation of the benzyl radical to the activation energy requirement for chlorination.

The reactivity of the chlorine atom can be greatly affected by the solvent. If the chlorine atom forms a complex with the solvent then its energy is decreased, and its reactivity is more like that of the bromine atom (i.e. it displays greater selectivity in hydrogen abstraction reactions).

1.2 Photochlorination of benzene

Addition of halogens to benzene takes place by a radical mechanism. It is usually carried out at between 15 and 40 °C and can be initiated in a number of ways, including the use of light or radical initiators such as peroxides or azonitriles. The photochlorination of benzene is a process of considerable industrial importance because one of the products, the so-called γ-isomer (4) of hexachlorocyclohexane (benzene hexachloride), is a powerful insecticide. As a mixture of stereoisomers, benzene hexachloride (BHC) is marketed under the trade names 'Lindane' and 'Gammexane' but, unlike most other chlorinated hydrocarbons, BHC has the advantage that it is degraded biolo-

4

gically with comparative ease. The efficiency of conversion of benzene into its hexachloride is greater than 95%, although only about 14% of the product is the γ-isomer.

2 Photobromination

Much of what has already been said about photochlorination is true generally for photobromination. In the case of methane, the chain length is comparatively short, and the kinetics support a mechanism in which hydrogen abstraction is reversible and is the rate-determining step. If the alkane has more than one type of hydrogen atom, more than one product is likely to be formed. However, as a hydrogen abstractor, the bromine atom is much more selective than the chlorine atom (Section 1). In toluene, the chain length exceeds that of most alkanes, with the possible exception of tertiary alkanes. The mechanism is

initiation $\qquad$ $Br_2 \xrightarrow{h\nu} 2Br\cdot$

propagation $\quad Br\cdot + C_6H_5CH_3 \longrightarrow HBr + C_6H_5\dot{C}H_2 \qquad \Delta H = -10.5\,kJ\,mol^{-1}$

$\qquad\qquad\quad C_6H_5\dot{C}H_2 + Br_2 \longrightarrow C_6H_5CH_2Br + Br\cdot \qquad \Delta H = -20.9\,kJ\,mol^{-1}$

termination $\quad C_6H_5\dot{C}H_2 + Br\cdot \longrightarrow C_6H_5CH_2Br$

$\qquad\qquad\quad 2C_6H_5\dot{C}H_2 \longrightarrow C_6H_5CH_2CH_2C_6H_5$

$\qquad\qquad\qquad\quad 2Br\cdot \longrightarrow Br_2$

Because both propagation steps are exothermic and the chains are long, both propagation steps must be rapid.

2.1 Bromination using N-bromosuccinimide

Allylic bromination (i.e. bromination at a saturated carbon atom situated adjacent to one of the carbon atoms of a double bond) using N-haloamides was first recorded by Wohl in 1919. However, it was not until 1942, when Ziegler reported the results of an extensive study in which he selected N-bromosuccinimide (NBS; **5**) as the best reagent, that this reaction received

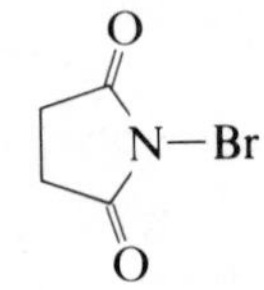

$$\text{5}$$

any significant attention. Bromination of organic compounds by NBS (Wohl–Ziegler reaction) can be initiated by radical sources or by light, for example:

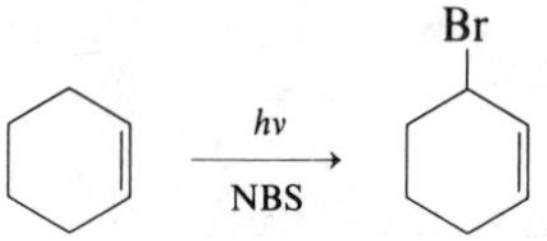

NBS serves as a reservoir of molecular bromine, which arises from the interaction of NBS with hydrogen bromide:

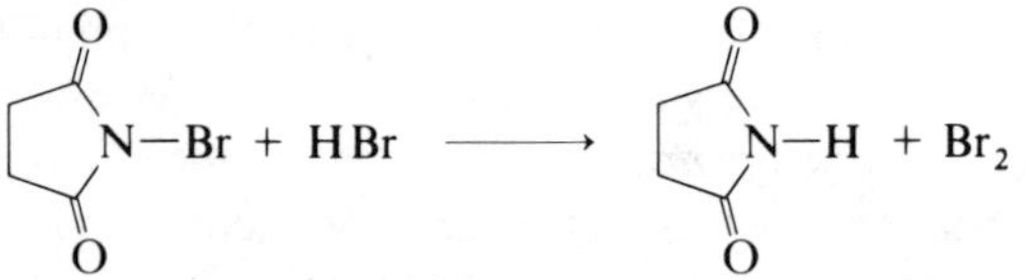

The bromination reaction is a radical chain process in which the low concentration of molecular bromine acts as the brominating agent:

$$Br_2 \xrightarrow{h\nu} 2Br\cdot$$

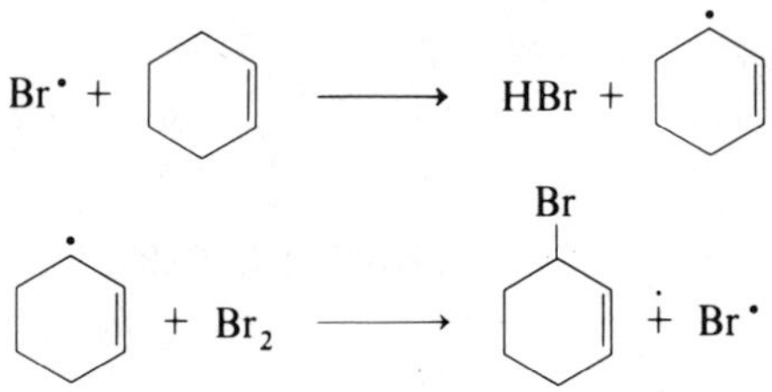

3   Photonitrosation

Like photohalogenation, photonitrosation is an important process for the functionalisation of unactivated C—H bonds and can be brought about as follows.

3.1   Photolysis of organic nitrites

Organic nitrites $(RO-N=O)$ have a longest wavelength absorption $(\lambda_{max} = 360\,\text{nm}, \epsilon < 100\,\text{l}\,\text{mol}^{-1}\,\text{cm}^{-1})$ corresponding to an $n \to \pi^*$ transition and involving a non-bonding electron on nitrogen. Excitation leads to cleavage of the RO—NO bond, and the alkoxy radical generated may undergo a number of different processes.

Fragmentation. This produces carbonyl compounds and alkyl radicals:

e.g. $(CH_3)_3CO—NO \xrightarrow{h\nu} (CH_3)_3CO\cdot + \cdot NO$

$(CH_3)_3CO\cdot \longrightarrow (CH_3)_2CO + \cdot CH_3$

Hydrogen abstraction. A competition exists between intermolecular abstraction from the solvent and intramolecular abstraction. In benzene, a poor hydrogen donor, irradiation of octyl nitrite (**6**) leads almost exclusively to 4-nitroso-octan-1-ol (**7**). Following loss of NO, intramolecular hydrogen abstraction occurs:

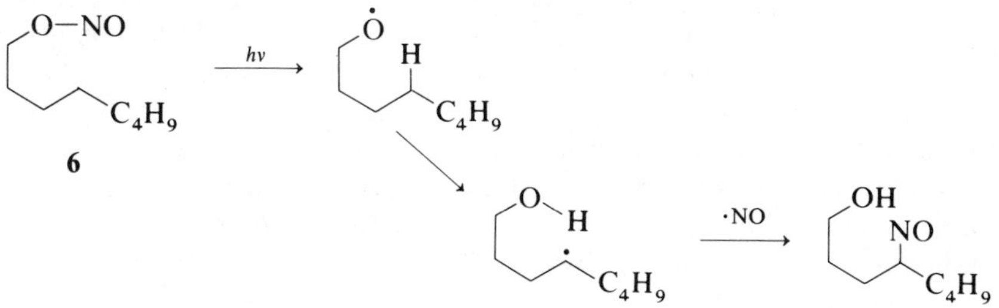

This transformation is known as the Barton reaction.

3.2 Photolysis of nitrosyl chloride

Nitrosyl chloride (NOCl) exhibits almost continuous absorption throughout the visible and ultraviolet regions. A maximum is apparent at 335 nm ($\epsilon \sim 32.5 \ 1 \ mol^{-1} \ cm^{-1}$) and excitation in this region promotes cleavage of the ON—Cl bond. Irradiation of nitrosyl chloride in cyclohexane leads to the formation of cyclohexanone oxime (**8**):

$$NOCl \xrightarrow{h\nu} \cdot NO + Cl\cdot$$

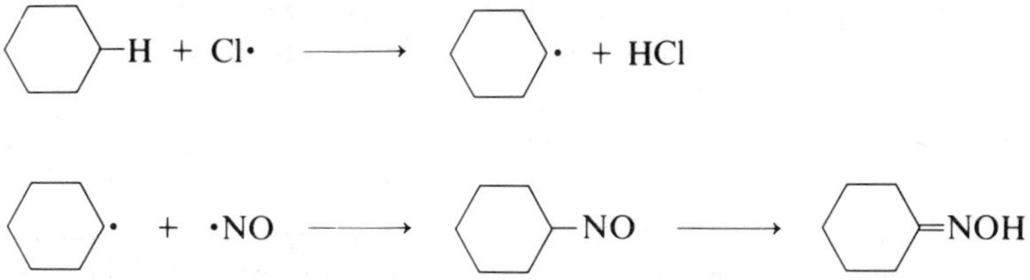

This process is used in the manufacture of nylon 6 (nylon 12 can be made in a similar way from cyclododecane).

4 Sulphochlorination

Sulphochlorination of alkanes is very important industrially, and under optimum conditions produces alkanesulphonyl chlorides (RSO_2Cl) with a quantum yield of about 2000. Most industrial production involves subsequent hydrolysis by NaOH to give the corresponding alkanesulphonates:

$$RSO_2Cl + 2NaOH \longrightarrow RSO_3Na + NaCl + H_2O$$

Formerly, alkanesulphonates were much used in detergent manufacture, but owing to the presence of di- and poly-sulphonates, which cannot be satisfactorily removed under industrial conditions, this is no longer the case. Instead, alkanesulphonates are now used mainly as emulsifiers for polymerisation. Alkanesulphonyl chlorides may be converted by ammonia into the corresponding sulphonamides (**9**), which are used in the textile industry. The sulphonamides themselves may be treated with chloroacetic acid to give sulphonylaminoacetic acids, which are used as emulsifiers and anticorrosion agents for mineral oils:

$$RSO_2Cl \xrightarrow{NH_3} \underset{\textbf{9}}{RSO_2NH_2} \xrightarrow[NaOH]{ClCH_2COOH} RSO_2NHCH_2COOH$$

Sulphur dioxide and chlorine are known to react with alkanes photochemically to give a sulphonyl chloride as the principal organic product, together with some chloroalkane impurity:

$$RH + SO_2 + Cl_2 \xrightarrow{h\nu} RSO_2Cl + HCl$$

The cleanest product is usually obtained in the absence of branched-chain alkanes, because these promote competing chlorination. However, the product is still a mixture, because the sulphonyl chloride group is normally randomly distributed over all the carbon atoms. Thus photochemical sulphochlorination of propane gives a mixture of isomeric propane-1- and propane-2-sulphonyl chlorides $(CH_3CH_2CH_2SO_2Cl$ and $(CH_3)_2CHSO_2Cl)$, which are not readily separable. Sulphochlorination is also capable of giving di- and poly-sulphonyl chlorides. Butane is found to lead not only to an inseparable mixture of butanesulphonyl chlorides, but also to a mixture of butanedisulphonyl chlorides from which the 1,4-disubstituted isomer $(ClO_2S(CH_2)_4SO_2Cl)$ can be obtained. It is interesting to note that neither the 1,1- nor the 1,2-isomer is ever produced in these reactions. The mechanism of the transformation is a chain process, involving initial cleavage of the chlorine molecule on absorption of a photon:

$$Cl_2 \xrightarrow{h\nu} 2Cl\cdot$$
$$Cl\cdot + RH \longrightarrow R\cdot + HCl$$
$$R\cdot + SO_2 \longrightarrow RSO_2\cdot$$
$$R\cdot + Cl_2 \longrightarrow RCl + Cl\cdot$$
$$RSO_2\cdot + Cl_2 \longrightarrow RSO_2Cl + Cl\cdot$$

This mechanism explains both the omnipresence of chloroalkanes in these reactions and also why the reactions are initiated by radical sources, such as peroxides or tetraethyl-lead.

Photochemical sulphochlorination can also be carried out using sulphuryl chloride, SO_2Cl_2, but in this case a catalytic amount of a base such as pyridine is necessary. For example, photochemical sulphochlorination of cyclohexane using pyridine as catalyst gives a mixture of 9.4% of chlorocyclohexane and 54% of cyclohexanesulphonyl chloride. A variety of substrates are known to react with sulphuryl chloride on irradiation. Toluene gives only chlorination products whereas ethylbenzene and methylcyclohexane give a sulphochlorination product in up to 30% and 44% yields respectively. It has been suggested that the base induces thermal decomposition of the sulphuryl chloride to SO_2 and Cl_2. The chlorine molecule so produced then undergoes photolysis and the reaction proceeds as shown at the top of the page.

Apart from alkanes, photochemical sulphochlorination can also be carried out on other substrates, such as aliphatic carboxylic acids, aminoalkanes, and organosilicon compounds. Lower aliphatic acids generally undergo sulphochlorination at the 3-position or 3- and 4-positions, and accordingly acetic acid fails to react. With higher aliphatic acids substitution occurs randomly but again there is no 2-substitution. The product is often a cyclic anhydride, and in the case of propanoic acid it is the cyclic anhydride (**10**) of 3-sulphopropanoic acid which is formed.

$$CH_3CH_2COOH \xrightarrow[SO_2Cl_2]{h\nu} \underset{\underset{SO_2Cl}{\mid}}{H_2C-CH_2COOH} \xrightarrow{-HCl} \underset{\mathbf{10}}{O_2S}$$

The mechanism is again thought to involve chlorine atoms and organic radicals, and it is interesting to note (but so far unexplained) that the use of peroxides leads only to chlorinated products.

Sulphochlorination of the hydrochlorides of aliphatic amines, such as propylamine, isobutylamine and butylamine, proceeds as follows:

$$Cl^- H_3\overset{+}{N}C_nH_{2n+1} \xrightarrow[SO_2 + Cl_2]{h\nu} Cl^- H_3\overset{+}{N}C_nH_{2n}SO_2Cl + HCl$$

Cyclic compounds can also arise:

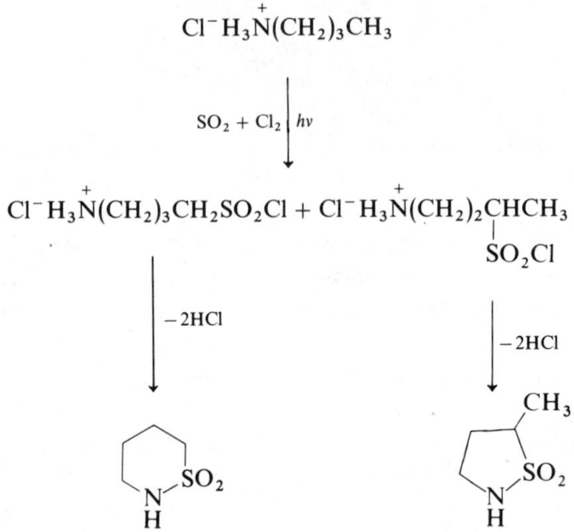

$$Cl^- H_3\overset{+}{N}(CH_2)_3CH_3$$

$$\Bigg\downarrow SO_2 + Cl_2 \bigg| h\nu$$

$$Cl^- H_3\overset{+}{N}(CH_2)_3CH_2SO_2Cl + Cl^- H_3\overset{+}{N}(CH_2)_2CHCH_3$$
$$\underset{SO_2Cl}{|}$$

$$\Bigg\downarrow -2HCl \qquad\qquad \Bigg\downarrow -2HCl$$

5 Sulphoxidation

The term 'sulphoxidation' usually refers to the photoinduced reaction between straight-chain alkanes, sulphur dioxide and oxygen:

$$RH + SO_2 + \tfrac{1}{2}O_2 \xrightarrow{h\nu} RSO_3H$$

As a method of synthesising alkanesulphonates it is more satisfactory than sulphochlorination, because it uses oxygen rather than the much more expensive chlorine as oxidising agent. This reaction gives a mixture of all possible secondary sulphonic acids, with the yield of primary sulphonic acids being lower because the rate of abstraction of primary hydrogen atoms is lower. With cyclohexane, the initial product has been shown to be the peroxysulphonic acid $C_6H_{11}S(O_2)OOH$, which is a very powerful oxidising agent and is, therefore, not isolated. In water, the peroxysulphonic acid slowly decomposes to give cyclohexanesulphonic acid and hydrogen peroxide, and in water containing sulphur dioxide the products are cyclohexanesulphonic acid and sulphuric acid. This process, which is known as the 'light–water process' and is the best of several variants, has been developed industrially by Hoechst.

Sulphoxidation can be brought about either by irradiation or by addition of small amounts of peracids to the reaction mixture. In both cases the transformation depends on the initial formation of an alkyl radical and proceeds as follows:

$$R \cdot + SO_2 \longrightarrow RSO_2 \cdot$$
$$RSO_2 \cdot + O_2 \longrightarrow RS(O_2)O_2 \cdot$$
$$RS(O_2)O_2 \cdot + RH \longrightarrow RS(O_2)OOH + R \cdot$$

In the absence of water, the peroxysulphonic acid decomposes to radicals:

$$RS(O_2)OOH \longrightarrow RS(O_2)O \cdot + \cdot OH$$
$$RS(O_2)O \cdot + RH \longrightarrow RSO_3H + R \cdot$$
$$RH + \cdot OH \longrightarrow H_2O + R \cdot$$

6 Photoaddition to alkenes

Alkenes undergo a wide variety of light-induced addition reactions, a common one being the addition of photochemically generated radicals to the ground state of the alkene. For example, hydrogen bromide shows continuous absorption, which has its onset at 254 nm, and on irradiation it has been observed to add readily to unsaturated compounds. The addition gives an anti-Markownikoff product and occurs by the following mechanism:

$$HBr \xrightarrow{h\nu} H \cdot + Br \cdot$$
$$RCH{=}CH_2 + Br \cdot \longrightarrow R\overset{\cdot}{C}HCH_2Br$$
$$R\overset{\cdot}{C}HCH_2Br + HBr \longrightarrow RCH_2CH_2Br + Br \cdot$$

A typical example is that involving propyne to give *cis*-1-bromopropene (**11**), showing that the addition is stereospecifically *trans*:

$$CH_3C{\equiv}CH \xrightarrow[HBr]{h\nu}$$

11

Hydrogen sulphide (H_2S) and thiols (RSH) undergo addition to alkenes either on direct irradiation at 280 nm or by use of a sensitiser such as acetone. The addition is thought to proceed as follows:

$$RSH \xrightarrow{h\nu} RS \cdot + H \cdot$$
$$RS \cdot + CH_2{=}CHR' \longrightarrow RSCH_2\overset{\cdot}{C}HR'$$
$$RSCH_2\overset{\cdot}{C}HR' + RSH \longrightarrow RSCH_2CH_2R' + RS \cdot$$

The orientation of addition is again anti-Markownikoff. Apart from such simple compounds as ethene and propene, a wide variety of molecules will undergo this addition including cyclohexene, styrene, various alkynes and many oxygenated alkenes, such as vinyl and allyl ethers, alcohols and esters. Organosulphur compounds prepared in this way are used as medicinal compounds and are present in a wide range of agricultural chemicals including herbicides, fungicides and insecticides. They also have applications in the rubber industry and as additives to fuel oil and lubricants.

Phosphine (PH_3) will add to unsaturated compounds on direct irradiation at $\lambda < 230$ nm, or at longer wavelengths if acetone is used as a sensitiser. The products are a mixture of primary, secondary and tertiary phosphines whose composition depends on the original ratio of phosphine to unsaturated compound. The reaction parallels the addition of hydrogen sulphide to unsaturated compounds, and the initiation step is:

$$PH_3 \xrightarrow{\ h\nu\ } \cdot PH_2 + H\cdot$$

Aliphatic polyhalo compounds, most notably CCl_4 and $CBrCl_3$, will undergo photochemically induced addition to alkenes. In the case of $CBrCl_3$ visible light is sufficient, but CCl_4 requires ultraviolet light. The generally accepted mechanism is:

$$CBrCl_3 \xrightarrow{\ h\nu\ } Br\cdot + \cdot CCl_3$$
$$RCH{=}CH_2 + \cdot CCl_3 \longrightarrow R\overset{\cdot}{C}HCH_2CCl_3$$
$$R\overset{\cdot}{C}HCH_2CCl_3 + CBrCl_3 \longrightarrow RCHBrCH_2CCl_3 + \cdot CCl_3$$

A photoaddition of this type has been used in the synthesis of an analogue **(12)** of the insecticide chrysanthemic acid

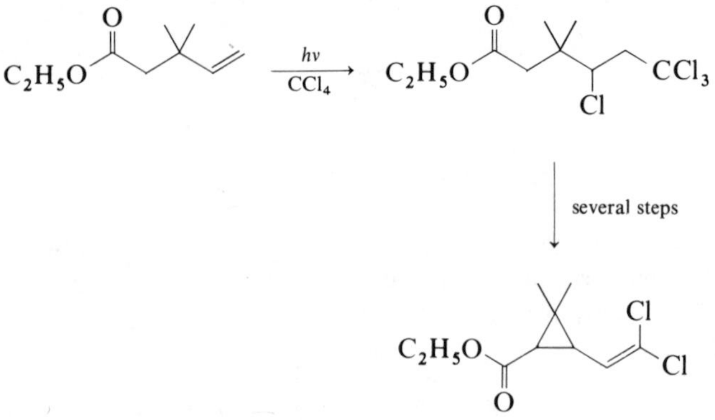

12

Alkynes are also reactive in this transformation, for example:

$$CH_3(CH_2)_5C{\equiv}CH \xrightarrow[CBrCl_3]{hv} CH_3(CH_2)_5CBr{=}CHCCl_3$$

However, as well as 1 : 1 addition products, both phenylethyne and oct-2-yne give products resulting from reaction of one molecule of the halo compound with two of the respective alkyne.

5·9 Photochemistry in fine chemical manufacture

by *Howard Carless (Birkbeck College, London)*

Photochemistry has developed very rapidly in the past 25 years as a laboratory method of synthesising organic compounds, but this growth has not been matched by a corresponding growth in its applications to commercial fine chemical manufacture. In fact, there are few examples of photochemical processes performed on a production scale. Nevertheless, the advances that have occurred in the design of photoreactors and in lamp technology over the past two decades make it likely that there will be further important photochemical syntheses in the fine chemical fields of pharmaceuticals, perfumery and flavourings.

In this chapter, we are concerned only with applications that are appropriate to *fine* chemicals; that is, those chemicals that are produced on a scale intermediate between that of the laboratory (where batch-scale methods involving grams of material are involved) and that of large-scale industrial processes (which use flow systems and may yield thousands of tonnes of material per annum). Photochemistry is especially suited to fine chemical manufacture, because such products are often chemicals with a high cost per tonne, and the use of light energy may contribute only a small fraction of the total cost. In addition, batch processes are often used in fine chemical production, and batch photochemical processes are relatively simple to introduce because they can be based on related laboratory-scale experiments; the cost of development is much less than that required for the continuous processes used in the manufacture of high tonnage chemicals. The main advantage of photochemical reactions applied to synthesis lies in the highly specific reactions brought about by light, giving transformations that would often be impossible to achieve by other (thermal) means. A photochemical reaction may be economic, even if it occurs in low *quantum* yield, if the *chemical* yield of the desired product is high.

A typical batch photoreactor consists of a stirred pot, into which is installed a light source. Either a low-pressure mercury arc (emitting mainly at 253.7 nm) or a medium-pressure mercury arc, available with powers up to 100 kW and emitting over a wide range of wavelengths, is a popular choice of ultraviolet lamp. The lamp surroundings are cooled by water, or by a filter solution to allow control of the wavelengths of the light passing into the pot. Conventional analytical techniques, such as gas–liquid chromatography or ultraviolet spectroscopy, may need to be used to monitor the progress of the

FIGURE 1   A large-scale photoreactor. (source: BASF)

photochemical reaction. An illustration of a large-scale photoreactor is given in Figure 1.

One criticism often levelled at potential photochemical processes is the high electrical costs required for the production of the light energy. However, these claims are sometimes without foundation, as the following calculation of the cost of a photochemical reaction shows.

The energy (E) of a photon of frequency v is given by

$$E = hv = hc/\lambda \tag{1}$$

where h is Planck's constant $(6.626 \times 10^{-34}\,\text{J s})$, c is the velocity of light $(2.998 \times 10^8\,\text{m s}^{-1})$ and λ is the wavelength of the radiation in metres.

The energy (E') per einstein $(6.022 \times 10^{23}$ photons) is therefore given by equation (2), where N_A is Avogadro's number:

$$E' = N_A hc/\lambda \qquad \text{in J mol}^{-1} \qquad (2)$$

Since 1 watt is 1 joule per second, the energy (E'') in kilowatt hours per einstein is shown in equation (3), taking into account that there are 3.6×10^3 seconds in 1 hour, and 10^3 watts in 1 kW.

$$E'' = \frac{N_A hc}{(3.6 \times 10^6)\lambda} \qquad (3)$$

In a perfectly efficient photochemical process $(\phi = 1)$, this energy would suffice to convert 1 mole of reactant into products. However, when the reaction becomes less efficient, then M, the number of moles of product formed per kilowatt hour of power consumed, is given by

$$M = \frac{(3.6 \times 10^6)\lambda \, \phi \, L \, f}{N_A hc} \qquad (4)$$

where ϕ is the quantum yield of the photoreaction, L is the fractional efficiency of the lamp, and f is the fraction of emitted light which is absorbed by the irradiated solution. Substitution of the numerical values for N_A, h and c in this equation gives equation (5), in which λ is the wavelength, in nanometres, of the absorbed light.

$$M = 0.03 \, \lambda \, \phi \, L \, f \qquad (5)$$

For an efficient photochemical process, such as the photoreduction of benzophenone in propan-2-ol:

$$2(C_6H_5)_2CO \xrightarrow[\text{(CH}_3)_2\text{CHOH}]{h\nu} (C_6H_5)_2 \overset{\overset{\displaystyle OH}{|}}{C} \mathbf{—} \overset{\overset{\displaystyle OH}{|}}{C}(C_6H_5)_2 \qquad (6)$$

the quantum yield is unity. Assuming total light absorption $(f = 1)$ from a low-pressure mercury arc lamp operating as the irradiation source with an efficiency of 20% (i.e. $L = 0.2$), and ignoring the weak absorption of light at 253.7 nm by the benzpinacol product, then $M \simeq 1.5$. The cost of electricity (at 1981 prices!) is therefore less than 8p per kilogram of product. To this must be added the cost of lamp replacement: making the reasonable assumption that a lamp has a lifetime of 5000 hours, this adds no more than 2p per kilogram to the cost of the product. Thus, the cost of electrical energy need not be the dominant feature of the economics of a photochemical reaction, and fine chemical processes can remain economically viable even when the fraction of absorbed light (f) or the quantum yield (ϕ) falls well below unity.

The only unifying feature of the following examples of photochemical reactions in the production of fine chemicals is that all the processes are economical, in competition with existing or possible non-photochemical routes.

1 Production of vitamin D

The photochemical production of vitamin D is the best known example of the application of photochemistry to the synthesis of fine chemicals. 'Vitamin D' is a term used for several compounds, which differ only in the nature of the long-chain alkyl or alkenyl group attached to the steroid rings. Whereas the original emphasis was on the manufacture of vitamin D_2 by ultraviolet irradiation of ergosterol, production of vitamin D_3 (structure **3**, Scheme 1) is nowadays of more interest. This latter compound, unlike vitamin D_2, is active in poultry, and most vitamin D_3 finds use as an additive in animal nutrition. The starting material for irradiation, cholesta-5,7-dien-3-ol (**1**) is obtained from cholesterol. When compound **1** is exposed to ultraviolet light, electrocyclic ring opening occurs to give the triene (**2**) (pre-vitamin D_3). Subsequent thermal reaction (50–80 °C) yields, via a 1,7-hydrogen shift,

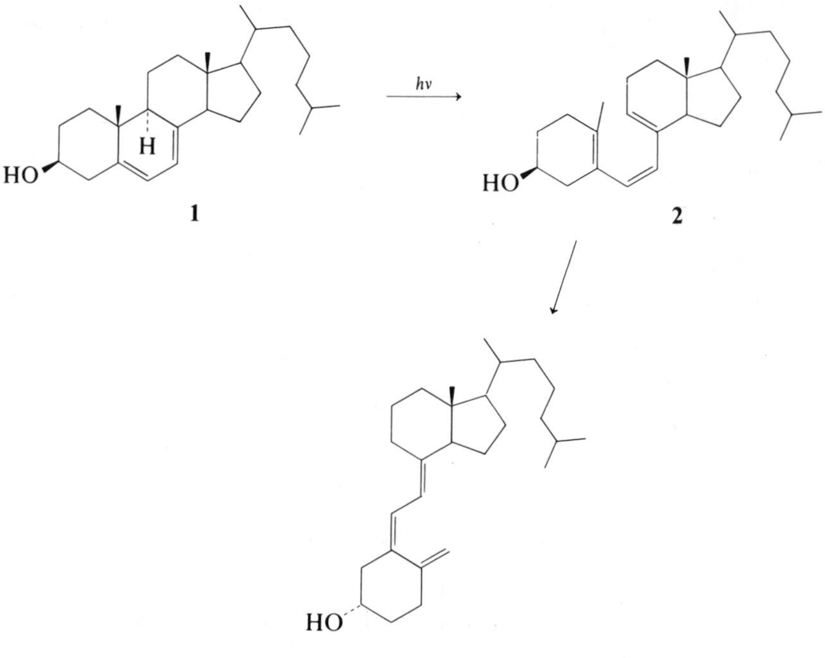

3   vitamin D_3

SCHEME 1

vitamin D_3. The absorption spectra of the diene (1) and triene (2) overlap; this means that only about 5% of the total emission spectrum of the mercury lamp can be exploited in the conversion of 1 into 2, and that reaction can be carried only to 30–50% conversion before the pre-vitamin D_3 (2) must be isolated. Nevertheless, the process is entirely viable; using a 40 kW lamp, about 30 kWh of energy are consumed per mole of vitamin D_3 produced.

2 Photoisomerisation of vitamin A

The photochemical *cis–trans* isomerisation of alkenes or polyenes is a well-established synthetic method used in the laboratory for changing the geometry about carbon–carbon double bonds. The Wittig process for the synthesis of vitamin A acetate (Scheme 2), performed on an industrial scale

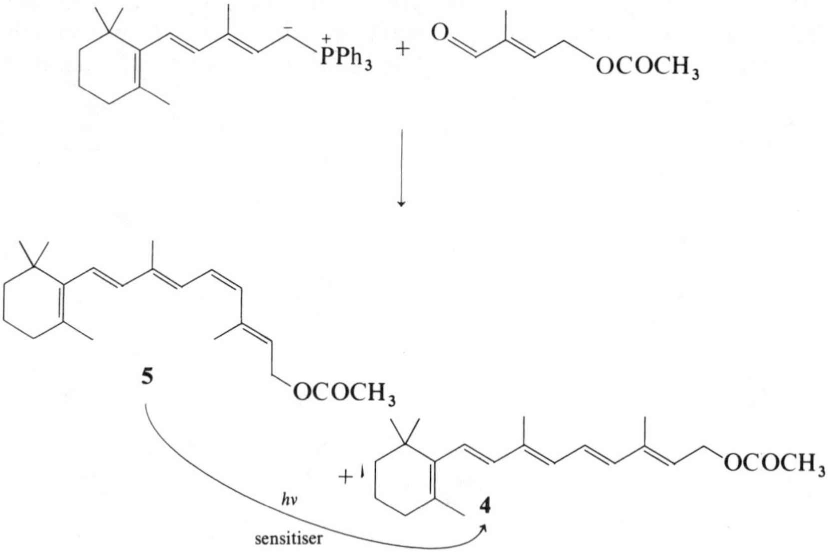

SCHEME 2

by the BASF company in West Germany, gives a mixture of the all-*trans* (4) and 11-*cis* (5) stereoisomers. Only the all-*trans* form is suitable for use in nutritional or pharmaceutical preparations. A mild photochemical method has therefore been developed for converting the 11-*cis* isomer into the all-*trans* form, in which the stereoisomeric mixture is irradiated with visible light in the presence of a sensitiser, such as chlorophyll.

3 Photochemical bromination

Bromination in the allylic position of suitably substituted alkenes is usually performed using N-bromosuccinimide (NBS) or N-bromoamides in an inert solvent. The reaction mechanism involves a radical chain reaction with hydrogen abstraction by bromine atoms occurring from allylic C—H positions. A variety of methods is used for the generation of the required radicals (such as heating in the presence of radical initiators) but among the best is the photochemical generation of radicals. Such photochemical reactions are often relatively free of by-products and give the highest yields.

An application of this method to fine chemical manufacture comes from the pharmaceutical field, involving synthetic cephalosporin antibiotics. The 3-bromomethylcephalosporin sulphoxides (compound **7**, Scheme 3) are

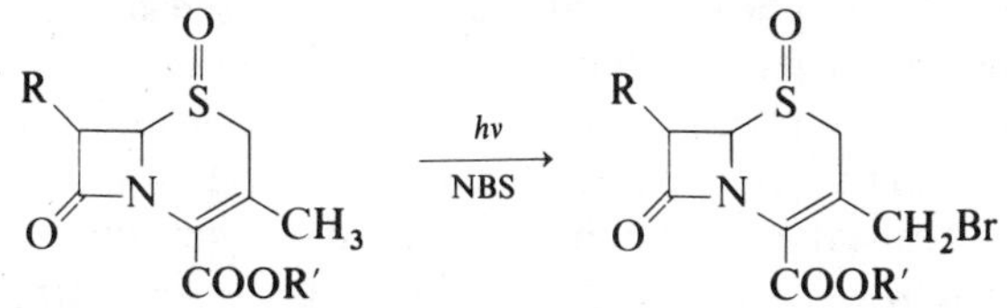

SCHEME 3

important intermediates in the preparation of various cephalosporin analogues. They are best prepared by allylic bromination of the corresponding 3-methyl derivatives (**6**) using NBS in an inert solvent such as chloroform or 1,2-dichloroethane, and irradiating with ultraviolet light. For example, the cephalosporin sulphoxide (**6**; $R = C_6H_5CH_2CONH-$ and $R' = CCl_3CH_2-$), on irradiation by a medium-pressure mercury arc in 1,2-dichloroethane at $-20\,°C$ in the presence of NBS, gives 55% isolated yield of the bromomethyl derivative (**7**).

4 Nitrite photolysis

The irradiation of organic nitrites is a well-investigated photochemical reaction, which can introduce functionality into an otherwise unreactive carbon–hydrogen bond. The reaction, outlined in Scheme 4, was pioneered by Sir Derek Barton, who was awarded the Nobel Prize for Chemistry in 1969, for the development of conformational theory. It was used for the preparation of aldosterone 21-acetate (**9**) by irradiation of the 11β-nitrite ester of corticosterone 21-acetate (**8**) and subsequent hydrolysis of the oxime with nitrous acid (Scheme 6). Aldosterone is the steroidal hormone that is responsible for the regulation of the sodium ion balance in the body, and for the correct

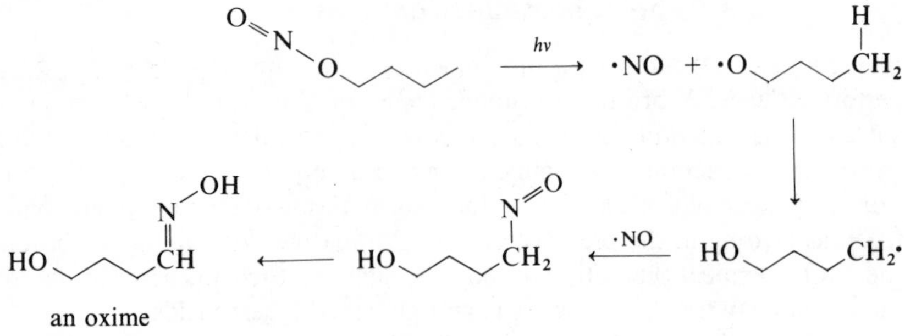

SCHEME 4

functioning of the kidneys. A similar photochemical reaction now allows the preparation of tritium-labelled aldosterone (**13**), used in the medical diagnosis of abnormalities in the functioning of the adrenal glands. Thus, the 11-nitrite ester of the pregnane derivative (**10**) (Scheme 5) is photolysed to give the oxime (**11**), in which the C-18 methyl group has been functionalised. Subsequent chemical conversions give 1,2-didehydroaldosterone acetate (**12**), which can be catalytically reduced in the presence of tritium and then hydrolysed to give the labelled aldosterone (**13**).

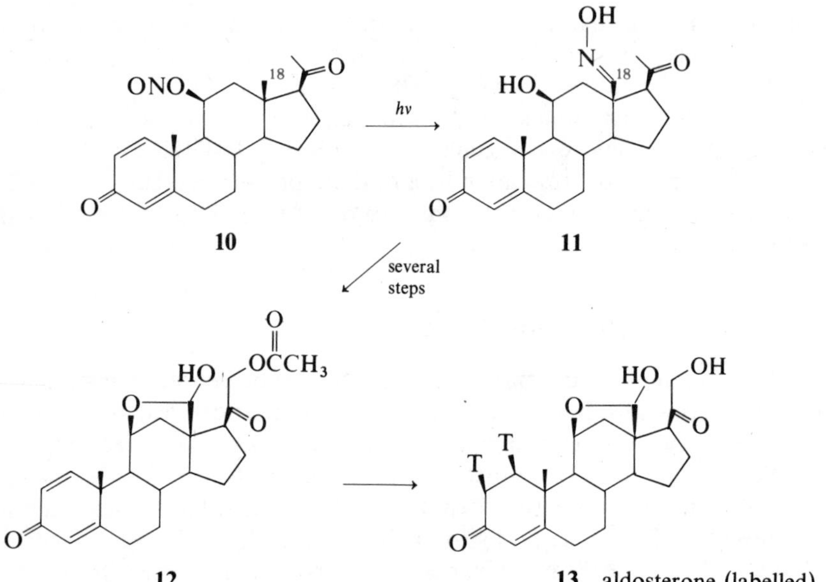

SCHEME 5

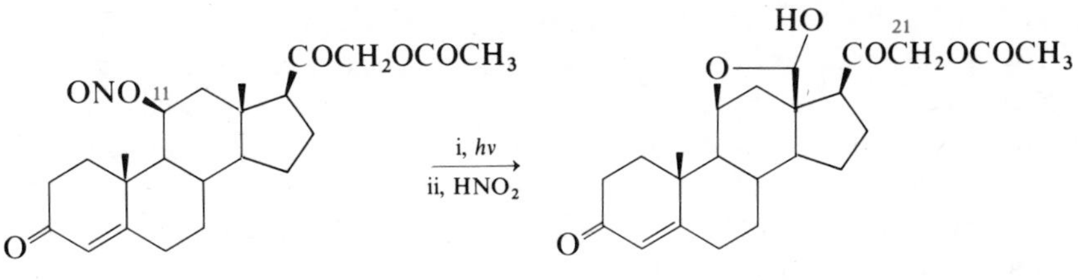

SCHEME 6

5 Photo-oxidation

Photo-oxidation methods employ oxygen and light as a source of energy, and are thus among the most promising of organic photochemical reactions for use on a larger scale. Photo-oxidation of alkenes is generally performed using visible light, with a dye as sensitiser in the presence of oxygen. The use of visible (rather than ultraviolet) light makes photo-oxidation especially attractive as a cheap but specific method for the oxidation of fine chemicals. Moreover, the starting materials and products are usually transparent (and thus inert) to the wavelengths of visible light used. Typical dye sensitisers used include chlorophyll, methylene blue and Rose Bengal. Under the reaction conditions, singlet excited oxygen is the reactive species generated:

$$^{3}\text{dye} + {}^{3}\text{O}_2 \xrightarrow{h\nu} {}^{1}\text{dye(ground state)} + {}^{1}\text{O}_2 \qquad (7)$$

Singlet oxygen reacts with conjugated dienes in a cycloaddition reaction, as shown in Scheme 7, to yield organic peroxides, such as (**15a**) derived from cyclohexa-1,3-diene. The active constituent of the natural oil of chenopodium is a peroxide, viz. ascaridole (**15b**). This natural oil has found use in

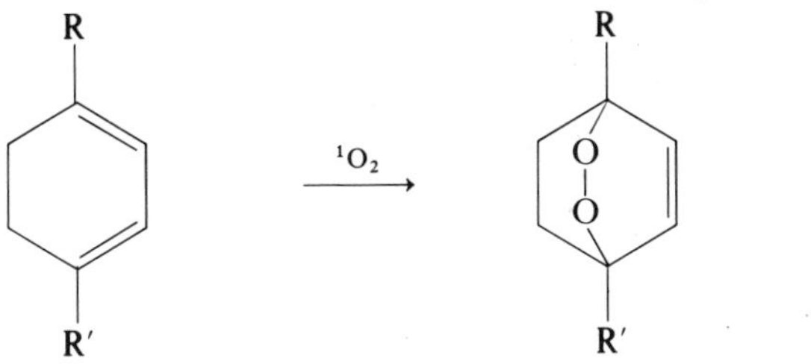

14a
14b

15a R = R' = H
15b R = CH$_3$, R' = CH(CH$_3$)$_2$

SCHEME 7

medicine and veterinary science as an anthelmintic, a compound that destroys parasitic worms (helminths) in the host. The peroxide concentration of chenopodium oil varies, and to give a more effective preparation, a convenient synthesis of ascaridole was developed in the 1950s. This route involved the photo-oxidation of α-terpinene (14b), which was itself derived from natural oils extracted from plants such as marjoram. The preparation has now fallen into disuse, not because of technological difficulties, but rather because of the recognised toxic effects of ascaridole.

Another promising application of photo-oxidation is in the synthesis of fragrances, utilising the reaction of singlet oxygen with alkenes to yield allylic hydroperoxides (Scheme 8). Hydroperoxides are easily reduced to allylic alcohols. Rose oxide (18) is currently being prepared on a scale of tonnes per annum by companies in West Germany (Dragoco) and Switzerland (Firmenich), using the route shown in Scheme 9. Photo-oxidation of citronellol (readily available by reduction of oil of lemon-grass) (16) with Rose Bengal as sensitiser gives a mixture of two allylic hydroperoxides which can be reduced by sodium sulphite in methanol to the

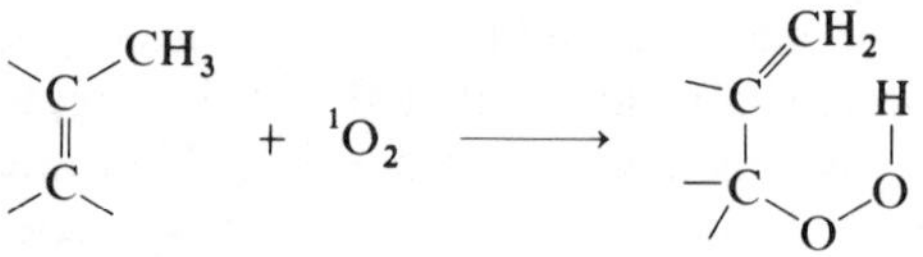

SCHEME 8

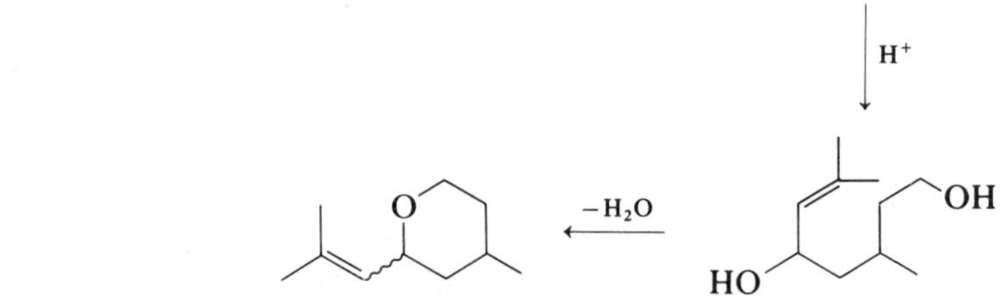

16 citronellol   35%   17 65%

18 rose oxide

SCHEME 9

respective allylic alcohols. The main product (17) undergoes allylic rearrangement in acid solution, followed by cyclisation with elimination of water. The resulting mixture of stereoisomers of rose oxide (18) is used as a perfume.

6 Production of prostaglandins

Prostaglandins are a naturally occurring group of hormones derived from unsaturated fatty acids, and they have wide ranging physiological effects. It appears that prostaglandin derivatives may become useful drugs in the treatment of bronchial disease and gastrointestinal ulcers, and as contraceptives. The synthesis of prostaglandins is at an exciting stage of development, and many pharmaceutical companies have active interests in the area. The high biological activity of prostaglandins ensures that synthetic methods that can be scaled up as far as the production of fine chemicals will suffice for the commercial preparation of prostaglandins and their analogues. There have been two recent reports of photochemical reactions that have been used in novel routes to various prostaglandins.

Ultraviolet irradiation of a cyclobutanone in solution results in ring expansion, via an oxacarbene intermediate that can be trapped by nucleophiles (Scheme 10). A similar ring enlargement on irradiation of the more complex cyclobutanone (19) in aqueous acetonitrile leads to a hydroxyaldehyde (21), drawn in Scheme 11 in its cyclic hemiacetal form (20). A subsequent Wittig reaction at the aldehyde group completes a nine-step synthesis (from cyclopentadiene) of prostaglandin-$F_{2\alpha}$ (22). The photochemical route represents an advance over a previous synthesis which used the hazardous reducing reagent di-isobutylaluminium hydride.

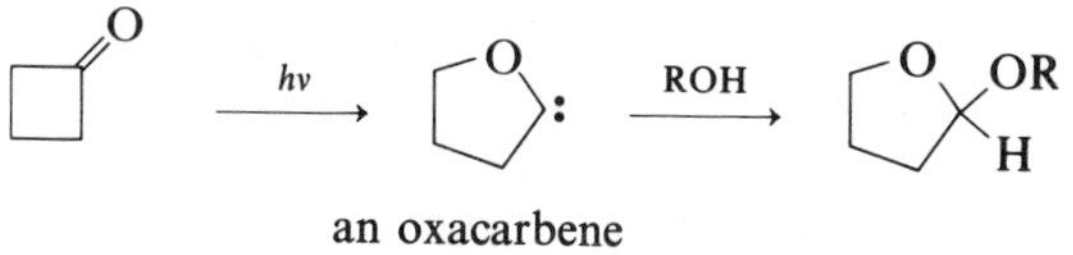

$$\text{cyclobutanone} \xrightarrow{h\nu} \text{an oxacarbene} \xrightarrow{ROH} \text{product}$$

an oxacarbene

SCHEME 10

Photolysis of cyclic ketones can produce an unsaturated aldehyde by the well-known route of α-cleavage and intramolecular hydrogen atom transfer. Application of this photochemical reaction to the norbornan-2-one derivative (23) gives the unsaturated aldehyde (24), having the precise ring stereochemistry for conversion into prostaglandin-C_2 (25) (Scheme 12).

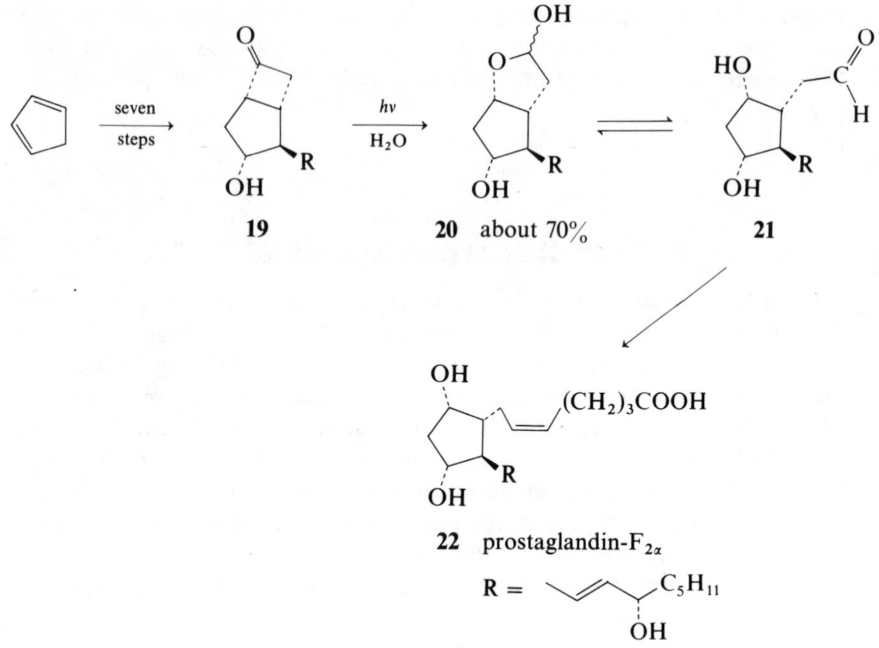

22   prostaglandin-F$_{2\alpha}$

R = (structure) C$_5$H$_{11}$, OH

SCHEME 11

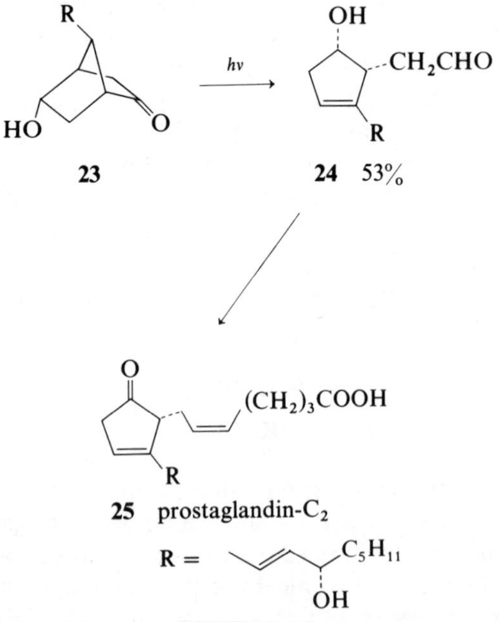

23   **24**   53%

25   prostaglandin-C$_2$

R = (structure) C$_5$H$_{11}$, OH

SCHEME 12

5·10 Photochemistry in large-scale synthesis

by Bill Horspool (University of Dundee)

Much research effort has been expended in the study of photochemical reactions over the past 25 years. Although industrialists have been slow to exploit the 'new' technique, it is rewarding for the photochemist to see the increase in involvement in this area. Clearly, before an industrialist will contemplate moving from a proven, thermal process for a specific marketable product to a photochemical reaction, he has to be convinced that the new method is superior in yield and quality of product and also that the product will still be competitive on the open market. Furthermore, the reactions must be suitable for scale-up from the laboratory process. An added benefit would be that the process could be run in a continuous manner rather than as a batch system. The obvious financial benefit of a continuous system is that it makes the best use of the usually expensive apparatus, with less unproductive down-time which is needed for the emptying of a batch reactor and its cleaning in preparation for the next run.

Most of the large-scale photochemical reactions currently in use involve radical reactions with chlorine atoms as the chain carriers. The resultant quantum yield can often be about 100, making good use of the available light. However, it is fairly easy to demonstrate by the use of the Einstein equation ($E' = N_A h c / \lambda$; see Chapter 5·9) that high quantum yields are not necessary for successful light utilisation. Incorporation of the quantum yield (ϕ), lamp efficiency (L) and the fraction (f) of light absorbed by the reactant yields the following equation:

$$M = 0.03 \, \lambda \, \phi \, L \, f \tag{1}$$

where M is the number of moles of product formed per kilowatt hour of power consumed.

This equation has been used to evaluate the cost of the photochemical conversion of benzophenone into benzpinacol:

$$2(C_6H_5)_2CO \xrightarrow[\text{(CH}_3)_2\text{CHOH}]{h\nu} (C_6H_5)_2\overset{\text{OH}}{\underset{|}{C}}\!\!-\!\!\overset{\text{OH}}{\underset{|}{C}}(C_6H_5)_2 \tag{2}$$

which can be carried out using a 253.7 nm lamp (a low-pressure mercury lamp with an efficiency of 20%, i.e. $L = 0.2$). The quantum yield for the conversion is unity ($\phi = 1$). With careful design of apparatus it is possible to arrange a situation where all the light is absorbed ($f = 1$). Under these conditions, and where the product, if it also absorbs at the exciting

275

wavelength, is removed from the reaction mixture, then product can be produced at 1.53 moles per kilowatt hour.

This would be true under ideal circumstances. In practice, several factors must be taken into account to minimise the reduction in the overall efficiency: (a) the materials used must be free from light-absorbing impurities; (b) the products and by-products must be transparent at the exciting wavelengths; (c) the light source must be efficient and have a reasonable life without exhibiting too great a drop in efficiency with use; (d) the photoreactive starting material should absorb in the long wavelength region, because long wavelength light is cheaper and high performance sources are more readily available; and (e) the quantum yield should not be much less than 1.

1 The problem of scaling-up

When an industrialist is looking for a new route to an existing compound he has several problems to take into account. (a) Has the necessary basic research been carried out in the laboratory? (b) What light sources are available? (c) Are there severe technical difficulties in the scaling-up? (d) What reactor design should be used? (e) Will the route be commercially viable?

These are some of the problems that faced Toray Industries of Japan when they adopted the photochemical route to cyclohexanone oxime (1). This compound is readily converted, by treatment with 98% sulphuric acid, into caprolactam (2), the monomer for the synthesis of the industrially important polyamide, nylon 6 (3). In 1970 the production of polyamides amounted to 41% of the world production of synthetic fibres, with nylon 6 having a 40% share of this market (in 1979 these figures were 31% and 57%, respectively). In Japan, however, the market share of nylon 6 was much higher—75% in 1970. This is probably one of the factors that directed industrial research in Japan to the development of a new route to caprolactam.

2 The laboratory experiment

One of the synthetic routes to cyclohexanone oxime (1) involves the photo-oximation of cyclohexane by a mixture of nitrosyl chloride (NOCl) and HCl. The German chemist Müller and his co-workers established the viability of the process, showing that cycloalkanes (cyclobutane to cyclododecane) could be converted into the corresponding oximes in high chemical yield (greater than 80%) with quantum yields in the range 0.6–1.5. The reaction was at first thought to be a chain process ($\phi > 1$) with chlorine atoms as the chain carrier. However, a detailed study established that Scheme 1 operates.

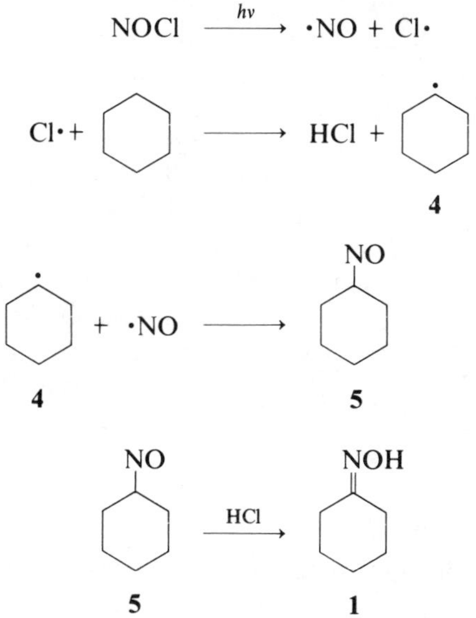

$$NOCl \xrightarrow{h\nu} \cdot NO + Cl \cdot$$

SCHEME 1

Homolysis of the weak ON—Cl bond ($159 \, kJ \, mol^{-1}$), with the formation of a molecule of NO and a chlorine atom, is brought about by irradiation with tungsten or sodium lamps (the absorption spectrum of NOCl is continuous in the ultraviolet and visible regions). The chlorine atom produced from NOCl behaves in a similar manner to that formed by photolysis of a chlorine molecule, substantiating the claim that atomic chlorine is the key intermediate. The chlorine atom abstracts hydrogen from the substrate, yielding an alkyl radical (**4**), which is trapped by molecular NO to yield a nitroso compound (**5**). Isomerisation of compound **5** yields the oxime **1**.

The reaction is not 100% efficient, and by-products of chlorine incorporation (chlorocyclohexane and dichlorocyclohexane) are the main contaminants. These are not a great inconvenience in the small-scale batch process, and become a problem only when the reaction is scaled-up and run continuously. The usual nitrosating mixture is NOCl/HCl (ratio 1:4), with the gases being mixed before entry into the reactor. Any change in this ratio leads to different products, compounds (6) and (7) being formed. Nitrosyl chloride is usually generated by the treatment with HCl of nitrosyl sulphuric acid, prepared commercially by the oxidation of ammonia.

Thus much of the basic research has been carried out, and the reactions have been shown to be efficient both chemically and photochemically. In a typical laboratory experiment the reaction in neat cyclohexane can be made to yield about 6 grams of product with the process carried out in an immersion well apparatus (see Figure 3 in Chapter 5·11). Extrapolation from this yield to the large-scale process is not possible, because the laboratory experiment typically uses thin films of solution and because NOCl does not absorb strongly. Is it therefore unlikely that all the available light is absorbed. Thus it is not possible with any certainty to determine the maximum amount of product for the lamp.

3   The large-scale continuous process

One advantage of the photo-oximation process is that the reaction is carried out in neat cyclohexane in which the product, as the oxime dihydrochloride, is insoluble. The bulk of the oxime salt settles out to the bottom of the reactor, thus facilitating its removal and making possible the continuous process. Research has shown that the separation can be enhanced if the oxime is extracted into concentrated sulphuric acid. Under these conditions the dihydrochloride salt is almost totally converted into the sulphate, with the resultant release of the HCl back into the reaction mixture.

The main problem encountered with continuous photo-oximation on a large scale is the build-up of a viscous, yellow, light-absorbing deposit on the immersion well. This acts as a light-screen, so diminishing the intensity of the irradiation and decreasing the overall efficiency. Careful study of the reaction has established that this deposit arises in part from secondary photolysis of the chlorocyclohexane by-products and of the oxime, and several methods have been described to minimise its formation. These include (a) the addition of the residues from a previous reaction to restrict the chlorinated material to 0.8–3.0%; (b) the use of $NO/NO_2/HCl$ as the nitrosating mixture; (c) careful choice of light source; and (d) the use of concentrated sulphuric acid to wash the immersion well.

This last method has the advantage that the addition of sulphuric acid down the immersion well affords a solution of the oxime in sulphuric acid. This solution can be used directly for the transformation of the oxime into caprolactam without the need for additional acid.

3.1 Choice of light source

The decomposition of chlorocyclohexane and of oxime deposited on the immersion well is brought about by short wavelength radiation (245–400 nm). Hence, NOCl is best irradiated in the 400–600 nm range. Thus for the scale-up of the reaction it would be most useful to have a lamp that produced light only in this wavelength range. Medium-pressure mercury lamps (Figure 1a) have the correct output, but have the disadvantage of generating light also in the 245–400 nm region. Attempts to eliminate these unwanted wavelengths by varying the pressure of mercury or by using xenon–mercury lamps proved useless. The problem was ultimately solved by using high-pressure mercury lamps doped with thallium iodide (Figure 1b).

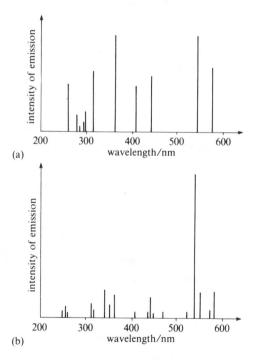

FIGURE 1   (a) The line spectrum of the medium-pressure mercury lamp. (b) The line spectrum of the high-pressure mercury lamp doped with thallium iodide. (sources: Horspool, 1976, and Fischer, 1974)

These lamps have enhanced emission at 535 nm, with diminution of all the other mercury lines. The residual light in the 245–366 nm region can be removed by adding sodium nitrite to the lamp cooling water.

The lamp used by Toray Industries is a 60 kW lamp, about 2 m long and 6 cm in diameter, enclosed in a water cooling jacket. The high temperature (600–800 °C) at which the lamps operate poses a serious fire risk. This can be minimised by operation in an atmosphere of nitrogen, and by fitting elaborate safety switches. The lifetime of the lamps is long and they can be operated for a year without serious loss of output (90% after 5 000 hours and 70% after 10 000 hours), providing the lamps are not switched off and on too often. The output from each lamp is of the order of 13.1 kW at 535 nm (this is equivalent to 210 moles of light quanta per hour). If the quantum yield of the reaction is 0.8 then the yield of product is about 24 kilograms per hour (about 200 tonnes per annum) for each lamp.

3.2 Reactor design

With the lamp design established, the final arrangement of the reactor could be undertaken. It is necessary to know the number of lamps needed for the projected output of the plant, as well as the optimum spacing of lamps in the photochemical reactor. The first point is readily dealt with because each lamp produces about 200 tonnes per annum. Thus for a plant producing 130 000 tonnes (the output of the Toray plant in 1980) 650 lamps are required. The optimum spacing of the lamps in a multiple-lamp reactor can be calculated from equation (3) (which relates to the lamp in Figure 2), in which it is assumed that the light is emitted radially and that light scattering is insignificant:

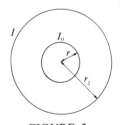

FIGURE 2

$$\log_{10} \frac{I_0}{I} = \log_{10} \frac{r_1}{r} + 2.3 \epsilon\, m (r_1 - r) \qquad (3)$$

where r is the radius of the immersion well (10 cm), $r_1 - r$ is the thickness of layer irradiated that absorbs 99% of the light (i.e. $I = 10^{-2} I_0$), ϵ is the absorption coefficient of NOCl at 535 nm ($\sim 0.90\, \mathrm{l\,mol^{-1}\,cm^{-1}}$), and m is the concentration of NOCl ($0.037\, \mathrm{mol\,l^{-1}}$).

Equation (3) reduces to

$$\log_{10} r_1 + 0.0766\, r_1 = 3.766 \qquad (4)$$

from which $r_1 = 30$ cm can be computed. Consequently most of the light is absorbed in a layer of 20 cm, which means that the lamps should not be more than 40 cm apart if dark spots are to be avoided.

A cross-section of the Toray reactor is shown in Figure 3. Because the reagents are corrosive, the outer vessel is made of titanium with only the lamp immersion wells made of glass. The heating effect of the lamps is minimised by passing cooling water around the lamps and the outer walls of the reactor, and by the use of immersion cooling coils in the reactants. This permits control of the reaction temperature within the optimum range of 5–30 °C. Further precautions are taken by pre-cooling, to 5 °C, both the reaction gases and the sulphuric acid used for cleaning the immersion wells. Mixing of the reactants is achieved by the NOCl/HCl gas, which enters towards the bottom of the reactor. Stirring the reaction mixture also helps to minimise the formation of the deposit on the immersion wells.

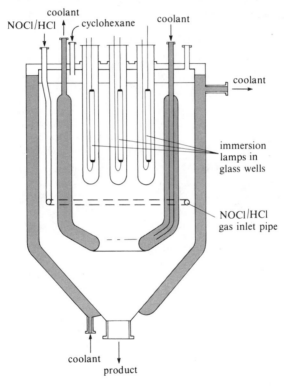

FIGURE 3   Cross-section of a Toray reactor. (source: Fischer, 1978)

The sulphuric acid solution of cyclohexanone oxime obtained from the base of the reactor is heated to convert the oxime into caprolactam. Neutralisation of this mixture with ammonia yields ammonium sulphate as a co-product. Ammonium sulphate is used to make agricultural fertilisers and is therefore a saleable commodity, which can be used to offset the cost of caprolactam. A further by-product, chlorocyclohexane, can be obtained by distillation of recovered cyclohexane.

4 Comparison of the Toray process with other routes to caprolactam

Caprolactam is obtained from the Toray process in 81.7% overall yield (Scheme 2). The reaction requires 0.91 tonne of cyclohexane, 0.82 tonne of ammonia and 1.72 tonnes of sulphuric acid to make 1 tonne of product at a cost of £99.97 per tonne (1970 prices). The plant represents a capital outlay of £8.8 million (1969 prices) and is capable of producing upwards of 135 000 tonnes per annum.

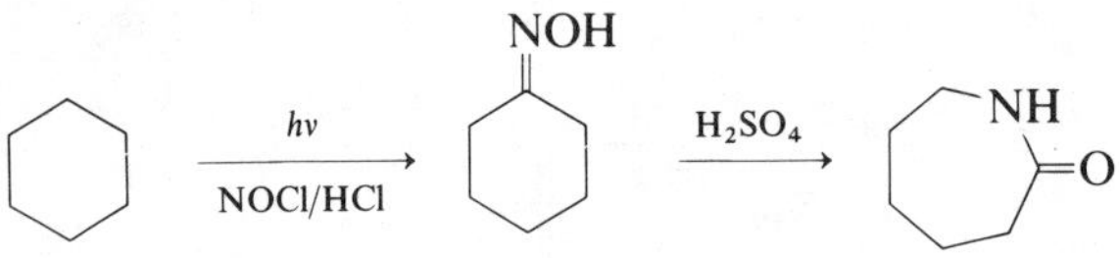

0.91 tonne

1 tonne costs £99.97
co-product $(NH_4)_2SO_4$ 1.8 tonnes
by-product $C_6H_{11}Cl$ 0.064 tonne

SCHEME 2   The Toray process

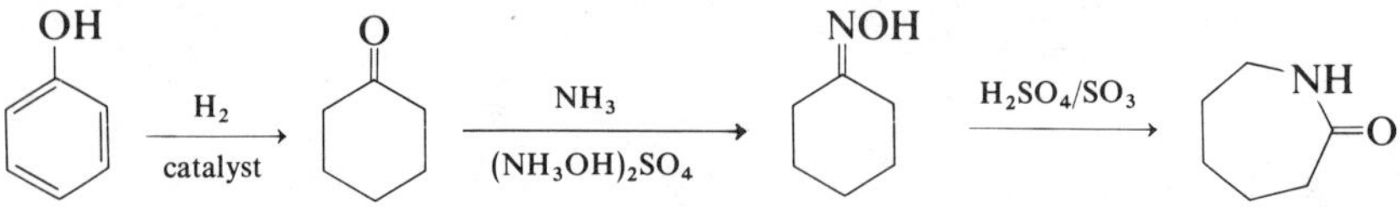

0.89 tonne

1 tonne costs £115.21
co-product $(NH_4)_2SO_4$ 4.6 tonnes

SCHEME 3   The Allied Chemical Corporation process

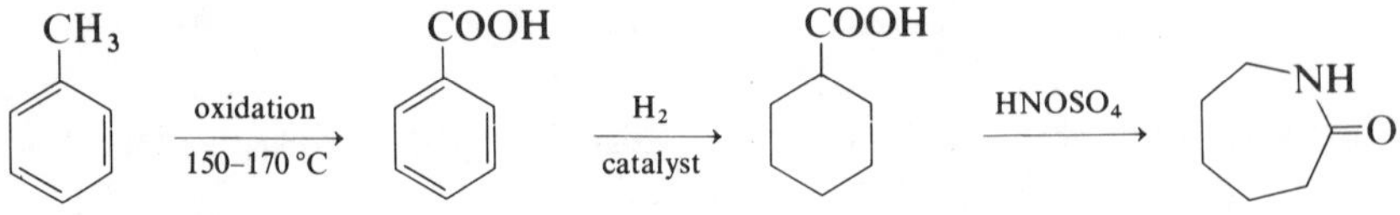

1.06 tonnes

1 tonne costs £88.90
co-product $(NH_4)_2SO_4$ 4.1 tonnes

SCHEME 4   The SNIA Viscosa process

The commercial viability of the Toray process can be compared with two of its non-photochemical competitors (Scheme 3 and Scheme 4). The costs of these processes are given again in 1970 prices. (This is the only year for which comparative costs are available for all three processes.)

5 Other large-scale photochemical processes

5.1 Dodecanolactam and nylon 12 production

The usefulness of photo-oximation is not restricted to the synthesis of caprolactam and nylon 6. Toray Industries of Japan also use the technique to manufacture cyclododecanone oxime (**8**), the precursor to nylon 12 (**9**; Scheme 5). This polymer is useful in the fabrication of plastic components for automobile construction, and for coating metals. Aquitanie of France also manufacture this oxime, using $(NO)_2SO_4/H_2SO_4$ as the nitrosating agent and light from a 60 kW mercury lamp (it was the intention to construct a plant capable of producing 8 000 tonnes per annum).

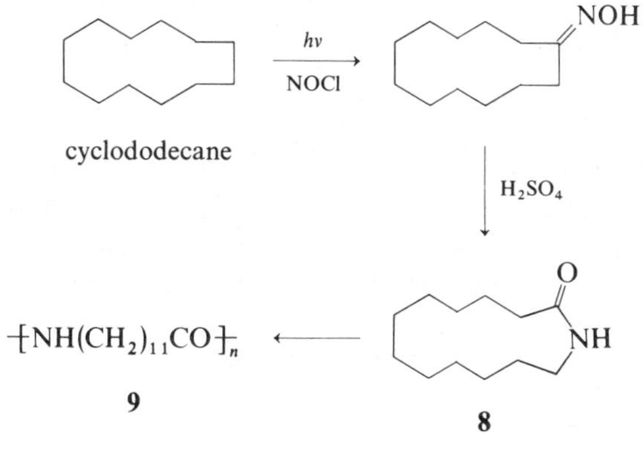

SCHEME 5

5.2 Photochlorination

The processes discussed so far do not involve photochemical reactions of high quantum yield and are not radical chain processes. There are, however, several large-scale synthetic processes using chlorine atoms as the chain carrier which have been developed commercially. As before, the over-riding considerations are that the reaction is competitive with alternative thermal routes and that there must be a market for the product.

The photochemical chlorination of benzene is used to make γ-hexachlorocyclohexane (**10**), an important insecticide ('Gammexane', 'Lindane').

The advantage of this route over thermal chlorination is that at the relatively low temperatures at which the photochemical radical chlorination takes place, formation of the required γ-isomer is favoured. This leads to a good yield of uncontaminated product.

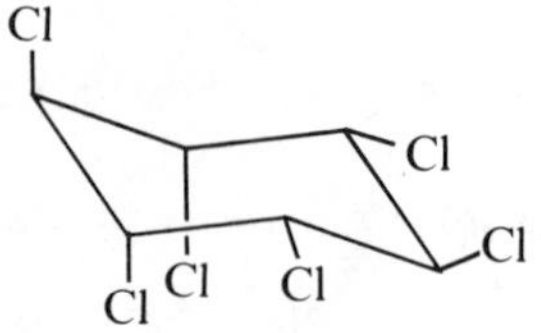

10

Photochlorination is also used to convert toluene into the chlorinated derivatives shown in Scheme 6, which are important intermediates in synthetic organic chemistry. Phillips Petroleum also used the technique in the early 1970s to synthesise monochloroalkanes from alkanes $(C_{11}$ to $C_{14})$ on a scale of 2000 tonnes per annum, but they have since discontinued this process.

$$C_6H_5CH_3 \xrightarrow[Cl_2]{hv} C_6H_5CH_2Cl \xrightarrow[Cl_2]{hv} C_6H_5CHCl_2 \xrightarrow[Cl_2]{hv} C_6H_5CCl_3$$

SCHEME 6

Photolysis of chlorine in the presence of sulphur dioxide is also used in the conversion of alkanes into sulphonyl chlorides. These reagents are important in the tanning and paper industries, and can be converted into many other useful chemicals. In the absence of chlorine, irradiation of a mixture of alkanes, sulphur dioxide and oxygen yields sulphonic acids, a process which is used by Hoechst to produce 50000 tonnes of acid per annum.

5·11 Photochemistry in laboratory synthesis

by John Mellor (University of Southampton)

The diversity of man-made compounds and the complexity of natural products ensure that organic chemistry is a subject dominated by *target synthesis* and the development of synthetic methods. Much scientific research in pharmaceutical and agricultural chemistry and in other disciplines depends on the success of synthetic programmes. Yet statistically, the role of photochemistry in organic synthesis has been slight. Could it be that the photochemical method is an esoteric tool of little consequence to the synthetic organic chemist? We shall consider the role of photochemistry in syntheses designed to afford a target molecule in amounts between a milligram and a few hundred grams. Such a target might be a thermodynamically unstable compound occupying a key position in the theory of organic chemistry, for which spectra might be recorded on a milligram; or a possible insect pheromone, for which a bioassay might again be achieved on a milligram; or a drug analogue, required in considerable amount for pharmacological testing.

Ideally, the synthetic chemist would like to use reactors of the simplest design and reactions of the maximum selectivity and yield. In large-scale synthesis directed towards products of commercial interest, economic factors and hence considerations such as quantum yield are of paramount importance. In laboratory synthesis economic factors are normally of secondary importance. The decision to use a multi-stage sequence involving a key photochemical stage, or a different synthetic strategy consisting entirely of thermal stages, may be based on many factors such as availability of photochemical equipment, yields and selectivity of reactions, ease of product isolation, and product purity. A choice between a photochemical reaction stage and a thermal stage is rarely necessary, because typically the photochemical stage will have no thermal equivalent. Here we consider only those factors relating to such a key photochemical stage. Reactors are considered first and then the reactions themselves.

1 Reactors

Reactors may be designed as flow systems (normally only used for amounts exceeding 1 mole) or as static reactors. In either case the radiation source is either external or internal (an immersion lamp). We will consider here only static reactors, and emphasise the possible light sources, cell materials and typical requirements of the photolysis conditions.

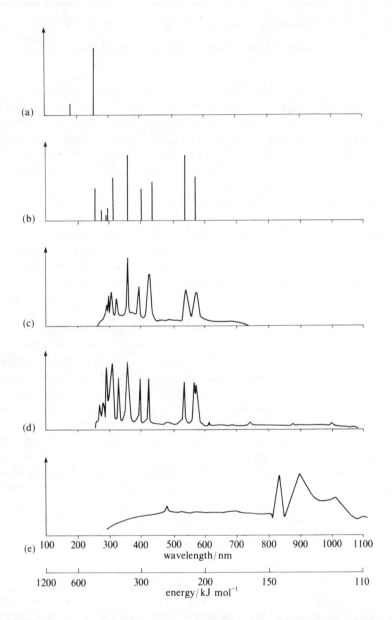

FIGURE 1 The relative spectral energy distribution of various light sources. (a) Low-pressure mercury lamp; (b) medium-pressure mercury lamp; (c) high-pressure mercury lamp; (d) high-pressure xenon–mercury lamp; (e) high-pressure xenon lamp. (sources: Schönberg, 1968, and Horspool, 1976)

1.1   Light sources

The earliest photochemical experiments in organic chemistry used the Sun as the external source. Some of the simplest photochemical transformations, for example benzophenone to benzpinacol with unit quantum yield, provide effective demonstrations of the use of sunlight. Because of the requirements of greater reproducibility and precise excitation wavelengths, however, the Sun is not greatly used today, although the development of solar reactors that will convert a more thermodynamically stable reactant into a less thermodynamically stable product remains an exciting possibility.

The spectra of some of the light sources used today are shown in Figure 1. Preparative photochemistry rarely requires sources more energetic (i.e. of shorter wavelength) than the low-pressure mercury lamp, because high energy sources rarely lead to the highly selective chemistry required. For molecules absorbing significantly at 254 nm, the low-pressure mercury lamp (Figure 1a) is normally used. If a low-pressure lamp is given a fluorescent coating, the secondary emission can be tuned to give effective output in the region 300–350 nm. Then the spectral distribution is fairly broad. Medium-pressure mercury lamps operating at pressures up to 50 atmospheres give emission lines through the spectral region 200–600 nm (Figure 1b). At higher pressures there is nearly continuous emission in the visible region (Figure 1c). An alternative to this high-pressure mercury lamp is a tungsten–halogen lamp, which emits only in the visible and near-ultraviolet regions.

1.2   Cell materials and design

A typical reactor that involves external irradiation by lamps held close to the sample compartment is shown in Figure 2, and the alternative arrangement of an immersion reactor in Figure 3. Reactors are normally made of quartz (transparent throughout the wavelength region 200–700 nm) or Pyrex (transparent above about 310 nm). If excitation in only the visible region is required, a soft glass cell may be used to filter out ultraviolet light. Additional filters may be used occasionally, but the normal lamp sources have a sufficiently narrow emission for most preparative work. Sometimes the problem arises of a close match of some spectral characteristics of the reactant and the product. In such cases the reaction may be slowed down by absorption by the product, or by a photochemical equilibrium between the reactant and the product, or worse by secondary decomposition of the product. Filters may often be used to reduce these difficulties.

With low-pressure mercury lamps the power output is much lower than with medium- or high-pressure lamps. In all cases, water cooling is used with an immersion arrangement. Low-pressure mercury lamps or sources of vis-

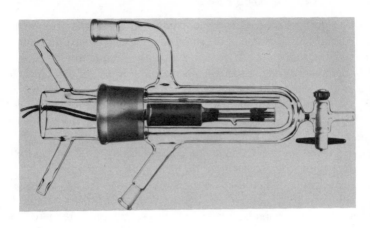

FIGURE 3   A small-scale immersion reactor. (source: Applied Photophysics Ltd., London)

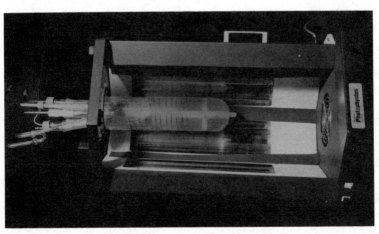

FIGURE 2   A photoreactor with an external bank of six lamps (two of which have been removed in this picture). Each lamp is an inverted U-shaped low-pressure mercury arc.

ible light are most frequently used for external irradiation, when a fan normally provides adequate cooling.

1.3   Choice of reaction conditions

If the experiment does not involve a photosensitiser, a non-absorbing solvent is chosen and typically a 1–2% solution is irradiated. The most commonly used solvents are saturated hydrocarbons (pentane, hexane, or cyclohexane), ethers (diethyl ether or dioxane), and the more polar solvents ethyl acetate, alcohols (t-butanol, ethanol or methanol), acetonitrile, and acetic acid. For sensitised experiments acetone is a common solvent, and a 2% solution of reactant is normal. For bimolecular photochemical processes, for example in addition reactions, one substrate is normally present in high concentration, frequently as solvent or cosolvent.

Oxygen can be an efficient quencher of excited states and may react chemically with photoproducts. Removal of oxygen by purging the system with nitrogen is often sufficient to avoid these complications.

A serious complication can be the formation of polymeric tars at the surface of the reactor close to the point of irradiation. This leads both to reduced yields and to the necessity for increased irradiation times. Usually an attempt is made to reduce the severity of the problem by changing the lamp position or changing the concentration of the reactant. In severe cases, mechanical scrubbers can be used.

The consequences of some of the above constraints can be more fully appreciated by the details† of the preparative conversion of butadiene into cyclobutene:

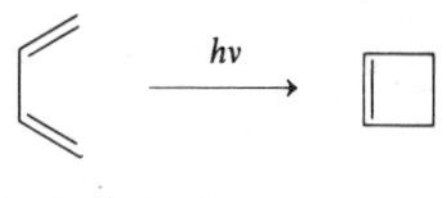

Irradiation of buta-1,3-diene (78 g) in cyclohexane (500 g) for 1200 h gives, after distillation, cyclobutene (24–30 g; yield 31–38%). In order to achieve this yield it is recommended that a clean cell should be used after 150, 400 and 800 h, to avoid the increased opacity of the vessel due to formation of polymers.

2   Reactions

Most of the important photochemical reactions used in synthesis are summarised in Tables 1–7. The examples in these Tables have been chosen to give an insight into the use of photochemical methods in the synthesis of a

---

† These details are taken from R. Srinivasan (Editor) (1971) *Organic Photochemical Syntheses*, Volume 1, Wiley-Interscience.

wide range of organic structures. In the synthesis of natural products the justification for the work may have been confirmation of structure. Over the past twenty years, the increasing use of X-ray methods to assign unambiguous structures to complex natural products has decreased the value of such synthetic work. More recently, the emphasis has been on the synthesis of complex structures for biological testing. Other examples are given in the Tables to show the generality of certain photoprocesses. Wherever possible, yields represent yields of product isolated.

2.1 Concerted photoassociative processes: [2 + 2]cycloaddition

In the first two volumes of the publication *Organic Photochemical Syntheses*, over one-third of the examples concern formation of four-membered rings by [2 + 2]cycloaddition reactions. The importance of the method stems not only from the satisfactory yields but from the paucity of thermal methods for producing four-membered rings. Table 1 lists typical examples of intermolecular cycloaddition, and examples of intramolecular cycloaddition are shown in Table 2. Although the examples in Tables 1 and 2 concern relatively simple reactants, the diversity of unusual skeletons produced underlines the importance of the method. More complex examples are gathered in Table 3, where we see that the synthetic target is normally obtained via a key photochemically produced intermediate by elaboration using conventional thermal stages (in some cases many stages). These reaction sequences illustrate the skill of the organic chemist in identifying the possible skeletal relationships between the target molecule and conceivable reactants. Today this type of analysis can be assisted by computer techniques. In such complex synthetic schemes an arsenal of possible synthetic methods is available to the organic chemist. Photochemical methods will always represent a minor contribution to the total, but the skilful chemist will not only be aware of those synthetic steps best achieved by photochemical methods, but also appreciate the limits imposed on a phototransformation by the other functional groups present in a complex molecule.

Other concerted photoassociative processes of some importance are the formation of four-membered rings by the electrocyclic ring-closure of conjugated dienes, and the related formation of cyclohexadienes by the closure of conjugated trienes. Examples illustrating these and other related processes are gathered in Table 4.

Table 1 Examples of intermolecular [2 + 2]cycloaddition

Type	Reactant(s)	Product and yield
dimerisation of a simple alkene		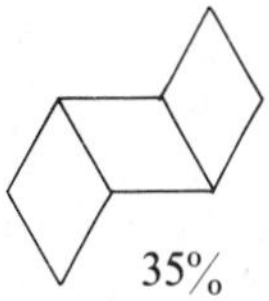 35%
dimerisation of a substituted alkene	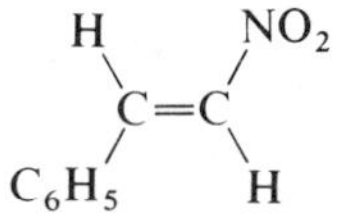	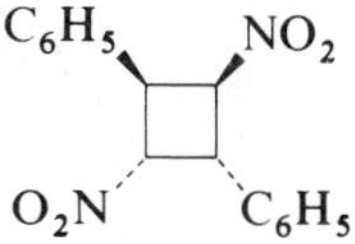 54%
dimerisation of a substituted alkene	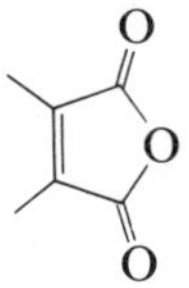	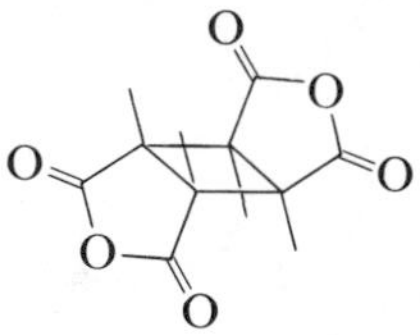 95%
addition of two different alkenes	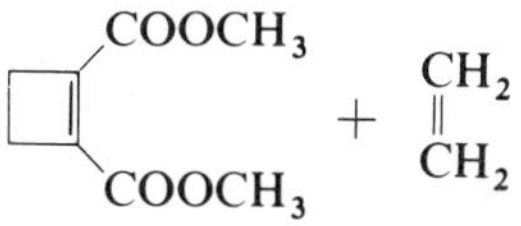	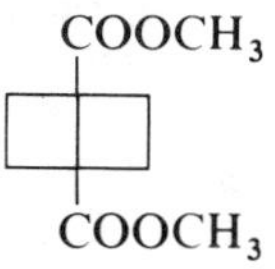 91%
addition of two different alkenes	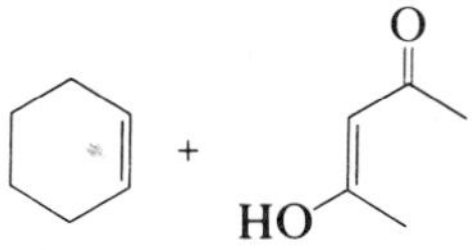	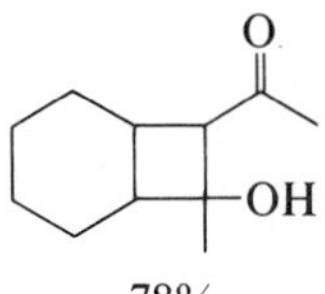 78%

(*continued*)

Table 1 (*continued*)

Type	Reactant(s)	Product and yield
addition to give a heterocyclic compound	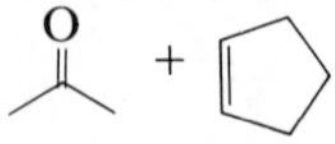	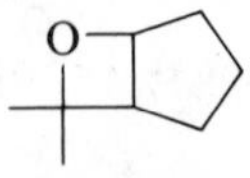 28%
addition to give a heterocyclic compound	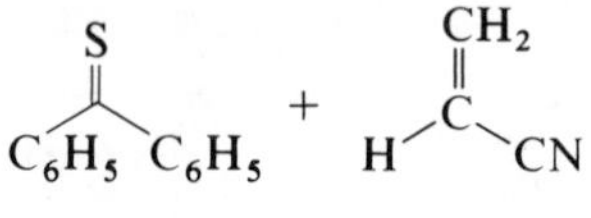	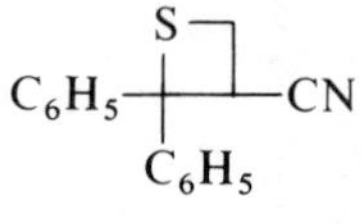 93%
addition to give a heterocyclic compound	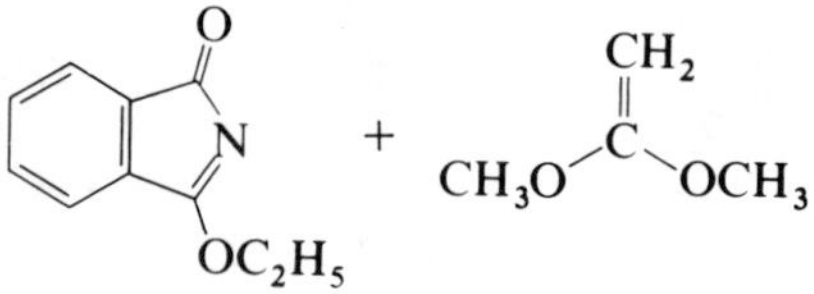	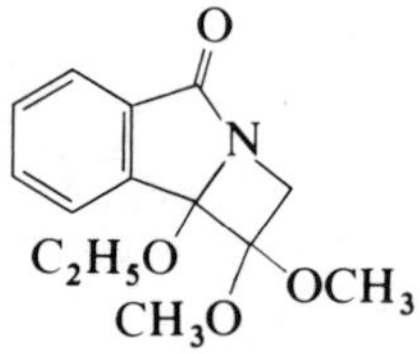 50%
addition to give a heterocyclic compound	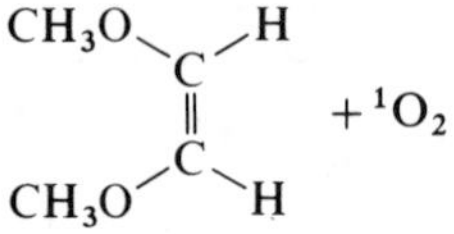	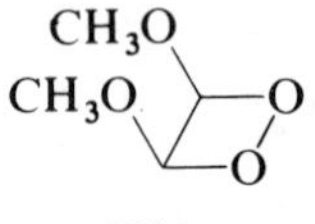 50%
addition to an alkyne	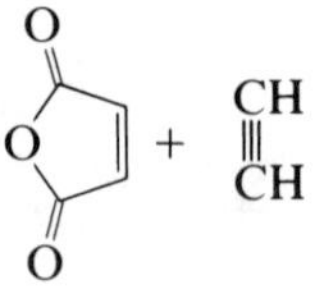	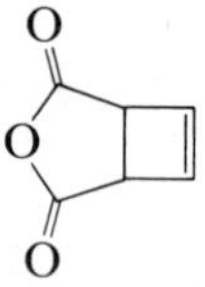 70%
addition to allene	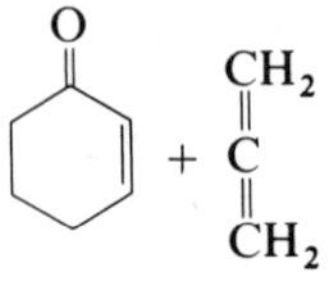	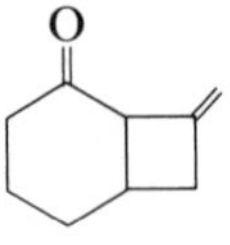 55%

Table 2   Examples of intramolecular [2 + 2]cycloaddition

Reactant	Product	Yield (%)
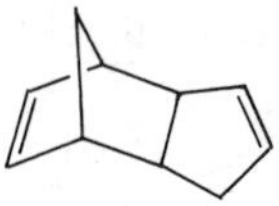	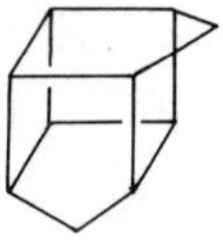	62
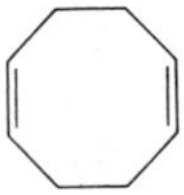	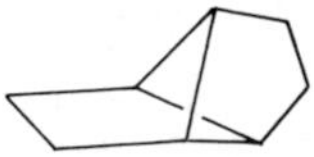	28
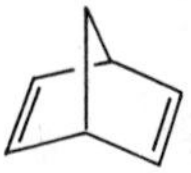	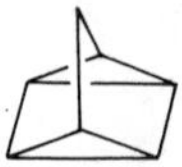	57
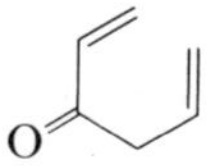	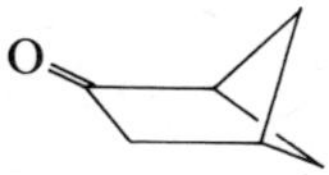	30
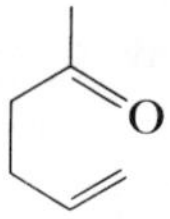	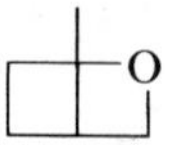	44

Table 3 Examples of the synthesis of complex molecules via [2 + 2]cycloaddition

Reactants	Photochemically produced inter- mediate	Target molecule and reason for synthesis
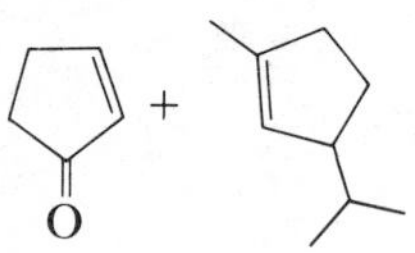	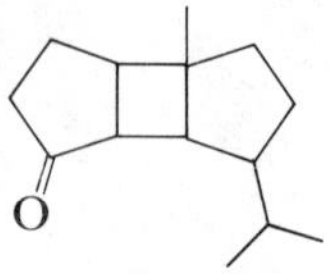	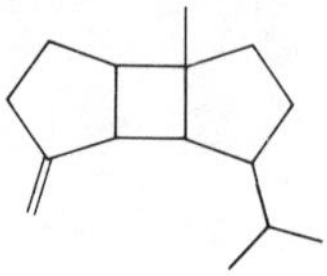 β-bourbonene (for confirmation of structure)
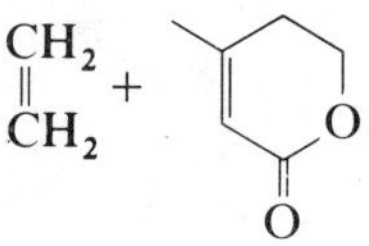	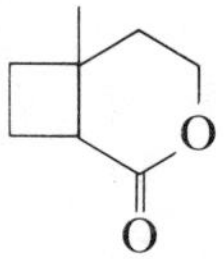	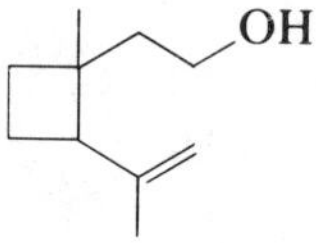 grandisol (for bioassays)
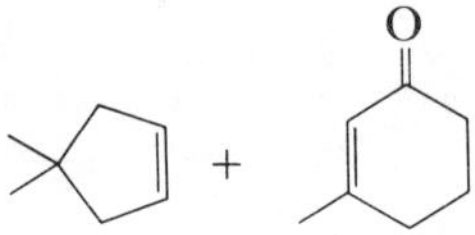	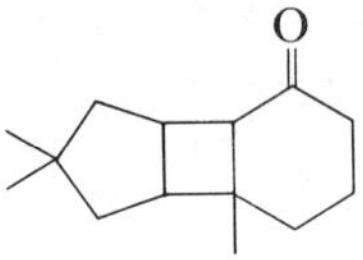	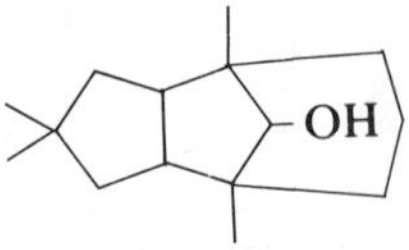 α-caryophyllene alcohol (for confirmation of structure)
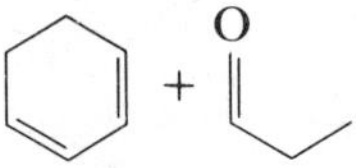	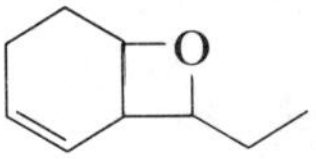	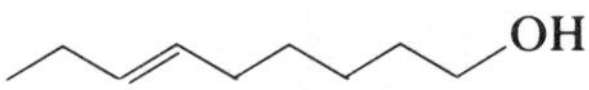 trans-non-6-en-1-ol (for bioassays)
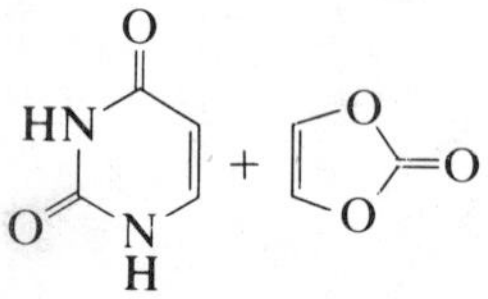	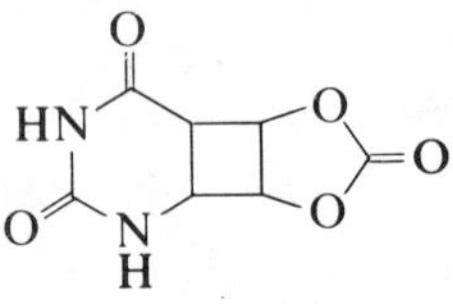	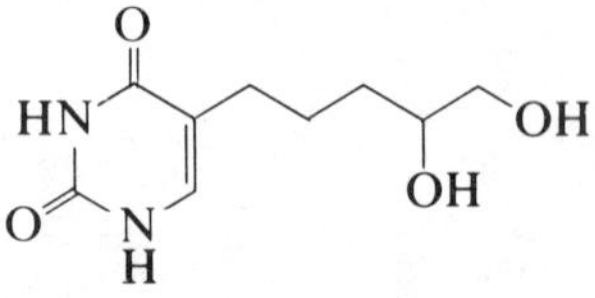 5-(4,5-dihydroxypentyl)uracil (for comparison with natural product from DNA)

Table 4 Examples of concerted electrocyclic processes

Reactant	Product	Target molecule
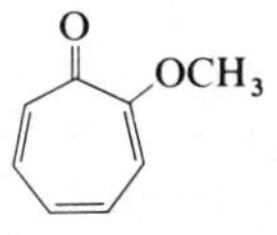	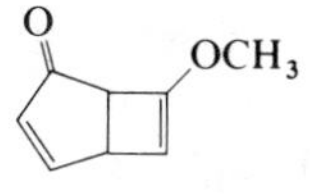	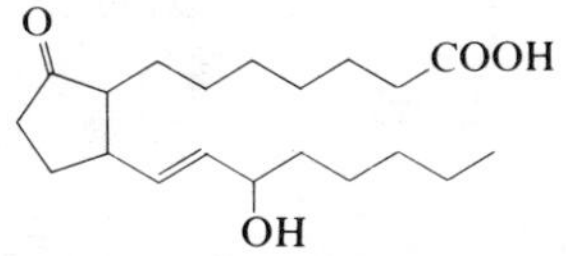 a prostaglandin
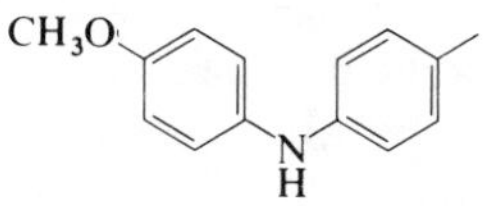		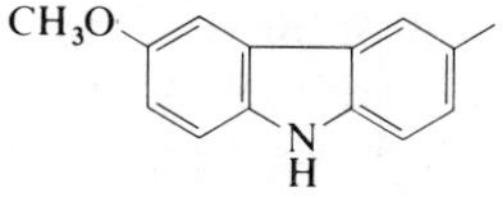 glycozoline (an alkaloid)
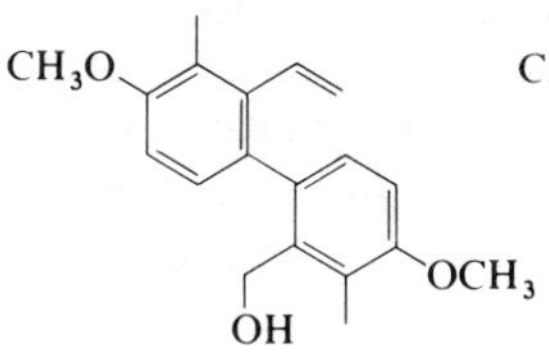	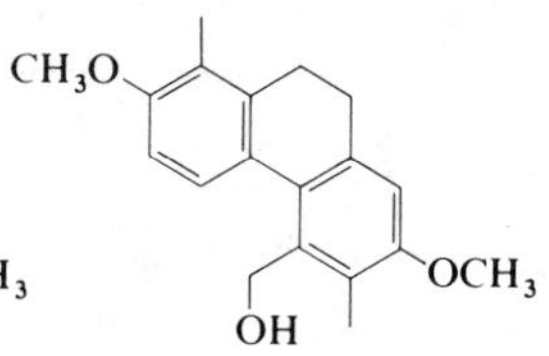	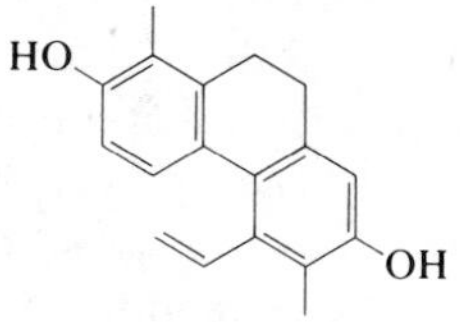 juncusol (a cytotoxic compound)
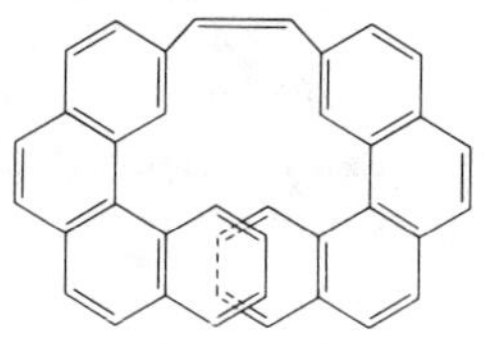		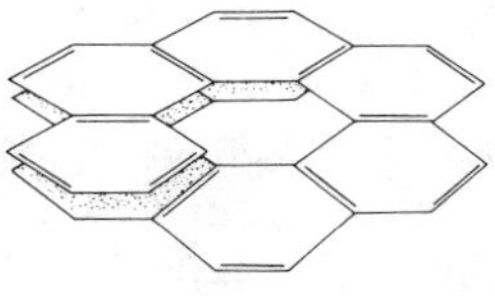 [9]helicene (of theoretical interest)

2.2 Photodissociative processes

When a reactant absorbs light at a given wavelength and the product does not, photochemical methods offer a possible route to highly strained and therefore thermodynamically unstable compounds. In particular, the use of low temperatures restricts thermal processes, and the synthesis of a wide range of strained compounds of interest to theoretical chemists has been achieved. Examples of the loss of chromophoric groups are given in Table 5, and these may be contrasted with the examples of electrocyclic ring-opening in Table 7 (p. 300). In the latter Table, the products have more extensive conjugation than the reactants and hence larger absorption coefficients. However, by careful selection of the wavelength of irradiation, it is frequently possible to excite the reactant selectively, and by limiting overall conversion, to obtain satisfactory routes to annulenes of low stability, for example. Electrocyclic ring-opening is a feature of some photochromic systems.

Formation of a strained compound by bond formation from a biradical intermediate represents one of the very many possible fates of the radical intermediates produced by a photodissociative homolysis. Photodissociation to radicals can be followed, for example, by addition of one of the radicals to an unsaturated system, by hydrogen atom abstraction, or by radical recombination with rearrangement. Some examples are listed in Table 6.

The diversity and complexity of skeletons available by photochemical synthesis imply that there must be both a knowledge of and an ability to execute such processes in a laboratory concerned with modern synthetic methods. This applies equally to academic laboratories, to pharmaceutical firms, and to companies concerned with the production, say, of complex agricultural chemicals.

Table 5 Examples of formation of strained compounds by photodissociative processes

Reactant	Product

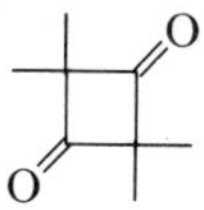

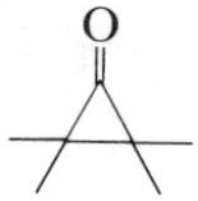

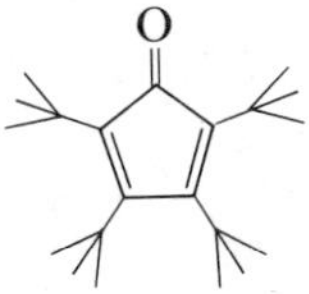

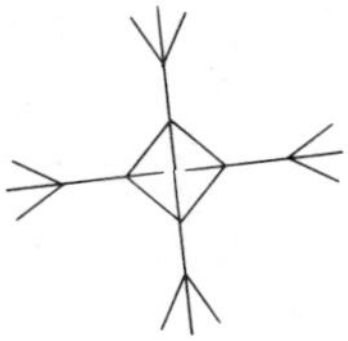

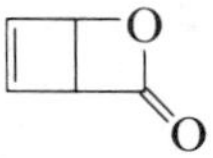

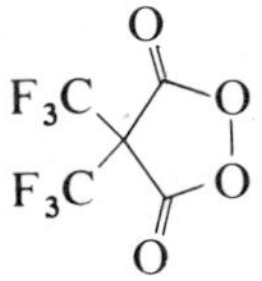

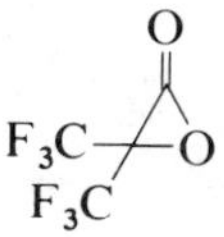

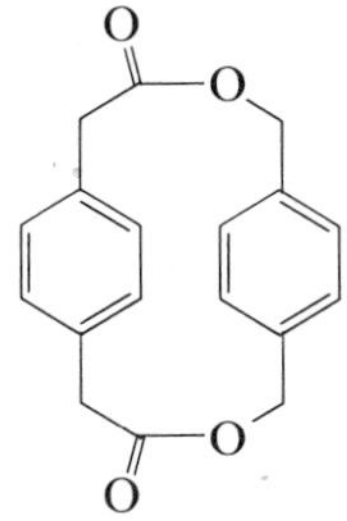

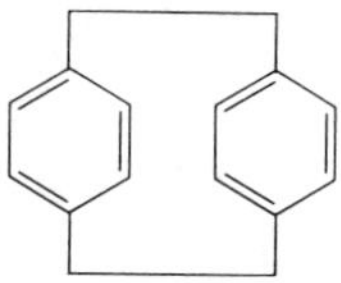

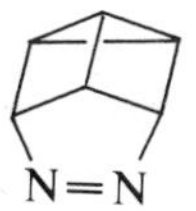

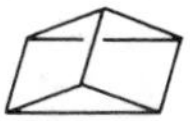

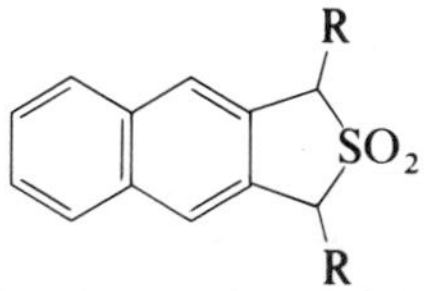

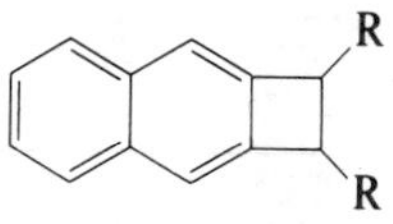

Table 6 Examples of homolysis in synthesis

Reaction type	Reactant(s)	Product	Target molecule
radical addition to an alkene	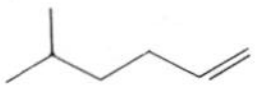 + HBr	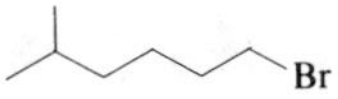 Br	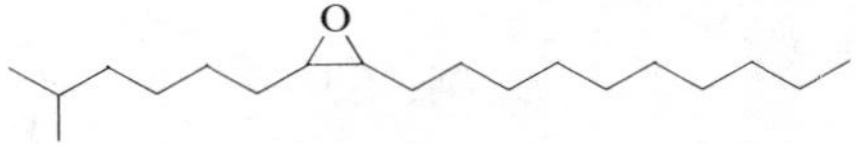 disparlure (Gipsy moth sex attractant)
Norrish type 1 (α-cleavage) followed by H transfer	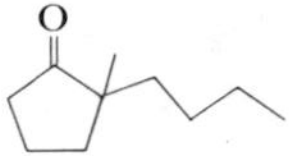	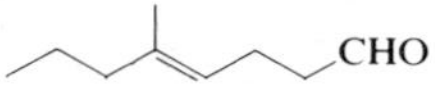 CHO	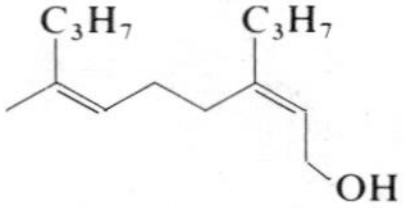 Codling moth hormone (presumed)
homolysis of an ester followed by radical recombination with rearrangement	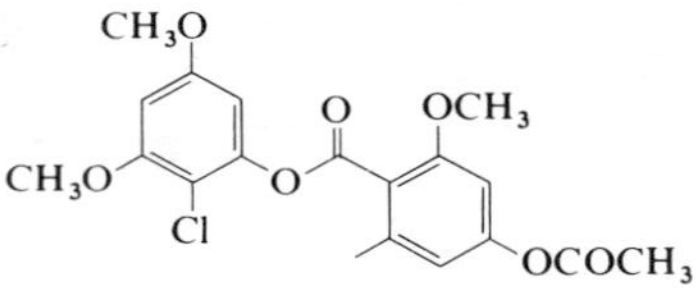	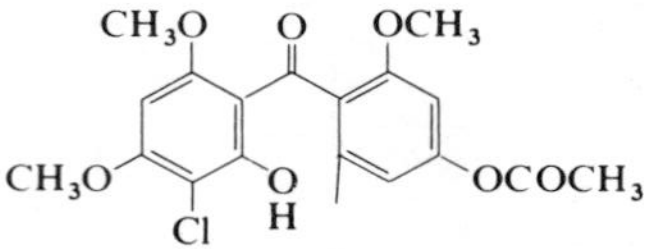	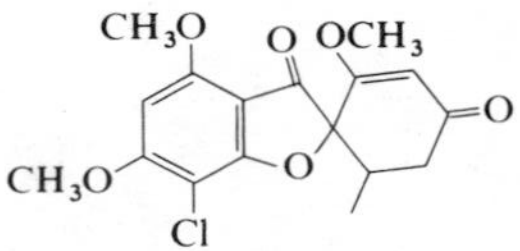 griseofulvin (an antibiotic)

298

Table 6 (*continued*)

photonucleo-
philic
substitution

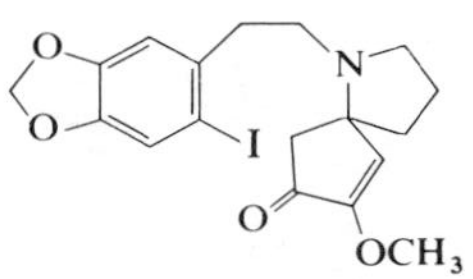

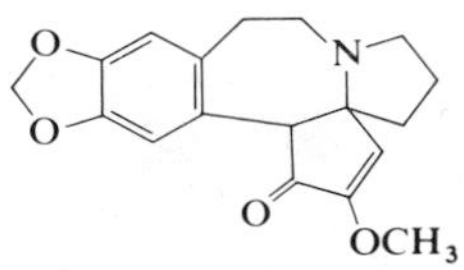

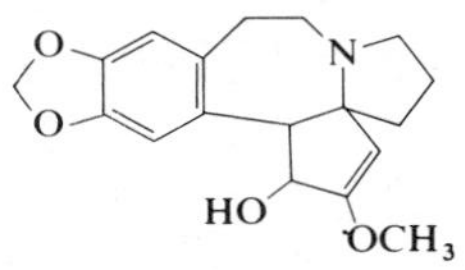

cephalotaxine (antileukaemic properties)

cyclisation

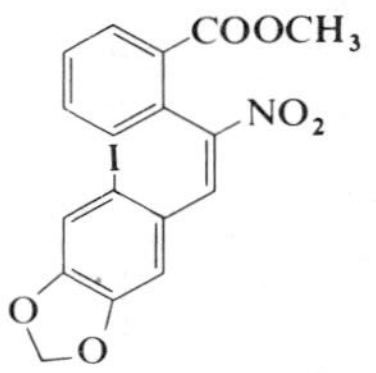

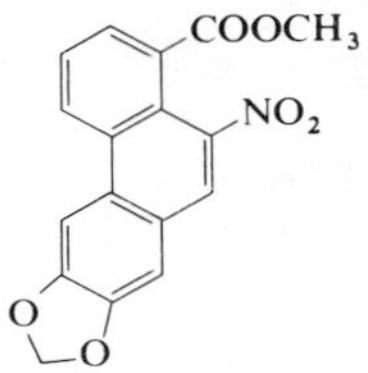

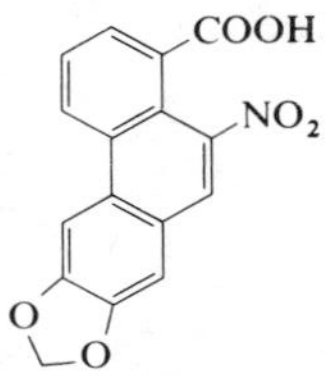

an analogue of aristolochic acid
(anti-tumour properties)

Table 7 Examples of electrocyclic ring-opening

Reactant	Product

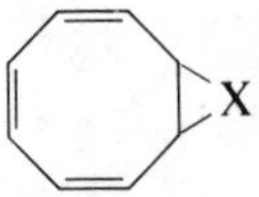

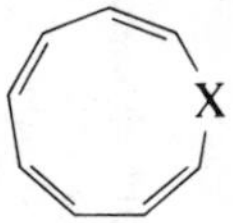

X = O, CH$_2$ or NCOOC$_2$H$_5$

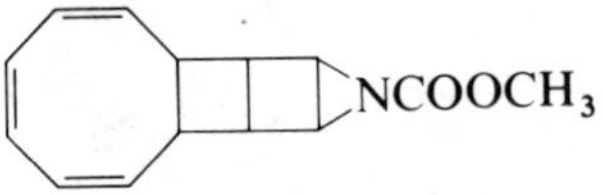

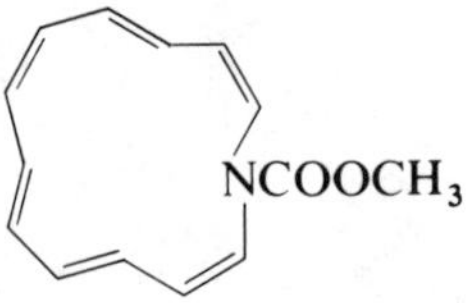

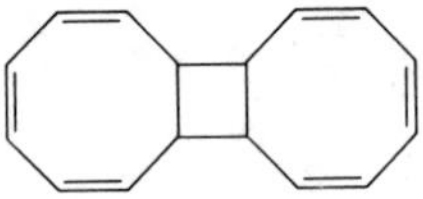

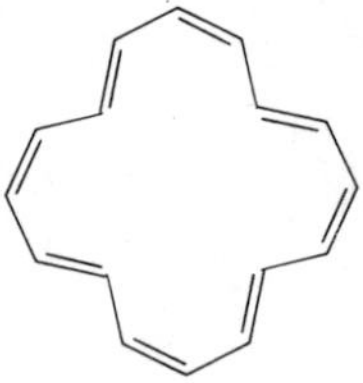

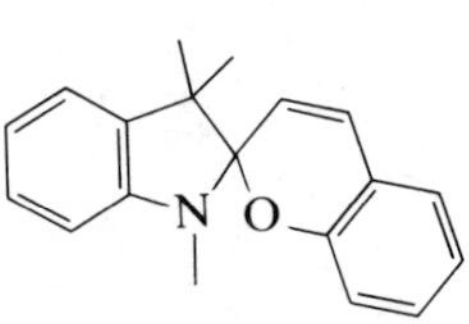

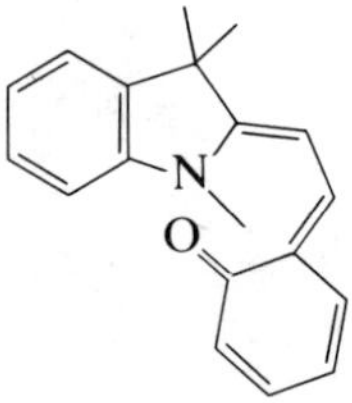

5·12 Non-conventional photoimaging

by Mike Ledger (Kodak Limited)

In principle, any photoinduced phenomenon that leads to a net change in some chemical or physical property of the light-absorbing material can be used to generate an 'image'. Here, 'image' simply means a record of the intensity pattern of the absorbed incident light. The usefulness of such a phenomenon in a practical imaging process is determined by a number of factors. Ultimately, exposed and unexposed areas in the imaging material should be clearly distinguishable. Final images are usually (though not always) for visual appreciation, so the distinction one seeks is in terms of actual visible appearance, with or without colour information. However, prior to this stage, one may be dealing with primary or 'latent' images, where exposed and unexposed areas differ not in appearance but in chemical reactivity, solubility, hardness, electrostatic charge, etc. Further treatment of the exposed material is then necessary to produce the desired result. To satisfy practical requirements, the primary image should be formed in high quantum yield, be sufficiently long-lived and, if necessary, be easily converted into a useable form in a convenient chemical or physical process.

A wide variety of phenomena have been exploited in forming images for different applications. Five broad categories of imaging systems have been identified, according to the type of process involved, namely: photographic, photochemical, thermographic, electrophotographic and photovisual. Because of their long history and diversity of application, materials based on silver halide as the light-sensitive element are described as 'conventional'. These are the true 'photographic' materials. This chapter aims to compare the photographic with the so-called 'non-conventional' imaging systems, with particular reference to photochemical systems, but excluding photopolymerisation.

1 Photographic systems

The enormous success of photography and the rapid growth of the associated industry since its discovery are due to the great sensitivity and versatility of silver halide imaging processes. The photographically active silver halides, AgX (X = chloride, bromide or mixtures of these with iodide), are water-insoluble, crystalline substances with absorptions in the ultraviolet and visible regions of the spectrum (up to about 500 nm). Photographic materials consist of microcrystals or 'grains' of AgX (typically about 100–1 000 nm in size) dispersed in a gelatin layer coated on a flat support (usually paper,

301

glass or transparent plastic film). Absorption of light by a grain generates mobile electrons within the crystal lattice (photoconductivity). In a process that is still not completely understood, photoelectrons are trapped at specific sites in the grain. These sites arise through physical imperfections or chemical impurities, and the photoelectrons eventually react with silver ions to give silver atoms. The quantum yield of silver formation at this primary stage can be close to unity. It is known that exposed grains have within them, or on their surfaces, a number of tiny clusters of silver atoms, Ag_n, where n is the number of atoms in a given cluster. In certain cases it has been shown that for a grain to be subsequently developable, it must possess at least one cluster with $n \geq 4$. Such a developable speck constitutes a 'latent image' and can be stable over extremely long periods.

For most photographic purposes, pure silver halides are insufficiently sensitive. Two forms of 'sensitisation' commonly employed are (a) chemical sensitisation, involving the introduction of certain impurity centres (silver sulphide is much used) that facilitate the formation of the latent image, and (b) spectral sensitisation, in which the response of AgX may be extended throughout the visible and into the infrared region of the spectrum by adsorption of dyes on to the crystal surface. Most of the useful sensitising dyes belong to the class of cyanine dyes, with the chromophore:

$$\diagup N {-} (CH{=}CH)_{\overline{n}} CH {=} \overset{+}{N} \diagdown$$

It is believed that in the majority of cases, spectral sensitisation involves a direct electron transfer from the excited singlet state of the dye into the conduction band. Thereafter, electron trapping and latent image formation occur in a manner similar to that operating in undyed AgX grains.

After exposure, simple black-and-white materials are chemically processed in two stages.

1   Development—with an alkaline aqueous solution of a reducing agent such as hydroquinone. A latent image catalyses the reduction to metallic silver of those grains where it occurs, other grains remaining unaffected. Since as few as four silver atoms can render a whole grain developable, an amplification factor of about 10^9 is possible at this stage.

2   Fixing—by removing the undeveloped AgX, which is still light-sensitive, from the layer with a suitable reagent, such as sodium thiosulphate, which forms a water-soluble complex with silver ions.

Developed silver particles are highly light-absorbing throughout the visible region, giving an image shading through greys to black in the areas which received the greatest exposure. The resulting image is 'negative', being darkest where the original was brightest. It is important to note that silver halide systems are inherently 'grainy', a factor which limits their resolution. If the mean grain size is decreased then the resolving power increases, but at the expense of sensitivity (see Table 2 on p. 311).

1.1 Colour photography

The photographic reproduction of colour is based on the principle that any hue can be obtained by mixing three basic colours. Modern colour photographic materials consist basically of three superimposed AgX–gelatin layers, sensitive to the blue, green and red spectral regions, respectively. All three layers have some sensitivity to blue light because of the intrinsic absorption of AgX. Blue light is therefore excluded from the lower two layers (see Plate 5) by a yellow filter layer containing a dye that is destroyed during development. Exposure to a coloured subject, followed by development, generates a different silver image in each layer, along with proportionate amounts of oxidised developer. A number of colour imaging processes have been devised, the best-known example making direct use of oxidised developer in the synthesis of image dyes.* Colour photography employs 'subtractive' colour reproduction, in which the hue of the image dye complements that of the light absorbed by the layer where it is formed. Thus, blue exposure produces yellow dye, green produces magenta, and red produces cyan, as in Plate 5.

Typically, the developer is a derivative of benzene-1,4-diamine (**1**), which, when oxidised, reacts with a 'colour coupler' to form an image dye. The overall reaction may be exemplified by:

$$+ \; 4Ag^+ \longrightarrow \qquad\qquad + \; 4Ag \; + \; 4H^+$$

1   magenta coupler   magenta dye

Couplers contain active methylene or methine groups, and are either incorporated in their respective colour layers or introduced during processing. Plate 5 depicts a colour negative system. Positive-working systems utilising

---

* Image dyes should not be confused with sensitising dyes, which are present in very small amounts and generally decompose during processing.

couplers and subtractive colour reproduction also exist (e.g. Kodachrome film).

After development, the silver image is removed with a mild oxidising agent such as ferricyanide, and the coloured image is then fixed as with black-and-white materials. Because the image dyes are formed in close association with developing silver centres, the dye image is also 'grainy'; this imposes limits on the resolving power of colour photography.

2 Photochemical systems for non-conventional imaging

Despite the success of silver halide materials, much interest has centred on non-conventional alternatives. The drive for research in this area has its origin in both economic and practical considerations; economic, because of the high price and possibly limited supply of silver, and practical, because of the inconvenience of silver halide materials for certain applications (e.g. when simple processing is required).

2.1 Diazo materials

Under this general classification come a number of imaging systems based on photolysis of a diazonium salt or related compound. As with silver halide, a single photoreaction has been exploited in a variety of ways to provide different types of image. Diazonium salts are decomposed via the excited singlet state:

$$ArN_2^+X^- \xrightarrow{h\nu} Ar^+ + N_2 + X^- \tag{1}$$

$$Ar^+ + X^- \text{ (or } H_2O) \longrightarrow ArX \text{ (or } ArOH + H^+) \tag{2}$$

Because diazonium salts absorb only weakly in the visible region, exposures are normally made with ultraviolet light. Spectral sensitisation has been demonstrated with certain dyes; photochemical redox reactions initiated by the dye produce radical intermediates, which attack and destroy the diazonium salt. Quantum yields for the decomposition range from about 0.3 to 2.0, values greater than unity arising through secondary reactions between the phenolic product (ArOH) of reaction (2) and the diazonium precursor.

Diazotype process. In this, the earliest photochemical imaging system to find commercial application, the active diazonium salt is coated directly on to a paper (or sometimes transparent) support. After exposure, a positive image of the original is developed by the reaction of undecomposed diazonium salt with a phenolic or amino coupler to give an azo dye, for example:

$$\text{ArN}_2^+\text{X}^- \quad + \quad \underset{\text{coupler}}{\bigodot\!\!\bigodot\text{—OH}} \quad \xrightarrow[\text{catalysed}]{\text{base}} \quad \underset{\text{azo dye}}{\overset{\text{Ar—N=N}}{\bigodot\!\!\bigodot\text{—OH}}} \quad + \quad \text{HX}$$

The colour of the image depends largely on the choice of coupler, which can be contained in the active layer or added to the processing solution. Note, however, that the diazotype process is strictly a monochrome system.

Vesicular processes. A diazonium salt is contained in a thermoplastic layer. Exposure decomposes the salt, with the release of molecular nitrogen (Figure 1a) which is temporarily trapped in the layer. Heat development expands these gas pockets and a reorientation of the resin occurs to form tiny bubbles (about 500–5000 nm) or 'vesicles' in the exposed areas. With a sufficiently intense light source, exposure and development can be performed simultaneously. Fixing may not be necessary, but can be accomplished by giving the film an overall exposure to decompose any remaining diazonium salt and allowing the nitrogen produced to diffuse out of the layer at room temperature. The vesicles scatter light efficiently so that in the final (negative) image, exposed areas appear opaque by transmitted light. Positive-working systems have also been devised. Vesicular images are very stable and, because of their particulate nature, can possess tonal similarities to conventional photographic images.

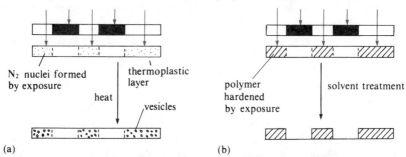

FIGURE 1 Diazo imaging. (a) Vesicular; (b) relief.

Diazo relief processes. In this application, diazonium salts are used to generate 'relief' images for printing purposes. In one process, the diazonium salt is contained in a layer of solvent-soluble polymer. The photodecomposition products of the salt harden the polymer in exposed areas, reducing its solubility. Solvent treatment then produces a negative relief image (see Figure 1b)—'negative' because it takes up and transfers printing ink in those areas that were brightest in the original.

2.2 Applications of diazo materials

Because of the 'molecular' nature of the dye image, diazotype materials possess high resolution, which makes them well-suited to the duplication of linework and script. Vesicular processes have a somewhat lower resolving power, but are still adequate for microfilm applications. Table 1 summarises some of the major uses for diazo systems.

Table 1   Applications of diazo systems

Process	Applications
diazotype	duplication of detailed linework and script (engineering drawings, microfilm, etc.); transparencies for overhead projection; proofing of colour negatives in the printing industry
vesicular	duplication of microfilm (with the capability to add to and update the unfixed material); black-and-white proofs from AgX negatives
diazo relief	production of positive and negative offset printing plates; colour proofing in the printing industry

2.3 Photochromism

Compounds that undergo reversible colour changes on exposure to light are said to exhibit photochromism. In Plate 6, chemical species A is converted by light of wavelength λ_A into species B, which has a different absorption spectrum:

$$A \underset{\text{heat or } \lambda_B}{\overset{\lambda_A}{\rightleftharpoons}} B$$

In many cases, B reverts thermally to A, but there are instances in which B is reasonably stable in the dark, the reverse reaction being induced by light only (λ_B). With thermal reversions, the rate of the back-reaction is one of the factors determining the usefulness of the system for imaging purposes. Preferably, B should be sufficiently long-lived and highly coloured that a readily observable image may be built up by exposures of moderate intensity. Both organic and inorganic photochromism are known, one of the more useful inorganic systems being based on glasses containing silver halide (e.g. photochromic spectacles). Organic photochromism may be conveniently categorised according to the type of photoreaction involved.

Cis–trans isomerisation.   The *cis-* and *trans*-isomers of many substituted alkenes and azo compounds are interconverted by light. The *trans*-isomer is usually the more stable and generally absorbs at longer wavelengths. However, the absorption spectra of *trans* and *cis* forms tend to overlap considerably, so that few of these sytems are of value for imaging purposes.

Bond homolysis. Photochemical bond rupture can lead to coloured radical products that recombine sufficiently slowly for visible photochromism to result. As early as 1899, photochromism was observed in the following system:

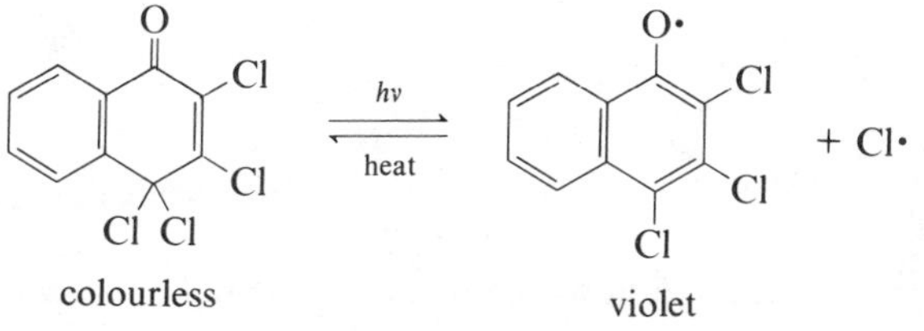

colourless   violet

Bond heterolysis. In some cases, excitation leads to the formation of ions. Photochromic spiropyrans have received much study, a large number of active derivatives being known, for example:

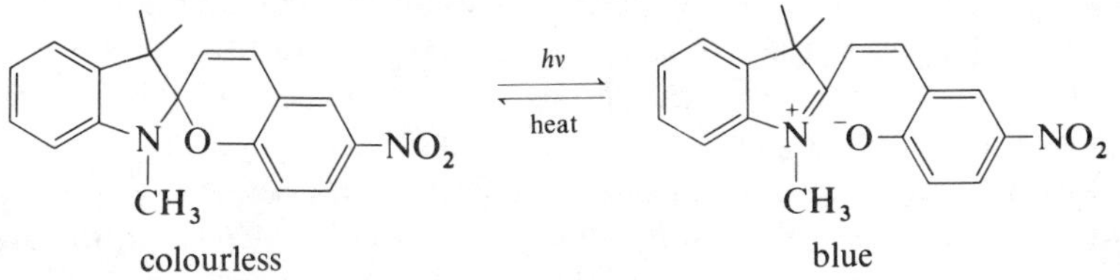

colourless   blue

Tautomerism. Photoinduced intramolecular hydrogen transfer or valence tautomerism occurs in a variety of compounds, and both have great potential in the design of photochromic systems. Hydrogen transfer is typified by the phototautomerism of the *o*-alkylbenzophenones, for example:

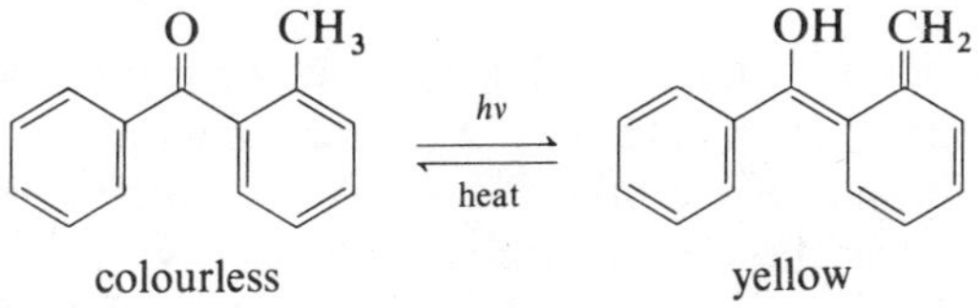

colourless   yellow

An important photoinduced valence isomerisation occurs in the compounds known as 'fulgides'. The colour-forming reaction may be illustrated by the generalised example in equation (3). B reverts to A only under the influence of light (λ_B); thermal ring-opening of B leads to an isomer of A in which R and R' are interposed. This, and other thermal side-reactions, can be minimised by the judicious choice of substituents. It is claimed that certain derivatives possess B-forms with high thermal stability which can be reconverted into A with light of wavelength λ_B, but are stable under illumination at another absorbed wavelength, λ_B' (see Plate 6). Thus, a 'write–read–erase' system of information storage is possible: in effect, an optical analogue of magnetic tape.

$$\tag{3}$$

(A) colourless   (B) coloured

2.4 Applications of photochromism

Many photochromic reactions have been shown to proceed efficiently in plastic layers, which makes them candidates for imaging processes. By their very nature photochromic images are transient, but some fixing techniques have been devised, often involving conversion of the coloured form, in one or more chemical steps, into a totally different chemical species. Fixable photochromic systems offer properties similar to those of the diazotype process; that is, they require some form of chemical or physical treatment to yield a permanent image, and possess relatively low sensitivity (quantum yields are usually less than unity) but high resolution. However, the great advantage of photochromism over other imaging processes is that an image appears immediately on exposure, without the need for further treatment. Until recently, photochromic materials had only limited application to imaging technology, but their 'no-process' advantage, together with their reversibility (i.e. re-useability), has aroused commercial interest. The following examples indicate the types of area in which photochromic imaging is used.

1   Because of their high resolution, photochromic films can record duplicates of originals at much reduced size (linear reductions of about 150 to 1 are possible without loss of information). These 'intermediate' images are useful in the preparation of microfilm because they can be inspected and corrected by additions or erasures before being committed to the final imaging material by contact printing.

2   Photochromic films are used in conjunction with computer- or operator-guided laser 'light pens' to generate rapid-access displays of diagrams, etc.

3   The no-process property of photochromism is advantageous in certain holographic applications, obviating the necessity for accurate repositioning of processed material within critical optical arrangements.

4   Although not necessarily an imaging application in the usual sense, photochromic films are being incorporated in 'optical memory' information storage systems (cf. fulgides), where lasers are again used for recording and reading purposes.

All these applications rely to some extent on the re-useability of the film, so that the 'fatigue' characteristics of the photochromic reaction concerned become important. Systems based on tautomerism seem to offer the best properties in this respect; cleavage processes often suffer from irreversible side-reactions.

2.5   Other colour-forming processes

Numerous other colour-forming (and colour-bleaching) organic photo-chemical reactions have been investigated for their potential in imaging systems. The prime objectives are to devise processes offering high sensitivity and/or total colour reproduction: that is, to match the capabilities of silver halide materials in the photographic field. The only photochemical systems that have so far come close to equalling the sensitivity of conventional materials are based on photoinduced radical reactions, where some degree of amplification is possible through chain processes. One such reaction to have formed the basis of a number of commercial and experimental imaging systems is the photolysis of polyhalogenated hydrocarbons, for example:

$$CBr_4 \xrightarrow{h\nu} \cdot CBr_3 + Br\cdot$$

The resulting radicals have been used to produce negative dye images in a variety of ways, for example:

1   By the oxidation of leuco-dyes (i.e. dyes in a reduced form).

2   By acid-induced colour changes in indicator dyes. For this purpose, use is made of the hydrogen bromide formed through hydrogen atom abstraction by bromine atoms from the polymeric matrix:

$$Br\cdot + RH \longrightarrow HBr + R\cdot$$

3   By the direct synthesis of dyes from other incorporated precursors. The classic example is the photoinduced reaction between tetrabromomethane and diphenylamine, successive radical condensations producing a triarylmethane dye (Scheme 1).

In all cases, fixing is accomplished by removing undecomposed polyhalogen compounds in a solvent rinse or by heat treatment. Polyhalogen systems are sensitive in the ultraviolet and blue-green spectral regions, depending on the halocarbon, but full spectral sensitisation is possible, and integral, three-layer colour reproduction has been claimed. Poor keeping

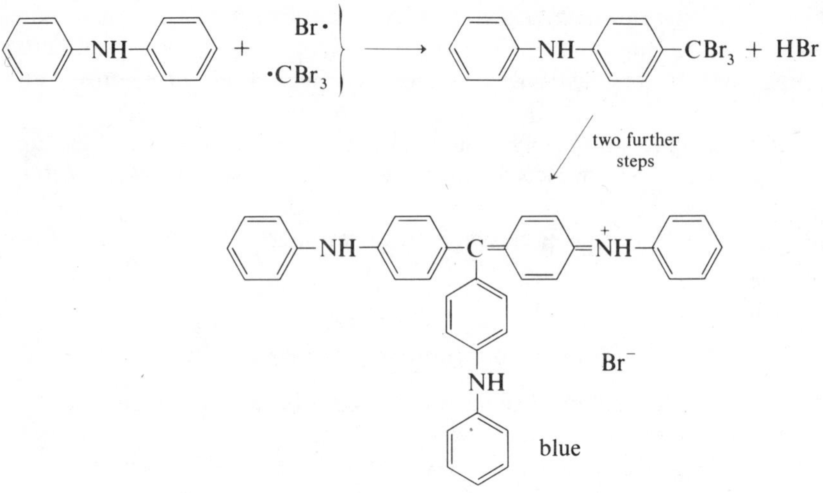

SCHEME 1

properties are a problem, particularly with the more sensitive materials for which speeds approaching silver halide capabilities have been demonstrated. Another serious drawback is that all polyhalogen compounds are toxic to some degree.

3 Thermographic and electrophotographic systems

In thermography, heat is used to bring about some physical or chemical change in a thermally sensitive layer. Electronically excited states are not involved in the imaging reaction. However, there exist a number of 'photo-thermographic' systems in which a thermally activated image-forming process is modified by a prior exposure to light. Such systems are of low sensitivity and resolution, finding application in office copying and the production of transparencies for overhead projection.

Electrophotographic systems make use of electrical phenomena to distinguish exposed from unexposed areas. In the well-known xerographic process, a metal plate is coated with a layer of photoconducting material (e.g. zinc oxide or selenium). The layer receives a positive electric charge, and the image to be copied is projected on to the surface, where the photoconductor leaks away the charge in the illuminated areas. The resulting electrostatic latent image is developed with a negatively charged pigmented powder. Coloured images can be provided. Xerographic processes have lower resolution but greater sensitivity than photochemical imaging systems, the images being particulate in nature.

4   Comparison of conventional and non-conventional imaging

In comparing the various types of imaging system, a number of factors need to be considered. Table 2 lists some chosen systems, together with their standing as regards three such factors. In this Table, sensitivity is defined as the minimum energy of the exposure required to produce an observable image. Processing conditions are loosely described as either 'wet' or 'dry', wet processes generally being considered less convenient. It should be pointed out that the photographic industry has recognised this problem. 'Instant' photography offers the customer a rapid-access, quasi dry-process product. Truly dry, thermally processed, silver halide materials are also available, finding application in specialised areas such as aerial photography.

Table 2   Properties of selected imaging systems

System	Sensitivity/ $mJ\,m^{-2}$	Resolving power/lines mm^{-1}	Processing conditions
human eye	10^{-3}	10	wet
fast silver halide	10^{-3}	60	wet
electrophotography (Se)	1	10	dry
fast polyhalogen	300	1 000	dry
very fine grain silver halide	10^3	1 000	wet
photopolymerisation	10^4	100–1 000	wet
diazo/photochromism	10^6–10^7	1 000	wet/dry

It is evident that few chemical systems can approach the sensitivity of silver halide materials, let alone offer the possibility of full colour reproduction. Furthermore, conventional materials possess other hard-to-match attributes, such as the great stability of the latent image and the capability for adjusting tone and contrast over a wide range. Only the photovisual (i.e. electronic) imaging systems present any real challenge. Sensitivities an order of magnitude greater than those achievable with silver halide materials are possible, and systems have been devised for in-camera application. Some kind of physicochemical imaging material will presumably still be required for the production of 'hard' copies, providing openings for non-conventional imaging when high sensitivity is not required.

For the present, within the restricted range of their capabilities, non-conventional systems can provide a convenient, low-cost alternative to materials based on silver halides.

5·13 Photopolymers for imaging and photoresists

by Ralph Jacobson (Polytechnic of Central London)

'Resist' is the term applied to protective coatings that inhibit chemical, physical or electrical attack on the underlying material. The term 'photoresist' is applied to protective coatings that are sensitive to electromagnetic radiation (in the ultraviolet and visible regions) and are capable of becoming insoluble or soluble so that the surface beneath can be modified by subsequent treatment to form an image.

Photoresists are involved in the manufacture of many articles we see around us. The list is extensive and includes: printed matter, textile patterns, nameplates, decorative panels and pictures, graticules and scales, small mechanical components such as camera shutter blades and electric razor heads, printed circuit boards, and integrated circuits (chips).

The origins of photoresists are as old as photography. The first successful photograph from nature by Nicéphore Niépce in 1826 was a photoresist. Niépce discovered that when bitumen, obtained from Judea asphalt, was coated on a metal plate and exposed to light for several hours it became insoluble in oil of lavender. In 1852 William Henry Fox Talbot (the originator of the negative–positive silver halide photographic process) patented the use of gelatin, containing dichromate, coated on a copper or steel plate as a photoengraving process. After exposure, the unhardened gelatin was washed from the plate and the underlying metal in the unexposed areas was then etched to give a relief image that could be used for printing. The hardened gelatin in the exposed areas protected the metal from the etchant.

The above are early examples of photoresists, and their principles of operation form the basis of modern photoresists, although the light-sensitive layers have been superseded by other materials that offer various technological advantages such as increased sensitivity, minimal dark reaction, better resolution, and higher resistance to etchants. These photoresists are based on polymers that become cross-linked via the action of a light-sensitive component, which may be separate from the polymer chains or may be chemically linked to them. They are negative working, which means that exposure renders them insoluble in a solvent which is used as the developer. A more recent innovation is to use positive working photoresists (Figure 1), in which the action of absorbed radiation is generally to change the solubility from organic solvent-soluble to water-soluble, in order to differentiate between the exposed and unexposed areas.

A distinction must also be made between the above types of photoresist

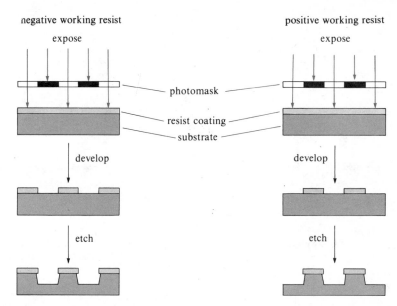

FIGURE 1 Negative and positive working photoresists. In negative working photoresists the unexposed areas are removed in the developer, allowing the substrate to be etched, whereas in positive working photoresists the exposed areas are removed in the developer.

and imaging systems that are based on the photopolymerisation of monomers. A number of different methods are available for distinguishing between the exposed (polymerised) and unexposed areas. These 'read-out' methods include: (i) solubility or adhesion, for relief images; (ii) light scattering; (iii) direct colour formation; (iv) indirect colour formation, by immersing the resist in a solution of dye (imbibition) or by transfer of pigment.

Photopolymerisation may be used as an imaging system itself, but it finds application mainly in the preparation of printing plates and in dry film resists for printed circuit preparation. Note that the above types of imaging system, which use photochemical cross-linking or photopolymerisation, differ from those that depend on the sensitivity of groups linked to polymer chains, i.e. photosensitive polymers, which are used in the preparation of lithographic printing plates.

1 Processes using photoresists and photopolymers

Photoresists are used in virtually all photomechanical printing processes. Four printing processes account for practically all printed matter: (a) lithography (also called planography, offset); (b) letterpress (flexography is a

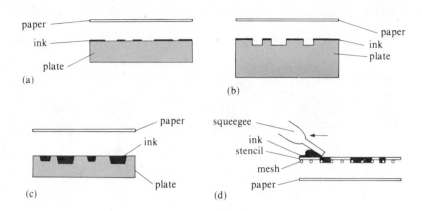

FIGURE 2   Four printing processes: (a) lithography; (b) letterpress; (c) gravure; (d) screen. (N.B. although the term 'paper' has been used for the printing surface, some of these processes are used for printing on to many other surfaces, such as glass, metal and plastic.)

rubber-plate version of letterpress); (c) gravure (also called intaglio); (d) screen-process printing (also called silkscreen, screen, stencil, serigraphy).

These four processes are illustrated in Figure 2. Lithographic printing relies on the ability of parts of the surface to retain a thin layer of ink whilst other areas repel the ink. The printing plate is dampened with water. A thin layer of water is retained in the non-image areas. The printing ink adheres to the image areas and is repelled by the water on the dampened parts of the plate, which remain clear when the ink is transferred to the paper. Thus lithographic printing relies on surface modification of the photopolymer, the image area being hydrophobic and the non-image area hydrophilic.

Both letterpress and gravure printing involve photoresists and subsequent etching to form relief images in the plate. In letterpress printing the raised areas of the plate transfer the ink to the paper, like metal characters on a typewriter. In gravure printing the ink is retained in etched hollows in the plate and transferred to the paper. In screen-process printing the ink is forced through holes in a resist that is supported on a fine mesh of silk, synthetic polymer, or metal that is held in contact with the image-receiving surface. These basic printing processes all use photopolymers or photoresists and find application in all types of printing, from reproducing colour pictures to the preparation of printed circuits.

Photoresists are used in various photofabrication methods, in which small metal parts can be manufactured simply and cheaply. The methods involve photography of the original design to make a mask, followed by the use of a photo-resist and etching. The ultimate application of the combination of photography and photoresists is in the manufacture of integrated circuits in the form of chips (Figure 3). This requires the accurate positioning of lines and points 2 or 3 μm in size. Each chip may require as many as nine levels of circuitry each positioned with an accuracy of ± 1 μm.

Photopolymerisation (Section 4) is used in the direct preparation of letterpress and lithographic printing plates. No etching is required, and the

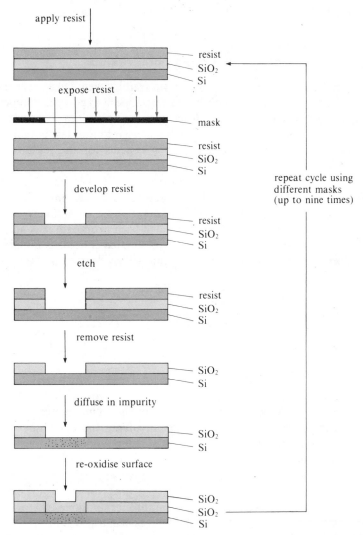

FIGURE 3   Simplified sequence for the preparation of integrated circuits (chips). (source: Kodak Limited)

relief images are formed in the photopolymerisable layer after exposure and development. Photopolymerisation is also used in materials for printed circuit boards (dry film resists), in the reproduction of engineering drawings, and in colour-proofing systems in the printing and advertising industries. Also photopolymerisation systems can be used for recording images for cathode ray tube displays and laser scanners, and displaying them on a near real-time basis (i.e. almost at the same instant as their original formation). They may be used for recording holograms on a real-time basis.

2 Negative working photoresists

The original photoresists of the nineteenth century were negative working (Figure 1). They used natural colloids or resins, such as gelatin, albumen, or shellac, in the presence of a sensitiser such as potassium dichromate or ammonium dichromate. These resists are still used to this day, but for many applications have been replaced by other systems for the reasons given earlier.

The exact mechanism by which both natural and synthetic polymers become cross-linked on exposure in the presence of a dichromate is still not known, but equations (1)–(3) have been proposed as a likely scheme. Although many other reaction schemes have been proposed, it is accepted that the photochemical cross-linking of dichromated colloids is initiated by the photoreduction of hexavalent chromium to trivalent chromium.

$$Cr_2O_7{}^{2-} \xrightarrow[\text{polymer}]{h\nu} CrO_4{}^{2-} + mCrO_3 \cdot nCr_2O_3 \tag{1}$$

$$mCrO_3 \cdot nCr_2O_3 \xrightarrow{H_2O} CrO_3 + Cr_2O_3 \tag{2}$$

$$\text{polymer} + Cr_2O_3 \longrightarrow \text{cross-linked polymer} \tag{3}$$

Most modern photoresists use synthetic polymers, which may be made photosensitive by the inclusion of a number of groups that can cross-link on exposure. A typical example is poly(vinyl cinnamate) (**1**), which undergoes a photodimerisation reaction involving the cinnamoyl group. However, poly(vinyl cinnamate) and related compounds are not very sensitive and their maximum sensitivity is in the ultraviolet region. Their sensitivity can be increased and extended to longer wavelengths by the inclusion of sensitisers. Many sensitisers have been patented for this purpose and include nitro compounds, nitroanilines, anthrones, quinones, ketones and various dyes. The addition of a sensitiser in concentrations of up to about 2% by weight of the polymer can lead to a 200-fold speed increase, and alter the wavelength of maximum sensitivity from 320 nm to 490 nm.

$$\sim CH_2-CH\sim \qquad\qquad \sim CH_2-CH\sim$$

$$
\begin{array}{ccc}
 & \overset{|}{O} & \\
C_6H_5 & \overset{|}{CO} & \\
\overset{|}{CH} & \overset{|}{CH} & \\
\parallel & \parallel & \xrightarrow{\;h\nu\;} \\
\overset{}{CH} & \overset{}{CH} & \\
\overset{|}{CO} & \overset{|}{C_6H_5} & \\
\overset{|}{O} & & \\
\end{array}
\quad + \quad
$$

Scheme with structure **1** (left, reactants) and product (right):

Left: $\sim CH_2-CH\sim$ with $-O-CO-CH=CH-CO-O-CH-CH_2\sim$ bearing C_6H_5 groups, plus $CH=CH$ with C_6H_5.

Right product: $\sim CH_2-CH\sim$ — O — $C_6H_5\;CO$ — $CH-CH$ — $CH-CH$ — $CO\;C_6H_5$ — O — $\sim CH-CH_2\sim$

1

Structure **2**:

$$\sim CH_2-CH\sim$$
$$\overset{|}{CH_2}$$
$$\overset{|}{O}$$
$$\overset{|}{CO}$$

(benzene ring) with $-COOCH_2CH=CH_2$

2

Partially polymerised diallyl phthalate (**2**) also finds application in negative working photoresists that become insolubilised on exposure.

Another class of polymers used in negative working photoresists are the polyisoprenes, the basic polymers of natural rubber. However, they must be cyclised before they can be used as photoresists; this also renders them ink-receptive for the preparation of printing plates. Scheme 1 shows some of the cyclised structures that have been identified from reactions of the isomeric polyisoprenes with acid or by heating them in a suitable solvent in the presence of a catalyst.

Cyclised polyisoprene resists are the most widely used resists for microelectronic applications. For use as a photoresist they require the addition of a sensitiser, usually bis-azides. Unlike many other types of sensitiser, which act by energy transfer or electron transfer to a photosensitive polymer that subsequently cross-links, bis-azides are involved in the formation of cross-links between the cyclised polyisoprenes, with the evolution of nitrogen (Scheme 2).

In practice, photoresists comprise a sensitiser, resin or polymer, solvent and additives to improve their properties (e.g. to inhibit thermal cross-linking and to improve adhesion). Also they are usually pre-baked under

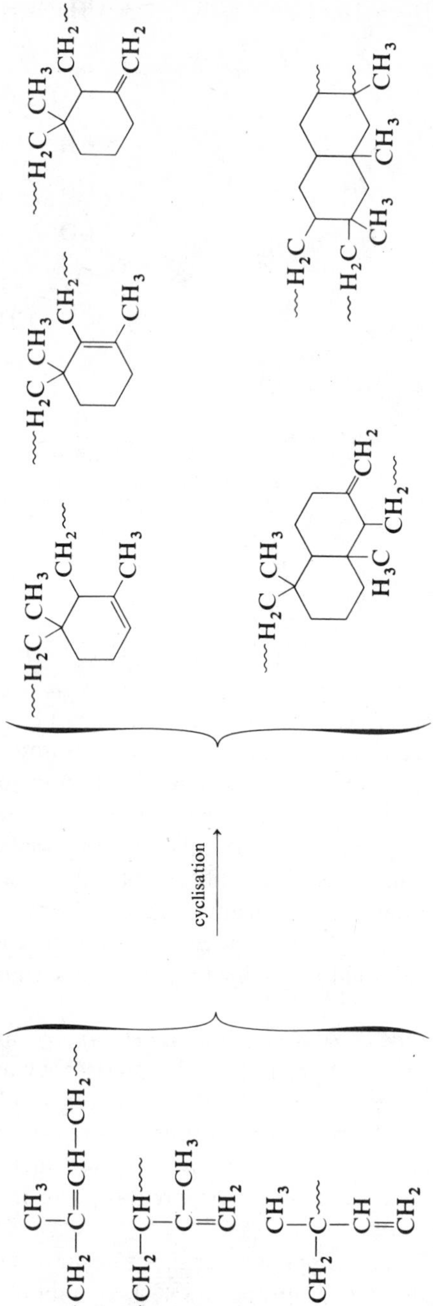

SCHEME 1

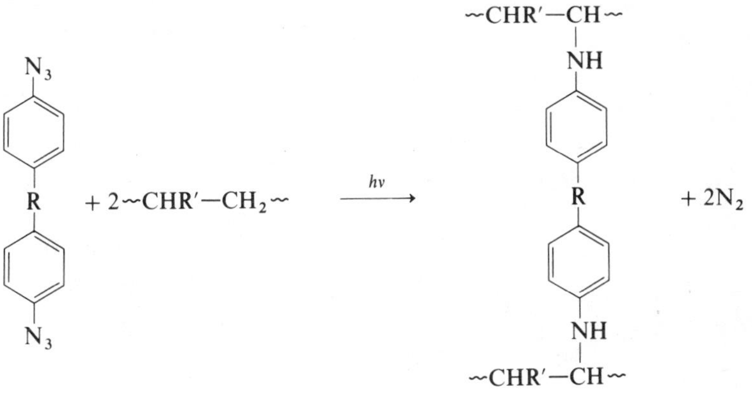

$$\sim CHR'-CH\sim$$
$$\text{NH}$$

where R is $\diagdown CO$; $-CH=CH-$; $-CH_2-$; $-NH-$; or

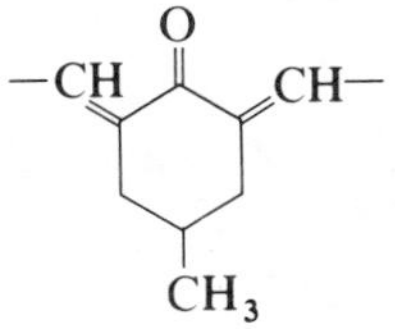

and $\sim CHR'-CH_2\sim$ represents cyclised polyisoprene

SCHEME 2

controlled conditions. This is carried out to expel any retained solvent, to harden the resist and so minimise damage in handling and developing, and to improve adhesion.

3 Positive working photoresists

The composition of positive resists is essentially the same as that of negative resists. They contain sensitisers, resins, solvents, and additives, but the nature and the reactions of the sensitisers and resins are completely different. The photosensitive reaction changes the photoresist, in the exposed areas, from being soluble in organic solvents to being soluble in water or alkali, and photochemical cross-linking reactions are not involved. The photosensitive component of most positive photoresists is a 2-diazoquinone (**3**; also termed a diazo oxide). On exposure, these compounds undergo a rearrangement of the ring structure to an indenecarboxylic acid or lactone, which is soluble in the aqueous alkali used as the developer (Scheme 3).

Resins or polymers are included in the photoresist. Usually these are not photosensitive but are added to improve adhesion, increase viscosity for ease of coating, increase chemical resistance and prevent the photosensitive component from crystallising. Phenol–formaldehyde resins are a good choice because they are slightly hydrophobic but are sufficiently soluble in the

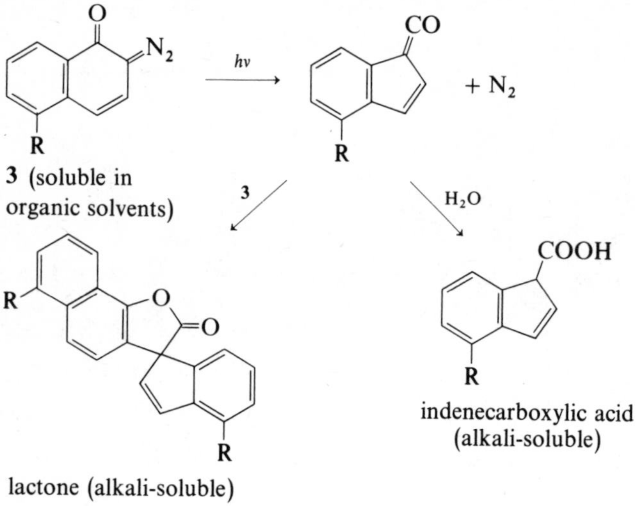
hν
$+ N_2$
3 (soluble in organic solvents)
3
H_2O
COOH
lactone (alkali-soluble)
indenecarboxylic acid (alkali-soluble)

SCHEME 3

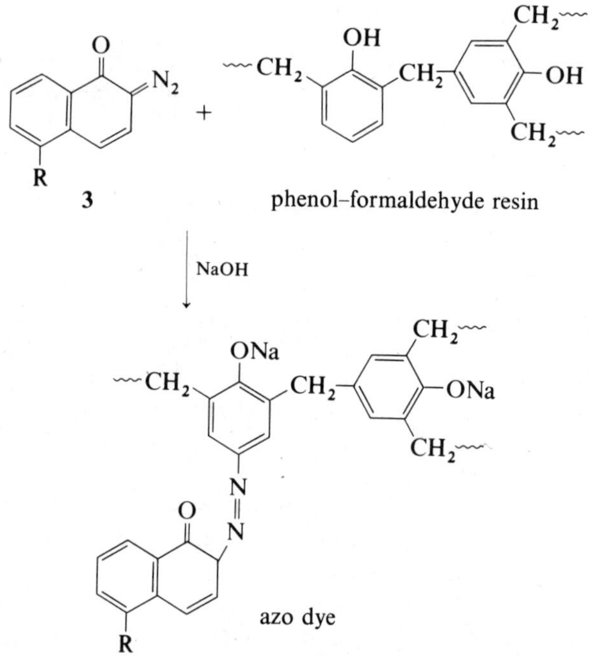
3
phenol–formaldehyde resin
NaOH
azo dye

SCHEME 4

alkaline developer that they can be removed from the exposed areas, without being too soluble or they would also be removed from the unexposed areas.

An additional advantage of phenol–formaldehyde resins is their ability to couple with the photosensitive component in the unexposed areas to yield a visible azo dye image during development in aqueous alkali (Scheme 4).

4   Photopolymerisation imaging

The photoresists outlined in the preceding sections depend on either cross-linking reactions to decrease their solubility in a solvent (negative photo-resists), or a photochemical reaction that changes their solubility (positive photoresists). Differentiation between exposed and unexposed areas can also be achieved by the photopolymerisation of monomers.

The photoinitiation of polymerisation is described in Chapter $5 \cdot 5$, and systems comprising a photoinitiator, monomers and binders coated on various supports, such as metal or plastic, form the basis of a number of imaging systems that are commercially available. The general scheme for initiating photopolymerisation in such systems may be written as follows:

$$I \xrightarrow{\;hv\;} I^*$$
(initiator)

$$I^* \longrightarrow R\cdot + R'\cdot \left.\rule{0pt}{12pt}\right\} \text{ initiating radicals for polymerisation}$$
$$\text{or} \quad I^* + RH \longrightarrow \cdot IH + R\cdot \left.\rule{0pt}{0pt}\right\} \text{ of ethylenic monomers}$$

In some systems, sensitisers (S) are used to extend the spectral sensitivity to longer wavelengths to which the initiator may be insensitive:

$$S \xrightarrow{\;hv\;} S^*$$

$$S^* + I \longrightarrow I^* + S$$

$$I^* \longrightarrow \text{ as above}$$

A large variety of photoinitiators are known that undergo photolysis to radicals that are able to initiate polymerisation of ethylenic monomers. These include: benzoin, diazonium compounds, azo compounds, peroxides, haloalkanes, and photoreducible dyes in the presence of a reducing agent. Ethylenic monomers such as acrylic acid ($CH_2=CHCOOH$), methyl methacrylate ($CH_2=C(CH_3)COOCH_3$), or styrene ($C_6H_5CH=CH_2$) may be used. Those with acidic groups have the advantage that the developer used to remove monomer from the unexposed regions can be aqueous alkali rather than an organic solvent.

A problem associated with the application of polymerisable layers in imaging systems is that the presence of oxygen, which acts as a radical scavenger, interferes with the initiation and propagation reactions. In practi-

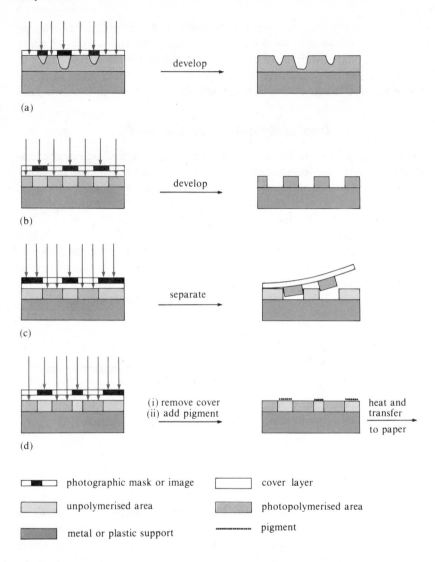

FIGURE 4   Examples of photopolymerisation imaging systems. (a) Letterpress printing plate (DuPont Dycril). (b) Lithographic printing plate (DuPont Lydel). (c) Process depending on change in adhesion (DuPont Crolux). (d) Process depending on change in adhesion and melting point (Custom Toning Film). (source: Walker, Webers and Thommes, 1970)

cal systems this severe limitation is overcome by pre-conditioning the material in an atmosphere of carbon dioxide, by using surface layers or laminates that are impermeable to oxygen, or by photoconditioning. In photoconditioning, the material is given a uniform exposure just sufficient to consume the oxygen but insufficient to initiate polymerisation:

$$I \xrightarrow{h\nu} I^*$$
(initiator)

$$I^* + MH \longrightarrow \cdot IH + M\cdot$$
(monomer)

$$M\cdot + O_2 \longrightarrow MO_2\cdot$$

$$\cdot IH + O_2 \longrightarrow I + HO_2\cdot$$

$$2HO_2\cdot \longrightarrow H_2O_2 + O_2$$

Oxygen is consumed by reaction with monomer and initiator radicals, and the products formed are not capable of initiating polymerisation.

A number of imaging systems based on photopolymerisation are illustrated in a simplified form in Figure 4.

5 Photosensitive polymers

A number of imaging systems are based on polymers that are sensitive to radiation because they contain photosensitive pendant groups. Unlike those described previously as negative photoresists, these polymers generally do

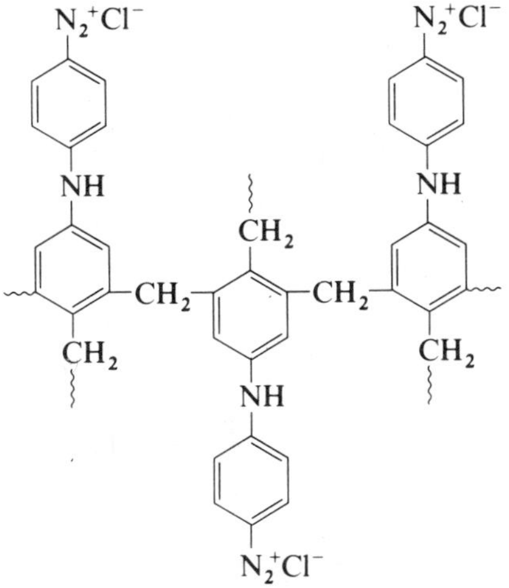

4

not depend on photochemical cross-linking for their action. Although cross-linking is involved in some examples, they are generally not used as photo-resists. A typical example is a diazo resin (**4**), formed by reaction between diazotised 4-aminodiphenylamine and formaldehyde. Although polymeric, this compound is water-soluble because of the ionic diazonium groups. The diazonium groups are destroyed on exposure and the exposed areas are insolubilised and rendered ink-receptive. They thus form the basis of many pre-sensitised lithographic printing plates. Other examples include aromatic azides linked to poly(vinyl alcohol), and photochromic monomers incor-porated in polymer chains.

5·14 Photochemical isotope enrichment

by Godfrey Beddard (The Royal Institution, London)

The separation or enrichment of isotopes using lasers is currently receiving considerable attention because of the necessity to provide sufficient fuel (uranium-235; ^{235}U) for nuclear reactors, which in the future are expected to provide an increasingly large supply of electrical power. Even a modest decrease in the cost of providing raw materials for nuclear power production will have a substantial economic impact. Separation of isotopes other than uranium is also important, such as ^{50}Ti for research into structural materials, and ^{10}B and ^{79}Br in medicine. Carbon, nitrogen and sulphur isotopes are important in providing non-radioactive tracers in agriculture, in environmental protection and in production control. The isotope separation techniques used also open up possibilities for instruments for the highly selective detection of atoms and molecules.

Because laser isotope separation deals with the radiatively related states of atoms and molecules, the change in the average thermal atomic (or molecular) velocity due to the change of mass that occurs on isotopic substitution (which forms the basis of the classical separation processes of gaseous centrifugation and distillation) is of no consequence. These classical processes are inherently inefficient, and only a minute enrichment is achieved on each pass through the separation device; consequently many stages of enrichment are needed, which makes the processes very expensive. In uranium, where there is only 1.26% difference in mass between ^{238}U and ^{235}U, the initial 0.7% of ^{235}U is reduced to only 0.2% in the residues (called the tailings), as this is the economic limit. With more efficient separation almost all the ^{235}U would be extracted—effectively making known supplies last approximately 40% longer. Moreover, because the radioactive content would be lower, the waste would also be far less dangerous.

The hitherto known schemes for laser isotope separation exploit isotope shifts (i.e. the shifts in the energy levels of atoms or molecules caused by isotopic substitution), which are observable as shifts in the ultraviolet, visible, and infrared spectra. First, the atom or molecule containing the required isotope must be selectively excited by absorption of radiation. This can be achieved only if the isotope shifts are larger than the width of the spectral line. Second, once the selected species is excited, differences between the physical or chemical properties of this isotopic species and those of the unexcited species, must be maintained against all competing photochemical and photophysical processes until separation is achieved, because these processes will tend to scramble the isotope selection. Figure 1 shows the basic idea of laser isotope separation; on the right-hand side of the diagram are the processes causing loss of selectivity, and on the left are those that selectively isolate the wanted isotope, A. A* is any excited state of the selected atom or molecule. Species B represents the unwanted isotopes, and X is a species that reacts preferentially with A* to facilitate its isolation, but that may also react with A and B.

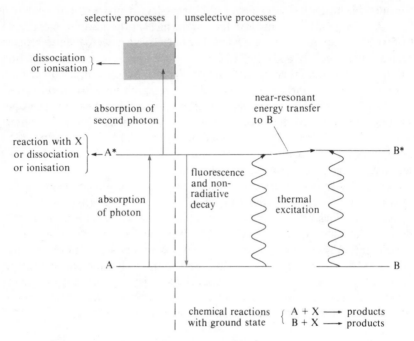

FIGURE 1   Isotopically selective and unselective processes.

Most laser isotope separation processes take place in the gas phase. Figure 1 shows two selective pathways. One pathway is photochemical and is the reaction of A* with X at a rate $k[A^*][X]$. The other pathway is photophysical and is the absorption of a second photon, at a frequency v, to excite A* further and cause ionisation if A is an atom, or dissociation if A is a molecule. The rate of absorption is then $I_v[A^*]$, where I_v is the light intensity (photons per second). The photophysical processes are controlled by the number of photons absorbed per second, and therefore the rates can be made very large.

In competition with these selective processes are the loss or scrambling reactions. These are (i) near-resonant energy transfer from A* to B, to form A and B* at a rate $k_R[A^*][B]$; (ii) radiative and non-radiative pathways out of A* at a rate $k_S[A^*]$; and (iii) thermal excitation of A to A* and of B to B*. For isotope selection to occur, the selective processes must be much faster than the unselective processes.

It is not absolutely necessary to use a laser to select the isotope, but its properties of a highly collimated beam, high power, narrow bandwidth, and broad wavelength tuneability make it in most cases the only viable light source. Low-pressure discharge lamps have been used, as in the selection of $CoCl_2$ isotopic species by an aluminium lamp at 281.6 nm. This requires the coincidence of an intense line from the spectrum of the lamp with the molecular absorption of just one isotopic species, which is generally difficult to obtain.

We now consider what properties of atoms and molecules lead to isotope shifts in the optical spectrum, and how the width of a particular line can be narrowed to allow selective absorption. Then we consider examples of single-photon and multiple-photon absorption processes leading to isotope separation.

1 Isotope effects on the optical spectrum

1.1 Atoms

Isotopes of the same element can have different spectra, which are caused by differences not only in the nuclear mass but also in nuclear shape and size (which affect the electric field in which the electrons move) and in nuclear magnetic moments. These various effects change the spectrum by different amounts. For example, the nuclear mass affects the atomic energy levels in inverse proportion to the square of the relative atomic mass (i.e. $1/A_r^2$). When A_r is greater than 100, the effect is less than the variation of the energy level caused by fluctuations in the speed of the atoms (the Doppler width), and nuclear size and shape are the most important considerations. In small atoms the isotope shift is caused mainly by the mass effect. For example, the relative isotope shift ($\Delta v/v$) between hydrogen and deuterium, for absorption at frequency v, is 2.7×10^{-4}; in a more massive atom, such as calcium, $\Delta v/v = 0.5 \times 10^{-6}$ and is only a quarter of the Doppler width; in uranium, where volume effects dominate, $\Delta v/v = 0.6 \times 10^{-4}$ and is 80 times the Doppler width of the spectral line. The Doppler width decreases as the mass increases because heavy atoms move more slowly at a given temperature than light ones. Isotope separation using lasers is thus very effective for heavy nuclei (e.g. uranium) in contrast to classical separation methods, for which the relevant parameter is always the relative difference between the atomic masses.

1.2 Molecules

Isotope shifts in rotational spectra are caused only by changes in the moments of inertia of the molecule, and hence isotopic substitution of sulphur in SF_6 would not be detectable in the rotational spectra. In vibrational spectra the change in mass is detected in a change in the vibrational frequency of the chemical bond containing the isotope. In the diatomic molecule HCl, containing ^{35}Cl or ^{37}Cl, the relative frequency change $\Delta v/v$ is 7×10^{-4} and is approximately 100 times larger than the Doppler width of the transition. In all molecules, departures of the intermolecular potential from that of a harmonic oscillator will lead to unexpected shifts in energy levels, which may dominate other effects.

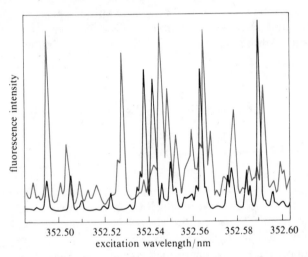

FIGURE 2   Rotational–vibrational structure in the fluorescence excitation spectra of $H_2^{12}CO$ (*black line*) and $H_2^{13}CO$ (*red line*). (source: Letokhov and Bradley Moore, 1977)

In polyatomics with limited symmetry, the rotational and vibrational spectrum becomes very complex with many lines overlapping within their Doppler width. Fortunately, in some cases not all lines overlap, as shown in Figure 2 for $H_2^{12}CO$ and $H_2^{13}CO$, where at 352.526 nm a clear difference is seen.

2   Narrowing the absorption linewidth

We now consider ways in which the width of an absorption line can be reduced to less than the isotope shift. This has to be done because if more than one isotope is excited, the enrichment of the final mixture will be low.

The absorption lines are broadened not only by fluctuations in the thermal velocity (Doppler effect) but also by molecular (or atomic) collisions, radiative decay and radiationless processes, and by effects associated with an intense (laser) radiation field.

At low pressures the Doppler width of a line is usually the dominant broadening process, and this can be reduced by cooling the gas thereby making all the molecules or atoms travel at the same speed relative to the laser beam (i.e. reducing the spread of their velocities). This latter effect can be achieved by producing, in high vacuum, a beam of the molecules (or atoms), with the excitation radiation in a direction perpendicular to that of the beam. As only comparatively few molecules can be put into a beam (in practice produced as a sheet rather than a pencil) the absorption cross-section of the beam is low. This means that intense excitation is required to select a significant fraction of the wanted isotopic species. The low pressure, however, favours the photoionisation method where a second photon ionises the isotope and a strong electric field separates the ions from the neutral species.

Another way of reducing the linewidth is to cool the gas to a very low temperature by allowing gas at high pressure to expand through a small nozzle. Because the expansion occurs at a supersonic rate, a considerable

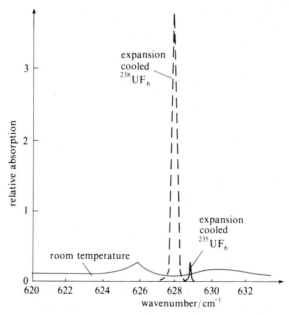

FIGURE 3 Absorption spectra of UF_6 at room temperature (*red line*) and following expansion cooling (*black line*). (source: Letokhov and Bradley Moore, 1977)

fraction of the internal energy of the molecules is transferred into bulk translational motion, so that the gas is cooled to near 1 K. Not only does the small spread of molecular velocities decrease the Doppler width, but also the low temperature brings all molecules to the lowest energy levels; the complex rotational band structure then collapses to a few lines. Similarly, the molecule goes into the lowest vibrational level. Figure 3 shows the effect on the UF_6 spectrum, where cooling to 50 K is sufficient to separate the ^{235}U and ^{238}U spectra. At room temperature the ^{238}U band swamps the ^{235}U band, because the isotope shift is only $1\,cm^{-1}$.

3 Photoionisation and photodissociation requiring one or two photons

The simplest process for producing isotopically pure material is shown in Figure 1, when state A* dissociates without absorbing a second photon, and leads to stable products. Such dissociation can be observed when the energies of non-repulsive and repulsive states of A overlap; furthermore, the non-repulsive state involved is usually sufficiently sharp that isotope shifts can be observed and isotopically selective dissociation can be performed. This type of dissociation has been studied most extensively with formaldehyde (methanal). Near the 0–0 band of the first singlet state the following primary processes can occur:

$$H_2CO \;\underset{\text{fluorescence}}{\overset{h\nu}{\rightleftharpoons}}\; H_2CO^* \begin{cases} \nearrow H_2 + CO \qquad (1) \\ \\ \searrow H\cdot + H\dot{C}O \qquad (2) \end{cases}$$

From Figure 2 it can be seen that $H_2{}^{13}CO$ can be selectively excited, and enriched ^{13}CO can then be produced. Similarly, if a mixture of H_2CO and D_2CO is used, then enrichment of hydrogen can be achieved. In this latter process the reactions

$$H\cdot + H_2CO \longrightarrow HH + H\dot{C}O \qquad (3)$$

$$D\cdot + H_2CO \longrightarrow DH + H\dot{C}O \qquad (4)$$

must be considered as they will degrade the isotopic selectivity. A scavenger can be added to inhibit these reactions by removing the radicals:

$$H\cdot(\text{or } D\cdot) + \cdot NO \longrightarrow HNO \text{ (or DNO)} \qquad (5)$$

Photochemical methods have also been used to separate chlorine isotopes. $I^{37}Cl$ is excited by a dye laser (605.4 nm) below its dissociation threshold, and the excited molecule reacts with 1,2-dibromoethene to yield small amounts of 1-bromo-2-chloroethene and 1,2-dichloroethene:

$$ICl \xrightarrow{hv} ICl*$$

$$ICl* + BrCH{=}CHBr \longrightarrow BrCH{=}CHCl + ClCH{=}CHCl + IBr$$
$$\qquad\qquad\qquad\qquad\qquad\quad \text{major} \qquad\qquad \text{minor}$$

The 1,2-dichloroethene was analysed to contain 85% of ^{37}Cl, corresponding to an enrichment factor of 17.

Uranium has been enriched by selective two-step photoionisation. The scheme is outlined in Figure 1, where state A* is photoionised by photons of frequency v. The excitation and ionisation wavelengths used vary between different laboratories. In one experiment, the 378.1 nm line from a xenon ion laser was used to excite ^{235}U, which emerged from a molecular beam oven (Figure 4). Photoionisation was accomplished using the 307.5 nm and

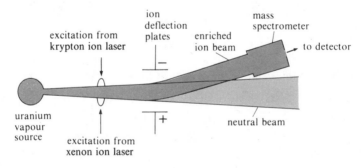

FIGURE 4   The experimental scheme for the separation of ^{235}U and ^{238}U, achieved by two-photon ionisation of uranium atoms in a beam. (source: Letokhov and Bradley Moore, 1977)

356.4 nm lines from a krypton ion laser. The molecular beam was placed *inside* the laser cavity, and as a result the power density at the beam increased to 30 watts. The $^{235}U^+$ ions were focused electrostatically on to collecting plates. In two hours irradiation, 4 mg of 3% enriched uranium, which is approximately the percentage enrichment needed for nuclear reactors, were obtained. One difficulty with this method is the optimisation of the intensities of the exciting and ionising lasers. The initial absorption is resonant and occurs with high probability, but the ionisation step does not. For instance in rubidium vapour, an intensity of $0.5\,W\,cm^{-2}$ is needed to saturate the absorption, but $10^7\,W\,cm^{-2}$ is needed to saturate the ionisation.

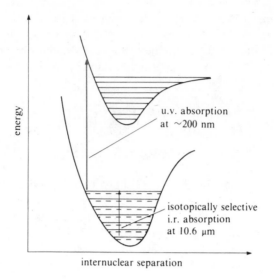

FIGURE 5   Two-photon ionisation of the ammonia molecule.

Ions are rarely produced from molecules, but dissociation to radicals or atoms occurs instead. The initial and selective absorption can be in the infrared region; for example, the dissociation of ammonia (Figure 5):

$$^{15}NH_3 + hv_1 + hv_2 \longrightarrow {}^{15}\dot{N}H_2 + H\cdot$$

$$2\,{}^{15}\dot{N}H_2 \longrightarrow {}^{15}N_2H_4$$

$$H\cdot + {}^{15}N_2H_4 \longrightarrow {}^{15}\dot{N}H\,{}^{15}NH_2 + H_2$$

$$2\,{}^{15}\dot{N}H\,{}^{15}NH_2 \longrightarrow 2\,{}^{15}NH_3 + {}^{15}N_2$$

4   Multiple-photon dissociation

When a source of intense infrared radiation illuminates polyatomic molecules, such as SF_6 or $CClF_3$, which are normally transparent to infrared radiation, sufficient energy can be absorbed for isotopically selective reactions to take place. The mechanism is not yet understood properly, but we shall now examine some current ideas on this problem, together with examples of this fascinating process.

Starting from SF_6 in its natural abundance (95% of ^{32}S, 4.2% of ^{34}S) a large enrichment ($^{34}S/^{32}S$) of 2 800 has been observed. The SF_6 decomposes by losing one fluorine atom at a time and $^{32}SF_6$ is selectively destroyed. The spectra before and after irradiation with a CO_2 laser are shown in Figure 6.

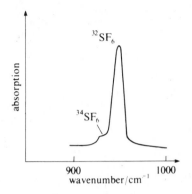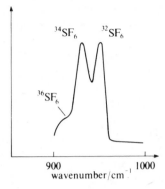

FIGURE 6   Infrared spectra of SF_6 before (*left*) and after (*right*) irradiation for isotope selection. (source: Letokhov, 1977)

Other examples of this isotope selection process are

$$CClF_3 \longrightarrow \cdot CF_3 + Cl\cdot$$

$$CH_2=CHCl \longrightarrow C_2H_2 + HCl$$

$$NH_3 \longrightarrow \cdot NH_2 + H\cdot$$

The process has an intensity threshold of $20-25 \times 10^6 \, W\,cm^{-2}$, and this is exceeded by focusing $100\,ns$ pulses from a CO_2 laser ($9-11\,\mu m$) to provide power up to $2 \times 10^9 \, W\,cm^{-2}$.

As the energy of a single photon from the CO_2 laser is no more than 10% of the dissociation energy of the S—F bond, dissociation occurs by multiple absorption of single photons, or multiphoton absorption, or both. The threshold in the excitation intensity for dissociation implies that there is a build-up of energy in the molecule rather than there being a single multiphoton step. Additionally, if the gas pressure is increased in the range 0.5–10 torr, the degree of dissociation decreases (at a constant excitation intensity), indicating that collisional effects are detrimental to the dissociation process.

The intriguing aspect of multiphoton processes is the way in which the molecule can be pumped up the vibrational ladder to dissociation (see Figure 7). A diatomic molecule may be excited to its first vibrational level by an infrared photon; because the molecule does not behave as a harmonic oscillator, however, a photon of lower frequency will be needed to reach the next vibrational level, and so on for higher levels. In polyatomic molecules the situation appears to be qualitatively different because there are numerous degrees of freedom. In these molecules the density of states $\sigma(E)$ (the number of states per wavenumber) increases rapidly as the energy increases, owing to the rapid expansion of the number of combinations and permutations of

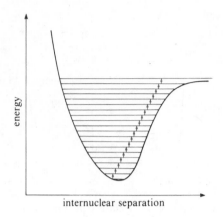

FIGURE 7   Multiple photon absorption.

vibrational modes. When $\sigma(E)$ is large enough, a 'quasi-continuum' of levels
is reached where the energy levels are packed so closely that they appear to
be continuous; at $1\,eV$ in SF_6, $\sigma(E)$ is about 10^8 per wavenumber. The
presence of the quasi-continuum means that energy from the initially excited
levels can be distributed to many levels, and then absorption from the quasi-
continuum to the dissociation limit can occur (Figure 8). The molecule must

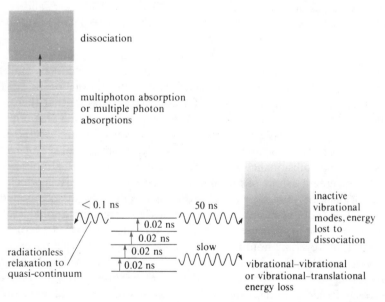

FIGURE 8   Isotopically selective photodissociation of polyatomic molecules. The
values given are for SF_6 at a pressure of 1 torr and an intensity of $1 \times 10^9\,W\,cm^{-2}$.

still, however, be excited into a high enough vibrational level of one mode (v_3 for SF_6) to reach the onset of the quasi-continuum. How is this possible when the energy spacings between vibrational levels are not the same? Possible explanations involve the strong oscillating electric field present with the laser radiation, which not only causes degenerate vibrational–rotational sub-levels to split, particularly in molecules with large dipole moments, but also changes the frequency dependence of the absorption of energy by the molecule. The stronger the electric field, the farther off-resonance this driving frequency (the laser frequency) can be to excite the oscillator (the molecule) to a given level. When the laser frequency is lower than the resonant frequency for the vibrational level and the field is sufficiently large, it is possible to drive the molecule up the vibrational ladder to an energy where a non-radiative transition to the quasi-continuum occurs. Further non-resonant excitation then occurs until dissociation is reached, as shown in Figure 8.

part SIX

The opening chapter of this Source Book referred to both photosynthesis and solar energy. It is fitting that the book should end with an examination of the greatest challenge to photochemistry—perhaps to chemistry as a whole—namely the search for photochemical means of converting and storing solar energy. The final five chapters describe the criteria that must be met by any practicable scheme, and some initial approaches to the problem.

The first of these five chapters describes the quality and quantity of solar radiation reaching the Earth's surface, and factors that determine the efficiency with which the radiation can be converted into fuel. Perhaps the most obvious approach one can take to solar energy conversion is to adapt the system that has emerged after billions of years of evolution, and the choice of topics that follows reflects this. There are other possibilities, however, and these are illustrated in the second chapter, before our principal subject is discussed in 'Photosynthesis' and 'Modelling Photosynthesis'. The final chapter outlines another very active area of research, photoelectrochemistry, which can also be seen to model photosynthesis in many respects.

6·1 Criteria for solar energy conversion

by Sir George Porter (The Royal Institution, London)

As with any other product, the usefulness of solar energy depends on its quality, its quantity and its cost. Of the many forms in which the energy of solar radiation may be collected, we shall here be concerned only with those that depend on electronic excitation, either through the physical processes of charge separation in a photoelectric device or through the chemical processes that follow the excitation of an electron in a molecule. Here the *quality* of radiation, in the sense of its spectral distribution, is of prime importance, whereas this is less important if the object is merely to convert the radiation into low-temperature heat.

1 Solar radiation

A black body (a body that is a perfect emitter at all wavelengths of the spectrum) has a characteristic radiation with an intensity and spectral distribution that depend only on its temperature. The Sun is not a perfect black body but its radiation, outside the Earth's atmosphere, approximates quite well to that of a black body at a temperature of 5 900 K.

As it traverses the Earth's atmosphere on its way to the surface, some parts of the Sun's radiation are absorbed. Ultraviolet radiation of wavelengths less than about 300 nm is almost totally removed by the ozone layer, and infrared radiation at certain wavelengths is removed by carbon dioxide and water vapour; the strong absorptions between 600 and 2 000 nm in curve (b) in Figure 1 correspond closely to the infrared spectra of water and carbon dioxide. There is also some scattering, by vapour, dust and the molecules themselves, so that the direct radiation in the direction of the Sun is reduced in intensity, and the rest of the sky, which would be black in the absence of scattering, appears blue (because short wavelengths, according to Rayleigh's law, are more strongly scattered than longer wavelengths). If mist or cloud is also present the scattered (indirect) radiation increases and may become predominant.

Even when the sky is clear, the spectral distribution of the radiation depends on the time of day and the time of year because these determine the length of the atmospheric path. This path is described in terms of air mass (A.M.), which is defined as follows:

$$\text{A.M.} = 1/\sin A$$

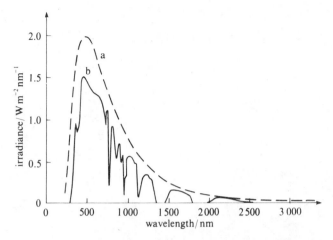

FIGURE 1   Spectral energy distribution for (a) a black body at 5 900 K, (b) the Sun at A.M. 2. (source: *Handbook of Geophysics and Space Environment*, by Air Force Cambridge Research Laboratories, edited by Shea L. Valley, McGraw-Hill Book Company, 1965)

where A is the Sun's altitude (i.e. the angle that the radiation makes with the Earth's surface). Thus A.M. 0 corresponds to radiation outside the Earth's atmosphere, A.M. 1 to the Sun overhead ($A = 90°$) and A.M. $1\frac{1}{2}$, 2 and 3 to $A = 42°$, 30° and 20°, respectively.

The energy flux (power) of the Sun's radiation at A.M. 0 is 1 350 W m^{-2}. This is reduced to about 900 W m^{-2} at A.M. 1 and to 750 W m^{-2} at A.M. 2 when the surface faces the Sun. This is for direct radiation; there is also a significant contribution from scattered radiation, which is about 100 W m^{-2} at A.M. 1. Because the area of the Earth's circle, πr^2, which intercepts the Sun's radiation is one quarter of the Earth's total surface area, $4\pi r^2$, the average energy flux per unit area (insolation) over the whole surface, day and night, winter and summer, is about 900/4 or 225 W m^{-2}. Owing to differences in the Sun's altitude at different latitudes, and to the effect of land masses on cloud formation, the actual average insolation varies from less than 100 W m^{-2} near the poles to over 300 W m^{-2} in several desert areas. These contours of insolation are shown in Figure 2.

The total solar flux at the Earth's surface (10^{17} watts) greatly exceeds all man's foreseeable energy requirements, but it is spread over large areas and the problem is to collect the radiation and convert it into useful forms, particularly free energy and work, in an economical way.

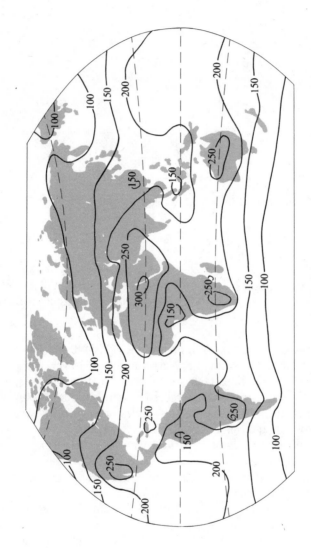

FIGURE 2 The intensity of solar radiation at the Earth's surface, in watts per square metre, averaged over a full year. (source: Porter and Archer, 1976)

2 Efficiency considerations

2.1 Thermodynamics

However carefully we design our solar energy collector we can never convert the radiation of the Sun into free energy or work with an efficiency higher than that dictated by the laws of thermodynamics, and these must therefore be our first consideration.

A combination of the first and second laws of thermodynamics leads to the following simple expression for the maximum efficiency with which heat energy can be converted into free energy capable of doing work:

$$w/q = (T_2 - T_1)/T_2$$

where w is the work performed or the free energy stored, T_2 is the temperature (in kelvins) of the heat source, in our case the Sun, T_1 is the temperature of the heat sink or the heat engine, in our case the Earth or that part of it to which we discard some of the heat, and q is the heat absorbed from the source at temperature T_2. It is implicit in this equation that some heat must be discarded at temperature T_1 because w must be less than q.

We can get a useful estimate of this efficiency of conversion by considering the Sun simply as a heat source at temperature T_2. If that temperature were 5 900 K and T_1 the temperature of the Earth, say 300 K, the maximum thermodynamic efficiency of the conversion would be 5 600/5 900, or 95%. However, if we place a black plate in bright sunlight it does not attain a temperature anywhere near 5 900 K, so we could not attain efficiencies of 95% in this way and we must now enquire why the temperature of the black plate is much lower.

If two black bodies are placed inside a perfectly reflecting vessel they will attain the same temperature, and this would be true if the Sun were one of those bodies and a black plate the other. The nearest we can come in practice to this ideal case is to place the black plate at the focus of a parabolic mirror so that the plate views the Sun over a large angle. Temperatures of over 3 000 K have been attained with solar furnaces of this kind. If smaller mirrors are used, the heated plate radiates into space as well as towards the Sun, and the temperature reached in the steady state is consequently less. If no mirrors are used, the solid angle subtended by the Sun is only a small fraction of the total solid angle; the effective temperature of the Sun turns out to be 1 333 K.

Under the black-body approximation, then, the maximum thermodynamic efficiency for conversion of solar energy into work without the use of focusing devices is therefore 1 033/1 333 or 77%, for a condenser temperature of 300 K. [One may ask why it is that a greater efficiency is possible, in principle, with a focused beam of radiation than with a dispersed beam, even though the quanta may be absorbed equally efficiently in the two cases. The answer lies in the fact that a beam of radiation has entropy E/T, as well as energy E, associated with it and, when a nearly parallel beam of light (low entropy) is absorbed or scattered by a material, it becomes isotropic, order is lost and its entropy consequently increases by an amount ΔS. When this radiation is destroyed in the absorption process, its entropy is also destroyed and, because the entropy of the universe cannot decrease, entropy of amount ΔS must be created as heat in the absorbing material at temperature T' and the available free energy is consequently decreased by an amount $T'\Delta S$.]

2.2 Efficiency of broad-band radiation

Suppose we irradiate some mercury vapour with its resonance radiation at 253.7 nm: the increase in energy, ΔE, of the excited atoms so produced will be exactly equal to the energy of the light absorbed (although, as we have seen, the increase of free energy, ΔG, will be less). If sunlight is used as the source, most of its radiation will be at other wavelengths, which are not absorbed. Now suppose that, instead of mercury, our absorbing material has a broadband absorption, like molecules in solution or a semiconductor. Again some wavelengths will not be absorbed, but an additional source of loss now appears because most of the photons that are absorbed will be of higher frequency and energy than the threshold frequency, v_0, corresponding to the energy $\Delta E_0 = h v_0$ necessary to excite the electron, and the surplus energy will generally be dissipated as heat. This situation is illustrated in Figure 3.

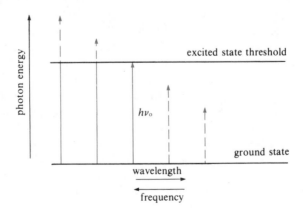

FIGURE 3   Diagram to illustrate the utilisation of a broad-band spectrum by an absorber that is black at $v > v_0$.

For a given threshold frequency, v_0, the best we can do is to arrange that all photons of frequency higher than v_0 are absorbed and used to excite electrons, (i.e. the absorber will be black at all frequencies above threshold). For such 'black-above-threshold' absorbers there will be one with an optimum threshold frequency v_0 for each particular distribution of radiation in the source. Many semiconductors and dyes, or mixtures of dyes, approximate to this black-above-threshold condition, and we can calculate the maximum efficiency of electronic excitation of v_0, and therefore of λ_0, for any given source. For solar radiation from a clear sky at A.M. 1 these efficiencies are as follows:

threshold wavelength/nm	400	500	600	700	800	1 100	1 500
maximum efficiency (%)	7	22	32	38	44	47	42

The optimum threshold is at 1 100 nm, which happens to be the long-wavelength absorption limit of silicon; the efficiencies are fairly similar for all near-infrared and red absorbers, but fall rapidly at shorter wavelengths. For climates more typical of temperate latitudes, with frequent cloud cover, the increased infrared absorption shifts the distribution to shorter wavelengths and the optimum threshold wavelength for the British climate is 700 nm, conveniently close to the absorption limit of the green plant.

In order to estimate the theoretical maximum efficiency of solar energy utilisation, the combined losses must be calculated for each increment of wavelength and integrated over the whole solar spectrum.

2.3 Other limitations on efficiency

Losses will occur when incident radiation is reflected, or is absorbed but does not lead to the necessary physical or chemical change; these need no further comment except to remark that they can usually be reduced to a few per cent. More important are the losses in the subsequent physical and chemical processes that convert the electronic excitation into electrical or chemical potential. Although the quantum yield of primary charge separation may be as high as unity, some recombination or reverse reaction is always possible and can probably never be completely avoided, as the following consideration will show.

The primary excited state R*, resulting from light absorption by R (Figure 4), must be short-lived because strong absorbers are needed, and the Einstein relations tell us that these necessarily have short lifetimes. Typically they will have lifetimes between nanoseconds and microseconds, and reaction or separation to form products P must occur in a shorter time than this if it is to be efficient. This in itself presents no difficulty and many photochemical reactions with unit quantum yield are known.

The products P, if they are to store energy, are thermodynamically unstable with respect to R, and therefore a very fast back-reaction $P \to R$ can be prevented only if there is a barrier E to this reaction, as shown in Figure 4. The height of this barrier cannot be greater than E_1, which is the energy wasted in the reaction $R^* \to P$; this wasted energy must therefore be great enough to inhibit the reverse reaction. Simple kinetic theory tells us that, in order to extend the lifetime of the products, before they back-react, to 1 second, an energy barrier of 77 kJ mol^{-1} (0.8 eV) is required at 300 K. Similarly, for a lifetime of 1 millisecond, a barrier of 58 kJ mol^{-1} (0.6 eV) is necessary. It might be

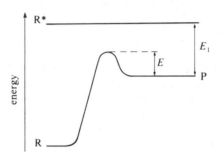

FIGURE 4   Energy relationships in the system $R \to R^* \to P \to R$.

thought that no activation energy barrier to back-reaction is necessary if the products fly apart in a large vessel, but this results in an increase in entropy and, because it is free energy that really concerns us in Figure 4, it is immaterial whether the back-reaction is retarded by an energy or an entropy barrier. These would represent very high proportional losses in a process such as photosynthesis, for example, where the energy of excitation is only about 1.8 eV. Fortunately, simple kinetic theory may not always be applicable, and products may have longer lifetimes than those calculated above, as a result of symmetry or spin restrictions, for example. Nevertheless, some losses must be incurred if energy is to be stored, and their magnitude is a matter of discussion at the present time.

3   Multiphoton processes

So far, our discussions have been about photochemical changes or molecular excitations brought about by a single photon, and indeed this is by far the most common case. Two-photon or multiphoton processes may be of three kinds: (a) no intermediate state is involved and absorption of the two photons is essentially instantaneous; (b) a short-lived metastable state or substance is formed in the first step and this absorbs the second photon; (c) the intermediate is a stable molecule. Types (a) and (b) are dependent on the light intensity (the rate is usually, though not always, proportional to the square of the intensity) and are therefore only observed at high intensities. Type (a) requires laser intensities, and type (b) may occur with conventional flash (or even intense continuous) sources if the intermediate has a fairly long lifetime (e.g. a triplet state).

The intensity of sunlight at A.M. 1 is about 10^{17} visible quanta $cm^{-2} s^{-1}$. A typical pigment molecule with an absorption coefficient 3×10^4 l mol^{-1} cm^{-1} will absorb 12 quanta s^{-1} under these conditions so that, for two-quantum processes to operate through one molecule, the lifetime of its intermediate state must exceed 0.1 second, a time longer than the lifetime of either the singlet or the triplet state of chlorophyll. It should be noted, however, that if a large number of pigment molecules operate co-operatively with very rapid energy transfer to a reaction centre, the probability of two-quantum processes is correspondingly increased.

6·2 Photochemical energy storage not based on redox systems

by Trevor Laird (Bridge Chemicals Ltd)

Although major efforts are being made to evaluate methods of photochemical energy storage based on photosynthesis, the criteria allow many other reversible organic and inorganic reactions to be considered. However, the requirements are critical. The portion of the solar spectrum useful for photochemical reactions lies in the range 300–700 nm, which corresponds to about 50% of the available energy. Some of this energy, however, is 'unusable' because quantum processes have energy thresholds below which photons are insufficiently energetic; above that threshold all photons contribute the same amount of energy to the chemical change. Thus a process with a high threshold energy will overlap with only a small part of the solar spectrum but will extract a large amount of energy per photon. A low-energy process has good spectral overlap but extracts correspondingly less energy per photon. A compromise must inevitably be sought. Two-component or three-component systems can be considered. This chapter concentrates on the former because they are the more promising.

1 Two-component systems—organic pericyclic processes

Figure 1 shows an energy diagram for a cyclic system that could convert solar energy into stored chemical energy. Material A is converted via its excited state A* into material B, which has a higher ground state energy, thus storing energy. B must be kinetically stable at ambient temperatures and therefore a minimum energy barrier of approximately $100 \, \text{kJ mol}^{-1}$ is required. The stored energy can be subsequently released as heat by applying heat initially or by using a catalyst to regenerate A.

Figure 1 shows the effect of trying to maximise storage capacity by increasing the ground state energy of B progressively. Possible ground state energy levels for reactions storing 40, 80 and $120 \, \text{kJ mol}^{-1}$ are depicted. Excited state energy levels are also shown for three materials that could be used to store energy, with excitation energies of 170, 210, $250 \, \text{kJ mol}^{-1}$ corresponding to λ_{max} at 710, 570 and 480 nm, respectively. As the storage capacity increases, the energy of the transition state for the reaction $B \rightarrow A$ increases to a point where the energy levels are of comparable energy with the first excited state energy levels of A*. It is likely that in the photochemical

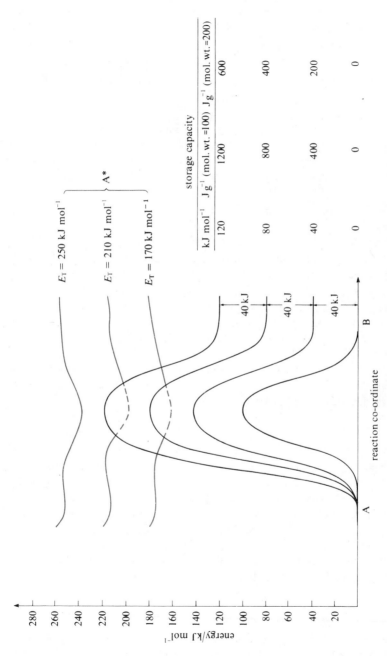

FIGURE 1   Potential energy diagram for a typical photochemical storage reaction, showing the effect on the storage capacity. (source: Jones, 1979)

stage the energy (E_T) required to raise A to its first excited state A* will be greater than this transition state energy. Thus as the potential storage capacity is increased, the excited state energy must also be raised, and the number of photons of solar energy usable will be consequently reduced. The maximum achievable efficiency therefore decreases as the storage capacity increases.

1.1 Criteria for efficient energy storage

In designing a photochemical energy store the following factors are important: (a) a good match of the ultraviolet–visible spectrum of A with the solar spectrum; (b) a high quantum yield for the photoreaction; (c) a high storage capacity: the molecules of B should be strained yet stable: a low relative molecular mass (M_r) is advantageous; (d) high chemical yields (more than 99.95%) in each step, otherwise byproducts will accumulate on repeated cycling; (e) A and B must be cheap and non-hazardous.

Reactions which produce, as B, small strained molecules by so-called pericyclic processes, meet these criteria. The products are kinetically stable, in part because of energy barriers imposed by orbital symmetry effects, but the conversion of B into A can usually be achieved catalytically. Many such processes are capable of storing $60–100 \text{ kJ mol}^{-1}$, so that for a material with $M_r = 100$, a storage capacity of $600–1000 \text{ J g}^{-1}$ could be achieved. This compares favourably with heat storage in water with a usable temperature difference of 50 K (209 J g^{-1}).

A feasibility study by the Battelle Institute in Ohio has compared a potential organic photochemical system with a conventional solar water-heating system. The design requirements to supply 80% of the heating and cooling load of a typical 200 m^2 house in a northern USA climate were assessed, the total installation costing about £5000 (1980 prices). Assuming that the solar water heater was between 25% and 35% efficient and an organic fuel costing £1200 per tonne would undergo about 5000 cycles in 20 years, the relationship between the storage capacity and efficiency of the photochemical system to match the performance of the solar heater could be calculated (Figure 2).

It is apparent that the minimum usable efficiency of a photochemical fuel is 15–20% with a storage capacity of at least 800 J g^{-1}. From recent calculations, an efficiency of 15% is the maximum likely to be achieved in any practical system, and therefore in searching for photochemical fuels a target storage capacity of greater than 800 J g^{-1} will be required.

1.2 Possible photochemical energy stores

Of the vast number of photochemical reactions suggested for energy storage, few meet the above criteria. For example, the isomerisation of benzene (1) to

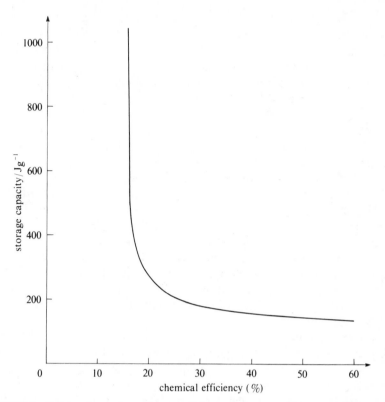

FIGURE 2 Efficiencies and storage capacities for a photochemical system to compete with a solar thermal storage system of 25% efficiency. (source: Talbert, Freiling, Eibling and Nathan, 1976)

prismane (**2**), if it were feasible, would store $4000\,J\,g^{-1}$, yet prismane has a half-life of 11 hours at 90 °C. At the moment, prismanes are photochemically accessible only from benzene with perfluoroalkyl groups attached (**3 → 4**). The increased molecular mass, however, reduces the storage capacity to an impractical $400\,J\,g^{-1}$.

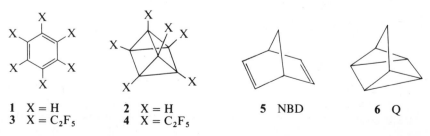

| **1** | X = H |
| **3** | X = C_2F_5 |

| **2** | X = H |
| **4** | X = C_2F_5 |

5 NBD

6 Q

The most widely studied reaction, the photoisomerisation of norbornadiene (NBD, **5**) to quadricyclane (Q, **6**) has many attractive features. (a) Both materials are liquids at normal pressures (NBD, b.t. 90 °C; Q, b.t. 111 °C). (b) NBD is readily available from cheap starting materials: cyclopentadiene and ethyne. (c) Although the enthalpy of isomerisation of NBD to Q is moderate ($1110 \, kJ \, mol^{-1}$) the low relative molecular mass (92) means that a very high storage capacity, $1200 \, J \, g^{-1}$, results. (d) Quantitative photochemical and chemical yields have been obtained in the forward and the reverse reactions. (e) The photochemical reaction is relatively insensitive to the presence of air. (f) Although Q is highly strained, it is extremely stable kinetically, the half-life for the conversion into NBD being 14 hours at 140 °C. Transition metals catalyse this reverse transformation quantitatively and exothermically. For example, when a rhodium complex catalyst is used the reaction has a half-life of 45 min at 26 °C. Complexes of iron, cobalt, nickel, platinum, palladium and silver have also been used.

The major disadvantage is that NBD does not absorb at wavelengths above 300 nm, and much of the research carried out recently has been aimed at overcoming this problem. Chemical modification of NBD by introduction of substituents causes an increase in the molecular mass and a reduction in the storage capacity.

The transition to the lowest triplet state of NBD requires $293 \, kJ \, mol^{-1}$. Triplet sensitisers such as acetophenone (E_T, $310 \, kJ \, mol^{-1}$) cause isomerisation of NBD to Q with high quantum yield ($\phi = 0.91$), but the use of sensitisers that absorb at longer wavelengths reduces the quantum efficiency as the triplet energy of the sensitiser is decreased. Energy transfer from these sensitisers is endothermic and normally inefficient, unless exciplex formation with NBD occurs.

For the substituted NBD (**7**), sensitisers such as camphorquinone (**8**) ($\lambda_{max} = 435, 480 \, nm$) are quite efficient ($\phi = 0.3$–0.6). Energy transfer to **7** must be endothermic, probably occurring via an exciplex. The design of sensitisers that complex with NBD in the excited state is therefore presently being investigated.

7   8

It has been suggested that if significant amounts of thermal energy can be used to boost triplet levels, the quantum yield of a normally endothermic sensitisation may be enhanced. This may allow low-energy sensitisers absorbing in the 500–600 nm range to be used for materials absorbing in the ultraviolet. Research on this 'thermal upconversion of triplets' is in its infancy, however, and it remains to be seen whether the elevated temperatures of solar collectors can improve photochemical efficiencies.

Transition-metal complexes have been examined as possible sensitisers. Many transition metals form complexes with NBD in the ground state, but only the copper(I) complex leads to the desired photochemical conversion into Q. The photoisomerisation ($\phi = 0.4$) is essentially catalytic, 400 moles of Q being formed per mole of copper(I) salt consumed. The system must be kept oxygen-free, however, otherwise copper(II) is formed and the reactions stop. Air-stable (triarylphosphine)copper borohydrides (9) also catalyse the photoisomerisation ($\phi = 0.8$), but in these examples no ground state complex with NBD is formed. Photocatalysis probably occurs via a complex between excited copper phosphine and NBD. The fact that these copper complexes absorb only below 350 nm means that the overall efficiency in the use of solar energy is only 0.2%. Research is now aimed at incorporating chromophores which absorb strongly in the visible region into the copper phosphines, to try to improve the solar efficiency of the NBD isomerisation.

$$
\begin{array}{c}
Ar_3P \diagdown \quad H \quad H \\
\quad\quad Cu \quad B \\
Ar_3P \diagup \quad H \quad H \\
\mathbf{9}
\end{array}
$$

In a study of a wide range of transition-metal sensitisers, only copper complexes and the iridium complex (10) were effective, the latter with a quantum yield of 0.7.

10   where N−N refers to 2,2'-bipyridyl

2,2'-bipyridyl

1.3   Immobilised sensitisers and catalysts

If transition metals are to be used as sensitisers for the energy-trapping stage or as catalysts for the energy-releasing stage in any practical system, it would be advisable to use immobilised materials, for two reasons: (a) to prevent interaction between sensitiser and catalyst, and (b) for ease of replacement or recycling of expensive transition metals.

Although there have been few applications of immobilised sensitisers in photochemical reactions, it has been found recently that immobilised sensitisers can be *more* efficient than homogeneous analogues. Thus the charged iridium bipyridyl complex (**10**) which is easily immobilised on acidic supports such as sulphonated polystyrene or carboxyphenylated silica, sensitises the photoconversion of NBD into Q with a quantum yield of 0.8.

A variety of transition-metal compounds catalyse the conversion of Q into NBD, the cheapest and most effective being cobalt porphyrins. These molecules are easily anchored to insoluble polymeric supports, and the resultant immobilised catalysts (0.28–0.44% cobalt) are extremely effective. The stability of porphyrins and related molecules (e.g. phthalocyanines) to prolonged exposure to heat and light, and the high turnover numbers already achieved (15 000 moles of Q per gram atom of cobalt) indicate that these materials are most likely to be chosen for any subsequent device.

2 Outlook for energy storage in organic compounds

The strict criteria needed for an organic fuel to store solar energy successfully are unlikely to be met unless ways are found of achieving a better spectral overlap of photosensitisers with the solar spectrum, without diminishing sensitiser efficiency. Two possible approaches are the thermal upconversion of triplets and the chemical modification of organometallic sensitisers. Even if these methods are successful, organic photochemical storage may still be less economical than other methods of solar energy conversion into low-grade heat. Methods of combining photochemical storage with solar hot water storage have therefore been examined.

2.1 Photochemically assisted hot water storage

Research in the USA has recently been aimed at improving solar water-heating systems by dissolving dyes in the water. The indigo dyes (**11**), for example, utilise the wavelengths 300–600 nm, normally inefficiently utilised by solar heaters, and store energy in the same manner as organic valence isomers, in the higher energy *cis*-isomers. Advantages are (a) excellent matching with the solar spectrum, and (b) the back-reaction is catalysed by simple acid catalysts, such as sulphuric acid). Properties that need to be improved are the storage capacity $(35\,kJ\,mol^{-1}, 100\,J\,g^{-1})$, the quantum yield (0.1–0.2) and the solubility in water. The half-life of the *cis*-isomers, several hours at room temperature, is satisfactory for use in a thermal system.

The potential overall improvement using photochemically assisted solar water heating has been calculated to be 24% (compared with a conventional

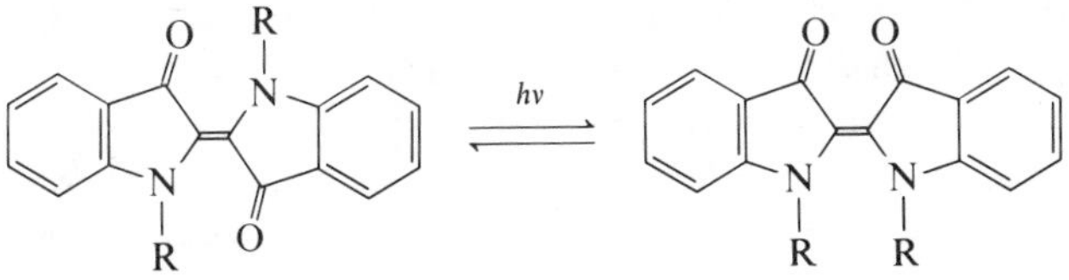

*trans-***11**   *cis-***11**

solar water heater) for summer months and 30% for winter months *provided* a photochemical efficiency of 20% can be achieved. It remains to be seen, however, whether the additional costs of a photochemically assisted system (mainly the cost of dye, because the equipment is essentially the same) outweigh the advantage of improved efficiency.

3 Three-component systems

The criteria for three-component systems

$$A \xrightarrow{hv} B + C$$

are similar to those for two-component systems, but additionally the products B and C must be separated and subsequently recombined when the stored energy is required. The most widely studied example is the photolysis of nitrosyl chloride (NOCl).

The visible spectrum of NOCl covers most of the range 300–640 nm and photolysis proceeds with a quantum yield of unity. Two processes occur at different wavelengths but the ultimate products are the same.

$$NOCl \xrightarrow{hv} NOCl^*$$

$$NOCl^* \longrightarrow \cdot NO + Cl \cdot$$
$$Cl \cdot + NOCl \longrightarrow \cdot NO + Cl_2 \qquad \lambda = 365\text{--}500\,nm$$

$$NOCl^* + NOCl \longrightarrow 2 \cdot NO + Cl_2 \qquad \lambda = 500\text{--}640\,nm$$

The starting materials and the products are both highly corrosive, toxic and very reactive. The products must therefore be separated within minutes otherwise the back-reaction occurs, and stored energy is lost.

Because nitric oxide is insoluble in chlorinated hydrocarbons, a solution of NOCl in CCl_4 can be used to facilitate product separation, but the quantum yield in solution drops to 0.2. Using such a system, a storage efficiency of 1.7% of the incident radiation between 300 and 640 nm (i.e. an overall storage efficiency of 0.65%) has been achieved.

The storage capacity $(414\,J\,g^{-1})$ coupled with excellent spectral sensitivity (potentially 38% of the solar flux is available) and potentially high quantum yield (0.2–2.0 depending on wavelengths) made this an attractive system for study. However, the problems associated with the toxicity, volatility, high reactivity and corrosive nature of the components are formidable, and the cost of developing a hazard-free NOCl storage system is likely to be prohibitive. Because none of the other three-component systems has the storage potential of NOCl there seems to be little future for this method for the storage of solar energy.

6·3 Photosynthesis

by Sir George Porter (The Royal Institution, London)

Natural photosynthesis is an energy-storing photochemical reaction that occurs in green plants and some other living systems. In all cases, except for photosynthetic bacteria, the overall reaction may be written:

$$H_2O + CO_2 \xrightarrow[\text{chlorophyll}]{\text{light}} (CH_2O) + O_2$$

$$\Delta H = 470 \, \text{kJ and } \Delta G = 500 \, \text{kJ per mole of } CO_2$$

(1)

In this equation the bracketed (CH_2O) represents carbohydrate (e.g. starch or sugar), and the energy increments in the system, ΔG and ΔH, are calculated for the carbohydrate glucose and for ambient conditions in the atmosphere.

Thermodynamically, the reaction is extremely improbable in the dark, both from the point of view of energy and entropy, and it can proceed only if energy is supplied from the Sun. The sunlight is absorbed by a number of pigments, of which chlorophyll is the most important. The reverse reaction does not occur spontaneously at normal temperatures; the carbohydrates are stable in air because of a high activation energy barrier to the reverse reactions. However, this reaction proceeds rapidly at higher temperatures (combustion) or at body temperature in the presence of enzyme catalysts. By releasing the stored energy in these two ways we use the photochemical product as a fuel or as a food.

The scale on which this process proceeds on Earth is vast, by any standards. All the carbon dioxide on Earth passes through the photosynthetic cycle, on average, once every 300 years, the oxygen every 2000 years and the water in the oceans every two million years. The mass of carbon fixed as carbohydrate is 2×10^{11} tonnes per annum, equivalent to ten times mankind's energy consumption, even though the overall efficiency of photosynthesis on land is less than 0.2%.

1 Mechanism and energetics

Reaction (1) describes the overall result of a very complex sequence of reactions, some of them photochemical and others occurring in the dark. The essential photochemical reaction is the splitting of water to form gaseous oxygen with the concurrent transfer of electrons and protons to other molecules which therefore become reduced. To produce one molecule of oxygen, four electrons must be transferred:

$$2H_2O \longrightarrow O_2 + 4e + 4H^+$$

(2)

355

and four electrons are also necessary to reduce one carbon dioxide molecule to the level of carbohydrate:

$$4e + 4H^+ + CO_2 \longrightarrow (CH_2O) + H_2O \qquad (3)$$

Reaction (1) is thus the sum of reactions (2) and (3).

If reaction (1) could be made to operate in a reversible electrochemical cell, the potential E of the cell would be given by

$$\Delta G = -nFE$$

where n, the number of electrons transferred, is 4, and F is the Faraday* (96 487 coulombs per gram equivalent), from which we find that $E = -1.30$ V. This is similar to the potential $(-1.23$ V) for the two-electron process which dissociates water into hydrogen and oxygen.

Let us now investigate the energetics of the photochemical reaction. The longest wavelength light absorbed by chlorophyll which is effective in photosynthesis is about 700 nm, corresponding to an energy of 170 kJ per einstein, or 1.76 eV. Comparing this with the energy required for each of the four electron transfers of reaction (1) (1.3 eV), we find that three photons of 700 nm light are just sufficient to transfer four electrons. However, it is known that the dark reactions by which carbon dioxide is finally reduced to carbohydrate require not only a reducing agent (NADP.2H) but also adenosine triphosphate (ATP) to fill its usual biochemical role as an energy source. Probably one molecule of ATP is formed from ADP for each electron transferred, and the energy required for this is 0.25 eV. The reaction now requires a minimum of four photons and, when the sources of inefficiency discussed in Chapter 6·1 are also taken into account, more than four photons would appear to be necessary. In fact, experimental measurements of the optimum quantum yield show that it corresponds to about eight photons per molecule of CO_2 reduced. This suggests that two photons are utilised for each electron transfer, which implies a two-step process with relatively long-lived intermediates connecting them.

In the 1940s, at the University of Illinois, Emerson provided evidence that there were indeed two separate photosystems operating in photosynthesis. By measuring the quantum yield of oxygen evolution at different wavelengths, he showed that the yield fell off at long wavelengths, even though these wavelengths were still being absorbed; this is known as the 'red drop' and occurs at wavelengths longer than 690 nm. However, he also found that, if he irradiated the photosynthetic system at shorter wavelengths, whilst simultaneously irradiating at wavelengths greater than 690 nm, the long

---

* One Faraday is the number of coulombs of charge required for one mole of a substance to gain one electron per molecule.

wavelength irradiation became effective in photosynthesis. The quantum yield of the system irradiated by both wavelengths at the same time was greater than the sum of the quantum yields obtained by separate irradiations at the same two wavelengths. Emerson concluded, therefore, that there are two photosystems (now called PS I and PS II) which operate in series and have slightly different absorption spectra. At wavelengths longer than 690 nm, only PS I absorbs and PS II cannot operate, so that photosynthesis is blocked.

In 1960, Hill and Bendall in Cambridge proposed a scheme for this two-photon excitation, which is still the basis of nearly all discussions of the mechanism of photosynthesis. A simple version of the scheme is shown in Figure 1; because of the shape of the diagram it is usually known as the Z scheme. The vertical co-ordinate, E'_0, is a scale of redox potentials* at pH 7,

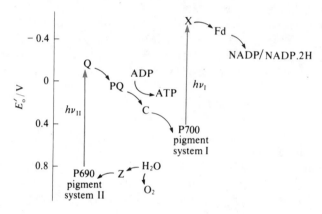

FIGURE 1   The Z scheme of photosynthesis.

and the position of any component in the diagram represents the redox potential of an oxidant/reductant couple. For example, $+0.81$ V is the potential of the $\frac{1}{2}O_2/H_2O$ couple in the reaction:

$$\tfrac{1}{2}O_2 + 2H^+ + 2e \longrightarrow H_2O$$

The positive sign indicates that the reaction tends to go as written, i.e. oxygen is a strong oxidant and water is a weak reductant. The negative redox potentials, for example NADP/NADP.2H at -0.32 V, indicate high reducing potential; this couple is capable of reducing all couples of higher E'_0.

Referring to Figure 1, the course of electron flow is as follows. A quantum of light absorbed by the pigment of PS II excites a molecule (called P 690

* See Appendix (p. 384)

because it absorbs at 690 nm) which mediates the transfer of an electron against the potential gradient from species Z to a species Q, to give Z^+ and Q^-. Although there is good evidence for intermediates at these potentials, their chemical nature is not yet known. There is strong evidence that Z involves a manganese ion in some form and that Z^+ oxidises water to oxygen, four steps being necessary to form one molecule of O_2. The reduced species Q^- transfers its electron, in a spontaneous dark reaction, to plastoquinone (PQ) and the reduced plastoquinone transfers its electron to cytochrome (C) and so on. There is a 'pool' of plastoquinone molecules, about 20 to each manganese ion, and the plastoquinone/reduced-plastoquinone couple appears to act as the intermediate reservoir of electrons between PS II and PS I.

The reaction centre of PS I (called P 700) has a lower redox potential than that of PS II, although both are thought to be molecules or dimers of chlorophyll *a* in different environments. A photon absorbed in the PS I pigment system excites P 700, which then mediates the second uphill transfer of the electron received from the PS II chain to the highly reducing component X. A second series of dark electron-transfers now occurs via the protein, ferredoxin (Fd), to NADP, which is reduced, by two electrons, to NADP.2H. This is the final stable product of the two quanta/electron transfer, and it acts as reducing agent in the dark reactions that reduce carbon dioxide. These occur in the fluid stroma outside the main photosynthetic apparatus in a series of catalysed steps known as the Calvin cycle. The reactions of the Calvin cycle require ATP as well as NADP.2H, and the ATP is synthesised in reactions that proceed in parallel with the Z scheme and utilise some of the energy that would otherwise be wasted in the downhill electron-transfer steps.

2 Light-harvesting antennae

If a green plant is irradiated with short (millisecond) flashes having a long (second) interval between them, the evolution of oxygen increases as the intensity of the flashes is increased until, at a certain intensity, a limit is reached and there is no further increase in oxygen evolution. At this limit, the number of photons absorbed is sufficient to excite only one out of every 300 pigment (mainly chlorophyll) molecules. If the other chlorophyll molecules were inactive the quantum efficiency, even at lower intensities, could never exceed 1/300, whereas it is near to unity under optimum conditions.

These light-flashing experiments indicate that there are approximately 300 pigment molecules associated with each reaction centre of PS I and PS II, and excitation of any one of these can lead to excitation of the reaction centre. The array of pigment molecules, reaction centre and intermediate molecules in the electron-transfer chain is called a photosynthetic unit, and the array of pigment molecules that transfer energy to the reaction centre is called the light-harvesting antenna. This is an elegant way of providing for efficient collection of incident light without the necessity of having one molecule of every component of the electron transport chain for every molecule which absorbs light. Energy transfer between pigment molecules in the antenna occurs by 'resonant transfer' (see Chapter 4·2), and its efficiency is proportional to the overlap of the emission spectrum of the donor molecule with the absorption spectrum of the acceptor. Because the peak of the fluorescence spectrum of a molecule occurs at a slightly longer wavelength than that of its absorption spectrum, the optimum conditions for transfer are those where the donor absorbs at slightly higher energy than the acceptor, though the overlap integral between two identical molecules can be quite large. This is so in the important case of chlorophyll a, for which R_0, the separation at which energy transfer is 50% efficient, is 7 nm.

The absorption spectra of some of the important pigments found in photosynthetic units are shown in Figure 2. It will be seen that chlorophyll a absorbs at a longer wavelength than any of the other pigments and will therefore always be the ultimate acceptor in the antenna. Chlorophyll a is present in all photosynthetic systems capable of evolving oxygen (i.e. all except bacteria) and is usually the major pigment. In green plants and algae the principal accessory pigments are chlorophyll b and carotenes. In red and blue–green algae the principal accessory pigments are phycoerythrin and phycocyanin. These pigments extend the region of the Sun's spectrum that is absorbed and provide a better match to the particular conditions in which photosynthesis takes place—for example, the red algae are usually beneath the surface of the ocean where green algae absorb and it becomes more important for them to utilise fully the shorter wavelengths.

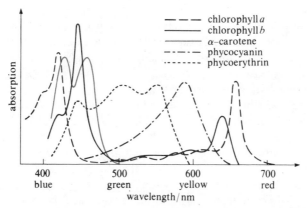

FIGURE 2   Absorption spectra of the principal light-harvesting pigments of plant photosynthesis. (source: Govindjee and Govindjee, 1974)

3   The photosynthetic apparatus

The process of photosynthesis occurs in lamellar membranes, which can be seen in electron microscope photographs of simple cells and of the chloroplasts of green plant cells. It is thought that the electron transfers occur from one side of the membrane to the other and in such a direction that oxygen is released on the inside (PS II), whereas reduction takes place on the outside (PS I).

Little is known with certainty about how the various chemical components of the electron transport chain, or even the chlorophyll and other pigments, are disposed. Very recently some progress has been made in isolating protein complexes from the lipid membrane, and at least three such complexes have been characterised in chloroplast membranes; these complexes seem to be associated with PS I, PS II, and a light-harvesting unit which contains most of the chlorophyll *b*. The light-harvesting chlorophyll *a/b* protein seems to contain three molecules of chlorophyll *a* and three molecules of chlorophyll *b* in a protein with a relative molecular mass of 30 000, whereas the PS I complex probably consists of trimers, each with a relative molecular mass of 48 000, and each containing seven chlorophyll *a* molecules. In algae, the auxiliary pigments (phycoerythrins and phycocyanins) occur in protein complexes (phycobilisomes) on the surface of the membrane and transfer their energy to chlorophyll *a* within the membrane.

4   Photosynthetic bacteria

Bacterial photosynthesis is a simpler process than that of the oxygen-evolving plants and, although it stores little energy, it has been much studied because it is more readily interpreted. Like plant photosynthesis, bacterial photosynthesis transfers electrons from a reducing agent to carbon dioxide but, unlike green plants, bacteria are unable to use water as the reducing agent. Instead, they use compounds such as H_2S, which is oxidised to elemental sulphur, and they are able to do this using only one photon for each electron transfer. Also, instead of chlorophyll, bacteria use a reduced form, called bacteriochlorophyll, as the principal pigment.

It has been possible to isolate several relatively simple protein complexes from bacteria. In one case, the complex has been crystallised and its structure determined by X-ray crystallography. In another case, the complex isolated is the reaction centre itself and very thorough investigations have been carried out on the reactions that occur immediately following light absorption, using electron spin resonance spectroscopy and flash photolysis techniques (particularly in the picosecond region). The results provide the first direct information about any photosynthetic reaction centre and are therefore of great interest. The sequence of reactions, as it is understood at present, is shown in Figure 3.

$$
\begin{array}{c}
\text{Cyt-c} \quad \text{BChl}^* \, \text{BPh} \quad \text{Q} \\
\downarrow 3\text{ps} \\
\text{Cyt-c} \quad \text{BChl}^+ \, \text{BPh}^- \, \text{Q} \\
\downarrow 200\text{ps} \\
\text{Cyt-c} \quad \text{BChl}^+ \, \text{BPh} \quad \text{Q}^- \\
\downarrow 1\text{–}20\mu\text{s} \\
\text{Cyt-c}^+ \, \text{BChl} \quad \text{BPh} \quad \text{Q}^-
\end{array}
$$

FIGURE 3   Electron transfer following excitation of the reaction centre in a photo-synthetic bacterium.

The components in the electron transport chain are thought to be the protein cytochrome c (Cyt-c), bacteriochlorophyll (BChl), bacteriopheophytin (BPh) (which is bacteriochlorophyll lacking its central magnesium atom), and ubiquinone (Q), arranged in that sequence. The bacteriochlorophyll is probably a dimer, and the ubiquinone is complexed to iron. The bacteriochlorophyll is excited and then a series of electron transfers occurs in the times shown in Figure 3. Further work on this and other reaction centres, using picosecond laser techniques, should lead to a better understanding of the primary electron-transfer reactions of photosynthesis.

6·4 Modelling photosynthesis

by Sir George Porter (The Royal Institution, London)

There are two reasons why organic synthesis is used in chemistry; first, it is a means of confirming the structure of a natural product and, second, it may lead to a commercial preparation for useful purposes. The same is true of the synthetic approach to photosynthesis, although there is here little hope of the total synthesis of anything as complex as a complete chloroplast. The practical purpose of modelling parts of the photosynthetic unit is ultimately to construct a simplified version of the photosynthetic process, which might be more useful than the living system for the collection and storage of solar energy.

Although it might seem a little presumptuous of the photochemist to believe that he can improve on a process which nature has taken three billion years to develop, we must bear in mind that the plant did not evolve as a source of fuel for man and, except in the form of their waste products (oil, coal and natural gas), plants are not very convenient sources of energy. The collection and transport of plants are labour-intensive and therefore expensive, and they also consume energy. Furthermore, agricultural processes are also energy-consuming because, if good yields are to be attained, fertilisers, weed-killers, insecticides and other manufactured products are necessary. Finally, in most parts of the world, irrigation is necessary because the living plant requires far more water than is actually used in the photosynthetic reaction—sugar cane, for example, may require several thousand times its own weight in water.

In addition to these disadvantages, the overall efficiency of solar energy collection by the green plant is far lower than what is theoretically possible, and this offers a great challenge. Various factors suggest that overall efficiencies of about 12% might be reasonably expected in a two-photon process; actual efficiencies compare very unfavourably with this:

Efficiencies of solar energy conversion by photosynthesis

whole-Earth biomass	0.15%
agriculture (annual)	0.1–1.2%
agriculture (best peak growth)	2–4.5%

Even at these efficiencies the products, sugar or cellulose, have to be further processed, by fermentation to alcohol, for example, unless they are merely to be burned. The most immediate problem is to provide a replacement for natural gas and oil, our two most convenient, but diminishing, sources of primary energy and chemical feedstock.

1 The essential reaction

With the exception of bacterial photosynthesis, which stores very little energy, we have seen that all photosynthetic systems oxidise water to oxygen. The reduced product of this reaction in photosystem II is the plastohydroquinone (reduced plastoquinone) pool, and this is utilised as the electron donor in photosystem I, which generates a product of still higher reducing power, first reduced ferredoxin, then NADP.2H. This reducing power is the primary fuel made in the photochemical reaction, and the dark reactions that follow serve only the purpose of producing the particular reduced product that is required. The most important is carbohydrate, from the reduction of carbon dioxide by NADP.2H, but nitrogen may be reduced instead to form ammonia by intercepting the reaction between ferredoxin and NADP with the enzyme nitrogenase, or the reduced product may be gaseous hydrogen if the enzyme hydrogenase is used. The energetics of the formation of these three products are not very different, as is seen from the following equations:

	$\Delta G/\text{kJ mol}^{-1}$	E_0'/eV
$CO_2 + H_2O \longrightarrow (CH_2O) + O_2$	124	-1.29
$\frac{2}{3}N_2 + 2H_2O \longrightarrow \frac{4}{3}NH_3 + O_2$	113	-1.17
$2H_2O \longrightarrow 2H_2 + O_2$	118	-1.23

where ΔG is the free energy change on liberation of 0.25 mole of O_2.

Even photosystem II alone, by forming plastohydroquinone from plastoquinone, stores, in a four-photon reaction, more than half of the energy stored in the overall eight-photon reaction.

Each of these reactions might be a useful substitute for natural photosynthesis. Hydrogen could replace natural gas, alcohols from reduced carbon dioxide could replace liquid fuels, atmospheric nitrogen might be 'fixed' in this way for agricultural use and, in principle, the oxidation of a hydroquinone could be made to power an electrical fuel cell. The essential reaction of photosynthesis, from the point of view of solar energy storage is, therefore, the photolysis of water to give oxygen and a reduced compound. The formation of oxygen is essential to complete the cycle if the reduced compound is to react with air. We could, of course, envisage other cyclic photochemical processes not involving oxygen, but they probably could not replace conventional fuels in existing equipment and the great advantage of having one of the reactants, oxygen, universally available in the atmosphere would be lost.

2 The photolysis of water in vitro

The photolysis of water into hydrogen and oxygen, using sunlight as the energy source can, in principle, be carried out in three ways: (a) a photovoltaic cell followed by electrolysis; (b) the photoelectrochemical generation of hydrogen and oxygen from water; (c) the photochemical generation of hydrogen and oxygen without electrodes.

The three methods are closely related and merge one into the other as we shall see later (Chapter 6·5). The third, which is the model closest to the natural process of photosynthesis, is the one that we shall be concerned with in this chapter.

If the overall process of formation of $H_2 + \frac{1}{2}O_2$ could be carried out without energy loss, then 1.23 eV would be required for each of the four electron transfers. On the other hand, if the mechanism is to involve the photolysis of water to hydrogen atoms or hydroxyl radicals, more than 2.5 eV would be required. Natural photosynthesis operates at wavelengths up to 700 nm, which corresponds to an energy of $170 \, kJ \, mol^{-1}$ or 1.76 eV, so it follows that fission into radicals or atoms is not energetically possible as a primary step.

Before proceeding, we need to be clear about how redox potentials are affected by light absorption. Absorption of a photon by a molecule raises one of its electrons to a higher energy level, and the molecule is a better electron donor in its excited state than in its ground state. Its reducing potential is raised. Furthermore, as electronic excitation also creates an electron 'hole' in the original molecular energy level, the molecule is also a better electron acceptor in its excited state.

Electronic excitation of the reducing partner, S, of a redox couple S^+/S makes it a better reducer, or *lowers* the redox potential of the couple, by an amount corresponding to the energy absorbed. Likewise, electronic excitation of the oxidising partner, S^+, makes it a better oxidiser, or *raises* the redox potential by an amount corresponding to the energy absorbed. Figure 1 shows the three situations where the wavelength of light absorbed is 700 nm. The couple, written S^+/S for simplicity, may be generalised to $S^{n+}/S^{(n-1)+}$ and $S^{n-}/S^{(n+1)-}$ where n is any integer, or zero.

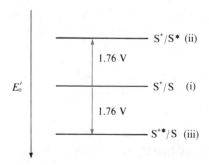

FIGURE 1   Relative potentials of a redox couple (i) in the ground state, (ii) with the reductant excited, (iii) with the oxidant excited by absorption of 700 nm light.

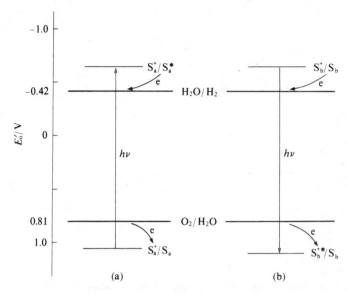

FIGURE 2 Redox schemes for the simultaneous photo-oxidation and photo-reduction of water: (a) light absorbed by the reductant; (b) light absorbed by the oxidant.

Let us now consider the various possibilities by which photochemical electron transfer reactions may be used to bring about the dissociation of water. Figure 2(a) shows a redox couple S_a^+/S_a with a potential of 1.05 V, in which S_a absorbs light of 700 nm wavelength, thus making available the couple S_a^+/S_a^* with potential $1.05 - 1.76$, i.e. -0.71 V. Such a situation makes it energetically possible for the couple in its ground state to oxidise water and in its excited state to reduce water, using a wavelength of 700 nm, provided the redox potential of the couple in its ground state lies between 0.81 and 1.34 V $(-0.42 + 1.76)$.

Figure 2(b) shows a different redox couple, S_b^+/S_b, with a potential of -0.66 V, in which S_b^+ will absorb light of wavelength 700 nm to make available the couple S_b^+*/S_b with potential $-0.66 + 1.76$, i.e. 1.1 V. Here, the ground state couple can effect the reduction of water and the excited state can oxidise water, provided the E_0' of this couple lies between -0.42 and -0.95 V $(0.81 - 1.76)$.

In either case, kinetics may prevent the reaction occurring at a measurable rate and the available spare energy of 0.53 eV $(1.76 - 1.23)$ may not be enough to overcome the energies of activation of the two reactions. If this is so, or if the rather stringent requirements for E_0' and light absorption cannot be fulfilled, it may be possible to carry out the reduction of water and the oxidation of an

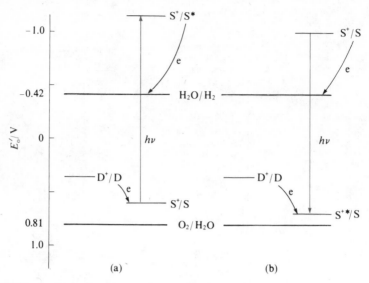

FIGURE 3 Redox schemes for the photoreduction of water using a sacrificial donor D.

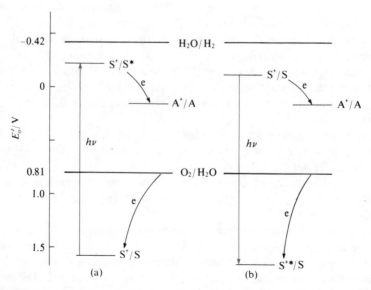

FIGURE 4 Redox schemes for the photo-oxidation of water using a sacrificial acceptor A^+.

added donor molecule, D (Figures 3a and 3b) or the oxidation of water and the reduction of an added acceptor molecule, A^+ (Figures 4a and 4b). These are all half-reactions as far as the oxidation and reduction of water are concerned but it is possible, in principle, to bring about the complete reaction by allowing electron transfer between the donor, D, and the acceptor, A^+. Because two systems are now used, two photons are required for each electron transferred. In the Z scheme of photosynthesis (see Figure 1 in Chapter 6.3), PS I is of the type in Figure 3(a) and PS II of type in Figure 4(a). The potentials of some redox couples relevant to the natural system and those to be described are listed in Table 1. We shall now consider, in turn, the experimental methods which have been used for the reduction (Figure 3) and the oxidation (Figure 4) of water.

Table 1 The potentials of some redox couples at pH 7, listed in the order in which they would appear in a redox scheme such as Figure 4 (The abbreviations are explained in Table 2 on p. 369)

Couple	Potential, E'_0/volts
$Ru^{2+}(bipy)_3/Ru^+(bipy)_3$	-1.3
$Ru^{3+}(bipy)_3/*Ru^{2+}(bipy)_3$	-0.83
proflavin/proflavin$^-$	-0.78
MV^{2+}/MV^+	-0.45
Eu^{3+}/Eu^{2+}	-0.43
H_2O/H_2	-0.42
Cr^{3+}/Cr^{2+}	-0.41
cystine/cysteine	-0.23
plastoquinone/plastohydroquinone	0.1
$EDTA^+/EDTA$	0.2
$Chla^+/Chla$	0.76
Fe^{3+}/Fe^{2+}	0.77
$TEOA^+/TEOA$	0.8
O_2/H_2O	0.81
$Fe^{3+}(bipy)_3/Fe^{2+}(bipy)_3$	1.0
$ZnTMPyP^{5+}/ZnTMPyP^{4+}$	1.2
$Ru^{3+}(bipy)_3/Ru^{2+}(bipy)_3$	1.27
H_2O_2/H_2O	1.36
Ce^{4+}/Ce^{3+}	1.4
Co^{3+}/Co^{2+}	1.82

3   Photoreduction of water

As might be expected, the two-electron photoreduction

$$2H^+ + 2e \longrightarrow H_2$$

has proved to be easier to bring about than the four-electron photo-oxidation

$$2H_2O \longrightarrow O_2 + 4H^+ + 4e$$

The reduction can be brought about by a number of reactions provided that, in addition to the sensitisers and the donor D of Figure 3, a catalyst is used to mediate the two-electron transfer from S* (type 1, as in Figure 3a) or S (type 2, as in Figure 3b). As will become clear, for some catalysts this will also require the use of an intermediate electron acceptor, A.

The general schemes of reaction for the two cases are as follows:

Type 1, with acceptor (A) and catalyst (cat)

$$S + h\nu \longrightarrow S^*$$
$$S^* + A \longrightarrow S^+ + A^-$$
$$S^+ + D \longrightarrow S + D^+$$
$$A^- + H_2O \xrightarrow{\text{cat}} A + OH^- + \tfrac{1}{2}H_2$$

Type 2, with acceptor (A) and catalyst (cat)

$$S^+ + h\nu \longrightarrow S^{+*}$$
$$S^{+*} + D \longrightarrow S + D^+$$
$$S + A \longrightarrow S^+ + A^-$$
$$A^- + H_2O \xrightarrow{\text{cat}} A + OH^- + \tfrac{1}{2}H_2$$

In some instances of type 2 the acceptor A may itself be the catalyst.

The overall result of these reactions is the reduction of water to H_2 and the sacrificial permanent oxidation of a donor. Some components that have been used are listed in Table 2.

We shall take as a specific example the system $Ru^{2+}(bipy)_3$, EDTA, MV^{2+} and colloidal platinum. The ruthenium complex is much used in this type of work; it has a strong charge-transfer absorption in the visible region, it luminesces strongly and its excited state has a relatively long lifetime (680 ns) and an excitation energy of 2 eV. The couple $Ru^{3+}(bipy)_3/Ru^{2+}(bipy)_3$ has a redox potential of 1.27 V (see Figure 5) which becomes -0.83 V for the excited state couple $Ru^{3+}(bipy)_3/*Ru^{2+}(bipy)_3$. Although it would be thermodynamically possible, the complex does not sensitise the photolysis of water directly but reaction of the excited state with methyl viologen occurs with an efficiency of 0.3 to yield the ion MV^+:

$$*Ru^{2+}(bipy)_3 + MV^{2+} \longrightarrow Ru^{3+}(bipy)_3 + MV^+ \qquad (1)$$

Table 2 Compounds that have been used as components of systems for the photo-reduction of water

Donors
triethylamine (TEA)
triethanolamine (TEOA)
cysteine (cyst)
ethylenediaminetetra-acetic acid
   (EDTA; **1**)

Catalysts
rhodium trisbipyridyl ($Rh^{2+}(bipy)_3$)
hydrogenase
platinum and other noble metals

Acceptors
methyl viologen (MV^{2+}; **2**)
rhodium trisbipyridyl ($Rh^{2+}(bipy)_3$)

Sensitisers
chlorophyll (type 1)
acridines (type 1)
proflavin (**3**; type 2)
ruthenium trisbipyridyl ($Ru^{2+}(bipy)_3$,
   4; types 1 and 2)
metal porphyrins, e.g. zinc
   tetramethylpyridylporphyrin
   ($ZnTMPyP^{4+}$) (type 1)

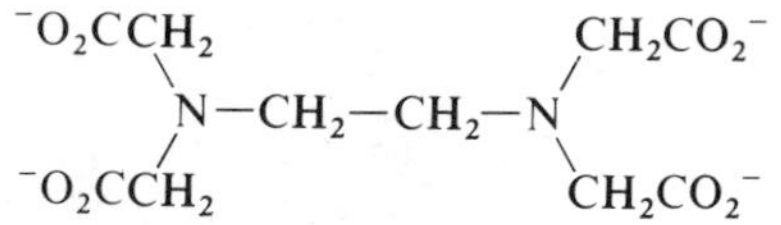

1 EDTA

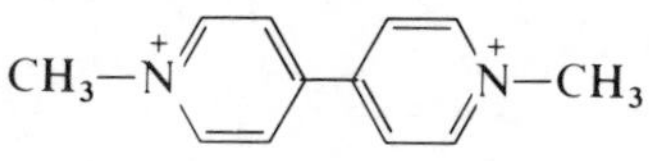

2 methyl viologen

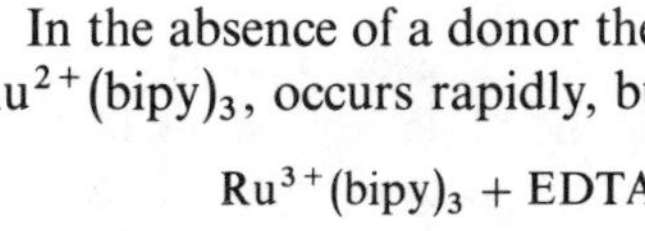

3 proflavin

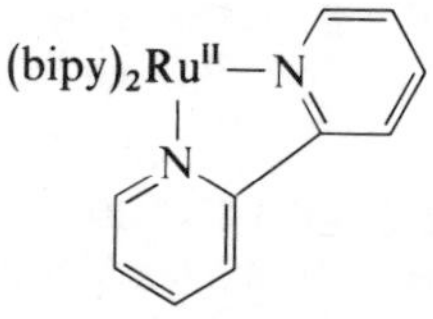

4 ruthenium trisbipyridyl

In the absence of a donor the reverse of reaction (1), to give ground state $Ru^{2+}(bipy)_3$, occurs rapidly, but in the presence of EDTA it is prevented:

$$Ru^{3+}(bipy)_3 + EDTA \longrightarrow Ru^{2+}(bipy)_3 + EDTA^+ \qquad (2)$$

and the reverse of reaction (2) does not occur because $EDTA^+$ is a weak oxidant. MV^+ is thermodynamically capable of reducing water but, again, the reaction does not occur spontaneously. It does occur readily, however, in the presence of the enzyme hydrogenase or with certain metal catalysts, of which colloidal plantinum has been the most studied. If a catalyst of colloidal platinum particles of radius 11 nm adsorbed on to polymer particles is used, reoxidation of MV^+ is complete in less than 100 μs and H_2 gas is formed quantitatively:

$$2MV^+ + 2H^+ \xrightarrow{\text{Pt}} 2MV^{2+} + H_2 \qquad (3)$$

The reaction is catalytic with respect to the ruthenium sensitiser and MV^{2+}.

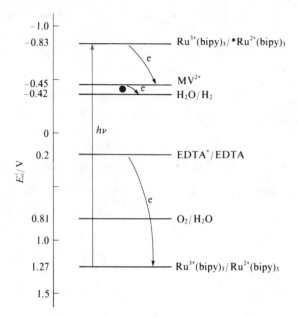

FIGURE 5   The photoreduction of water by the system $Ru^{2+}(bipy)_3$, MV^{2+}, EDTA and a platinum catalyst (marked with a circle).

A similar reaction, but of type 2 instead of type 1, occurs with proflavin (P) as sensitiser (see Figure 6), and it is now possible with three components rather than four (counting the catalyst as a component):

$$P^* + EDTA \longrightarrow P^- + EDTA^+$$
$$2P^- + 2H^+ \xrightarrow{\text{cat}} 2P + H_2$$

The reason that an acceptor is necessary in the type 1 reaction, but not in the type 2, is that excited states must react during their relatively short lifetime, and diffusion to a catalyst surface is a slower process than encounter with a molecular species in solution at high concentration.

The role of the platinum catalyst in these reactions is probably that of a microelectrode. The reducing component of a redox couple will donate electrons to the platinum until the particle attains the potential of the couple. This potential will, of course, be determined by the relative concentrations of the two components of the couple as well as by its standard redox potential. When the potential of the platinum becomes more negative than $-0.42\,V$, the reduction of H^+ to $\frac{1}{2}H_2$ can occur in exactly the same way as it does on a platinum cathode during the electrolysis of water. The connection with photoelectrochemistry is therefore quite close.

There is one case of catalytic hydrogen evolution in which the catalyst is in

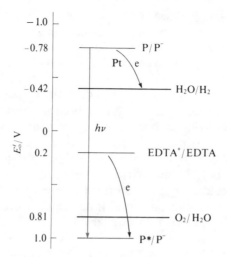

FIGURE 6   The photoreduction of water by the system proflavin (P), EDTA and a platinum catalyst.

homogeneous solution. It involves the rhodium complex $[Rh^{3+}(bipy)_2Cl_2]^+$ as a replacement for both the MV^{2+} and the platinum catalyst in the $Ru^{2+}(bipy)_3$ system described above, but using TEOA as donor. The mechanism of hydrogen liberation by this rhodium(III) complex is believed to involve two successive electron transfers to give the Rh^I complex, which then eliminates H_2 from the water molecules co-ordinated to it and reverts to the Rh^{III} complex in a single step, thereby acting as a two-electron accumulator.

An alternative to using a two-electron transfer in a single molecule would be to use two single transfers in a dimer. This approach has led to the synthesis of another rhodium complex, in which two Rh^I atoms are bridged by four ligands (of dicyanopropane). Irradiation at 546 nm in HCl $(12 \, mol \, l^{-1})$ gives clean conversion into the corresponding complex of Rh^{II} atoms and the elimination of hydrogen in low yield.

4   Catalytic photo-oxidation of water

Until very recently no attempts to bring about this four-electron transfer, with the generation of O_2, had been successful. Efforts were directed to schemes similar to those of the last two paragraphs, and particular attention was given to manganese complexes because there is good evidence that manganese is involved in the oxygen evolution process of natural photosynthesis. To accumulate a charge of $+4$, one possibility would be to employ a complex containing two Mn^{II} atoms and oxidise both (photochemically) to the Mn^{IV}

state. The $(Mn^{IV})_2$ might then be reduced by water to $(Mn^{II})_2$, liberating O_2. It has been reported that the use of manganese porphyrin complexes will produce small amounts of oxygen, but reaction soon ceases because of competing back-reactions. The avoidance of back-reactions is the main problem attending all electron transfer sequences and, when four successive transfers are necessary at one site, the difficulties become very great.

Very recently, an important advance has been made with the discovery that certain metal oxides will catalyse the elimination of oxygen in redox reactions in the same way as platinum catalyses hydrogen production. It has been shown that ruthenium oxide powder catalyses the reduction of Ce^{4+}, $Ru^{3+}(bipy)_3$, or $Fe^{3+}(bipy)_3$ with the liberation of oxygen in the dark. With Ce^{4+}, one molecule of oxygen is liberated for every four Ce^{3+} ions formed. With $Fe^{3+}(bipy)_3$, reduction at the RuO_2 catalyst occurs almost instantaneously on mixing at pH 7 although the redox potential difference is only 0.2 V.

If, now, the oxidant is formed photochemically, we have a scheme of the type shown in Figure 4(a). The process must, as always, be made irreversible by using an acceptor which does not back-react and, so far, this has been achieved only with a net expenditure of energy.

5   Combined oxidation and reduction of water

It is now possible to effect the two-electron transfer process for reduction of water to H_2 with the formation of an oxidised donor (like PS I), and it is also possible, in a separate reaction, to effect the four-electron transfer process for the oxidation of water to O_2 with the formation of a reduced acceptor (like PS II). In each case, one photon per electron transfer is involved in the stoichiometric equation.

The accumulation of the reduced and oxidised compounds in amounts equivalent to the oxygen and hydrogen produced is clearly not desirable, and we must therefore seek to link the oxidative and reductive reactions. In natural photosynthesis this is achieved by using a common redox system to link PS I and PS II which incorporates a number of intermediate couples but which seems to operate principally through a pool of plastoquinone. Using the same principle, we may try to link the oxidation and reduction processes by using, for example, a quinone Q as the acceptor A in Figure 4, and its hydroquinone Q^{2-} as the donor D in Figure 3, so as to have a fairly complete model of the Z scheme.

It has not yet been possible to combine the two systems through use of any common redox component Q/Q^-. The main reason for this is that success with the separate systems usually depends on rapid removal of the acceptor in Figure 4 and of the donor in Figure 3 so as to prevent the back-reactions, and this is clearly not possible if the Q/Q^- couple is to be both acceptor and donor. In fact, quinones are satisfactory acceptors (Figure 4) (benzoquinones, naphthoquinone and plastoquinone have all been used), and the corresponding hydroquinones are able to act as donors in Figure 3, using sensitisers of the type already described. However, the back-reactions occur very rapidly.

There are several ways in which these difficulties might be overcome:

1 With a suitable choice of the redox potentials for each couple, rates may be chosen that will still allow the overall reaction to proceed in competition with back-reactions.
2 Reaction rates may be modified by incorporating reactants in charged micelles made up of several hundred surfactant molecules.
3 By chemical linking of the components in the correct sequence, back-reactions between non-adjacent components may be retarded or prevented.
4 The reaction may be carried out in two stages, with separation of the reactants between them.
5 The two reactions may be separated in space, by the use of membranes which allow transport of electrons and protons but not transport of the other components.
6 The reaction may be made into an electrochemical system, with the reduction and oxidation reactions occurring in two half-cells connected by electrodes.

By linking together the two reaction schemes of Figures 3 and 4 we obtain a four-electron, eight-photon photochemical change similar to that of natural photosynthesis. Figure 7 illustrates one conception of how such a scheme

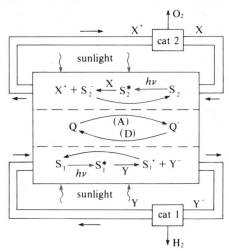

FIGURE 7   Conceptual scheme of a complete system for the dissociation of water.

might be put together. It is a flow system consisting of a photochemical reactor of large area and two small catalytic units (cat 1 and cat 2) for the release of hydrogen and oxygen separately. The principal difficulty is the separation of the two photosystems within the reactor; this might be spatial using membranes (represented by broken lines) or temporal, by using alternating flow of the two systems (sensitiser S_1 and Y; sensitiser S_2 and X) over the reversible couple Q/Q^-. This couple acts as both D^+/D and A/A^-.

There are still many difficulties and no complete system of this kind has yet been devised. However, very recently, evidence has been provided that the four-photon reaction of Figure 2 may be possible. The reaction system used had only four components, $Ru^{2+}(bipy)_3$ acting as photosensitiser and primary electron donor, methyl viologen as primary electron acceptor, and two catalysts, colloidal platinum for reduction and RuO_2 powder for oxidation. It was reported that H_2 and O_2 were evolved together according to the reactions:

$$*Ru^{2+}(bipy)_3 + MV^{2+} \longrightarrow Ru^{3+}(bipy)_3 + MV^+$$
$$2MV^+ + 2H^+ \xrightarrow{Pt} 2MV^{2+} + H_2$$
$$4Ru^{3+}(bipy)_3 + 4OH^- \xrightarrow{RuO_2} 4Ru^{2+}(bipy)_3 + O_2 + 2H_2O$$

The ion MV^+ is known to react rapidly with oxygen, but in this system MV^+ was apparently oxidised competitively by water on the colloidal platinum. This is a remarkably simple example of a Figure 2 type of reaction which, if confirmed as a four-photon process, will encourage further work on these thermodynamically less favourable systems.

Most of the work on the photolysis of water that has been described here was published between 1977 and 1980, and progress is so rapid that much more will have been achieved by the time this discussion is printed. Other work in progress is attempting to model the light-harvesting antenna of photosynthesis, and much attention is also being paid to photochemical reactions in micelles and across membranes as a means of facilitating charge separation. Our emphasis here has been on the photochemistry in homogeneous solutions, partly because reaction mechanisms and rates must be studied first, and partly because it is probably desirable to eliminate membranes, and the additional complexities they bring, if that is possible.

Much remains to be done before we can say whether an economic process for solar energy storage or the production of chemical feedstocks is possible on these lines, but many avenues have been opened up and there is the ever-present challenge of the very successful natural process.

6·5 Photoelectrochemical cells and their potential for conversion and storage of solar energy

by Laurence Peter (University of Southampton)

1 Definitions and classification

Photoelectrochemical cells are devices in which an electrochemical reaction takes place under illumination. An electrochemical reaction involves the transfer of electrons across the interface between an electrode and an electrolyte; a simple example is the reaction that takes place when a voltage is applied between two pieces of carbon dipped into a solution of sodium chloride. In a photoelectrochemical cell the driving force for the electrochemical reaction is provided by the light absorbed by the system, rather than by an external battery.

There are three distinctly different types of photoelectrochemical cell.

1   Electrochemical photovoltaic cells, in which a semiconductor in contact with an electrolyte solution absorbs light and generates electrical power.
2   Photoelectrolysis cells, which are similar to type 1 except that they produce hydrogen as a fuel.
3   Photogalvanic cells, in which a soluble dye in an electrolyte solution absorbs light and initiates electron transfer reactions in solution, which indirectly generate electrical power.

Here we shall consider briefly the first two types of cell. The key component of both the electrochemical photovoltaic cell and the photoelectrolysis cell is a semiconductor, which absorbs solar radiation and converts it into electrical or chemical free energy. We therefore begin with a brief summary of the properties of semiconductors. This will allow us to use energy diagrams to examine the basic mechanism common to all semiconductor devices for solar energy conversion.

2 Semiconductors

When atoms or molecules are brought together to form a solid, the individual discrete energy levels group themselves together to form energy bands. These bands are separated in energy by regions where there are no energy levels at all; this is the *band gap*. Many semiconductors are coloured materials, for instance cadmium sulphide (CdS) is bright yellow and mercuric sulphide (HgS) is red. *The absorption of visible light in these semiconductors results in the excitation of electrons across the band gap.* The absorption coefficient for these transitions can be as high as 10^4 or 10^5 cm^{-1}. The lower energy band, which is filled with electrons, is the *valence band*, and from it electrons can be excited to the next vacant energy band, the *conduction band*. The electron vacancy left behind in the valence band is known as a *hole*. For absorption to occur, the energy of the photon must be sufficient to promote an electron across the band gap, i.e.

$$h\nu \geqslant \text{band gap energy, } E_\text{g}$$

For example, the band gap energy of CdS is 2.4 eV so that it absorbs light with wavelength shorter than 515 nm. The discussion of these processes is best conducted using energy diagrams, such as that shown in Figure 1.

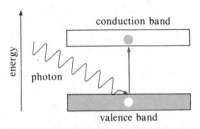

FIGURE 1   Absorption of a photon by a semiconductor results in the excitation of an electron across the band gap, and the creation of a hole in the valence band.

In most practical applications, small amounts of impurity are added to semiconductors in order to control their conductivity. For example, silicon is almost insulating when pure, and in semiconductor devices it is doped, either with an electron donor such as phosphorus or with an electron acceptor such as boron. Because silicon is tetravalent, each atom of pentavalent phosphorus can release an electron to the conduction band to make the silicon *n-type* (i.e. an electron conductor). In the same way, each atom of trivalent boron can accept an electron from the valence band and, because a hole is left behind, the silicon is now *p-type* (i.e. a hole conductor). In both cases the conductivity of the sample can be adjusted by the controlled addition of the appropriate impurity; typical concentrations are in the range 0.1 to 10 parts per million. The energy diagrams for the two conductivity types are shown in Figure 2.

Semiconductor devices, such as transistors and diodes, rely on the properties of the contact between n-type and p-type regions in silicon. These properties are also exploited in the silicon photovoltaic cell and in its 'wet' relative, the electrochemical photovoltaic cell.

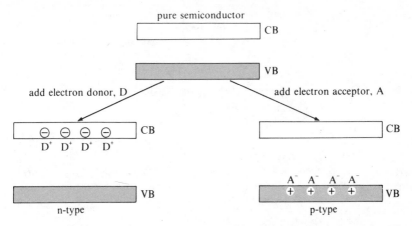

FIGURE 2   Addition of controlled amounts of impurity (doping) determines the conductivity type of a semiconductor. Acceptor atoms (A) make the semiconductor p-type, whereas donor atoms (D) make it n-type.

3   The electrochemical photovoltaic cell

Silicon solar cells are usually made from thin slices cut from a single crystal of silicon, although polycrystalline and amorphous silicon are now replacing the expensive crystal wafers. The key to the successful operation of the silicon cell lies in the nature of the contact between the n-type and p-type regions. Here the electrons and holes diffuse across the junction in opposite directions, setting up a potential difference across the contact which modifies the electron energy bands in such a way that the hole and the electron, formed when a photon is absorbed, are driven in opposite directions before they have a chance to recombine.

The p–n junction is not the only contact that can develop the potential gradient needed in a photovoltaic cell; under certain circumstances the contact between a semiconductor and an electrolyte solution containing a redox couple behaves in a very similar way. A redox couple consists of the oxidised and reduced forms of an ionic species; examples are the Fe^{3+}/Fe^{2+} couple, the I_3^-/I^- couple and the S_x^{2-}/S^{2-} couple (the S_x^{2-} ion is the poly-sulphide ion, and it has been used in several experimental cells). In the electro-chemical photovoltaic cell the p–n junction is replaced by a liquid junction, and the cells are often referred to as *liquid-junction solar cells*. The liquid junction overcomes the problem of lattice mismatch, which occurs when two solids of different structure are brought together. The strained region in a solid junction can greatly increase the rate of the wasteful recombination of electrons and holes.

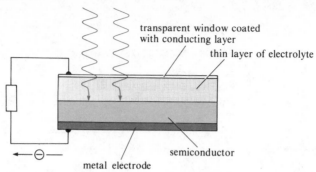

FIGURE 3   The electrochemical photovoltaic cell (liquid-junction solar cell). The direction of electron flow through the external load is shown for the case where the semiconductor is n-type.

Figure 3 is a simplified schematic diagram of an experimental liquid-junction cell. The potential gradient in the semiconductor is set up by choosing as the electrolyte a redox system that withdraws charge carriers (electrons or holes as the case may be) from the semiconductor. For example, if a sufficiently oxidising redox couple is brought into contact with an n-type semiconductor in the dark, electrons will begin to pass to the oxidised partner in the redox couple. The positively charged donor atoms left behind in the lattice give rise to a potential difference in the semiconductor, which soon compensates exactly for the original tendency of electrons to escape. A similar argument holds for the case of a p-type semiconductor, only in this case a reducing redox couple withdraws holes from the semiconductor leaving behind a cloud of negatively charged acceptor species. Figure 4 is the energy diagram for the case of the illuminated n-type semiconductor. This diagram

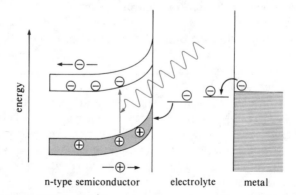

FIGURE 4   Energy diagram for the illuminated electrochemical photovoltaic cell. The hole is shown reacting with the reduced species at the semiconductor, whereas the oxidised species receives an electron from the metal electrode.

also shows the energy levels for the inert metal electrode, which returns the electron to the oxidised redox species in order to complete the circuit.

Because the current through the solution is carried by ions, an electrochemical reaction must take place at the electrodes. For example, if the redox couple is Fe^{3+}/Fe^{2+}, the reactions are

at the illuminated n-type semiconductor

$$Fe^{2+} + hole \longrightarrow Fe^{3+} \quad \text{(oxidation)}$$

(i.e. an electron from Fe^{2+} fills a hole in the valence band)

at the inert electrode

$$Fe^{3+} + electron \longrightarrow Fe^{2+} \quad \text{(reduction)}$$

So *no overall chemical change occurs*, because the cell reactions are regenerative.

Silicon is not a suitable material for electrochemical cells because it is rather easily oxidised to SiO_2. Other more stable semiconductors have been used in experimental cells, although many of these have less suitable absorption characteristics than silicon. Figure 5 shows where the band gaps of a number of semiconductors fall on a theoretical curve of the efficiency of conversion of solar energy. At the time of writing (1980), the most efficient experimental electrochemical solar cell consists of a slice of gallium arsenide (GaAs) in contact with a selenide redox electrolyte (Se_2^{2-}/Se^{2-}); it has a solar efficiency of 12%, compared with the 17% achieved with the best solid-state silicon cells. Details of some of the liquid-junction cells that have been tested are collected in Table 1. The data refer in all cases to cells tested in the laboratory; no extended field trials with electrochemical cells have yet taken place.

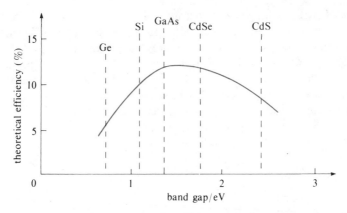

FIGURE 5 The theoretical curve for the efficiency of solar energy conversion for photovoltaic cells as a function of the band gap of the semiconductor. Band gaps for several materials are shown by the vertical lines.

Table 1 The characteristics of some liquid-junction solar cells

Semiconductor electrode	Band gap/eV	Redox electrolyte	Solar efficiency (%)	Stability
n-CdS	2.4	Na_2S_2/Na_2S	1.5	good
n-CdS	2.4	$K_3Fe(CN)_6/K_4Fe(CN)_6$	5.5	poor
n-CdSe	2.8	Na_2S_2/Na_2S	8	moderate
n-GaAs	1.4	K_2Se_2/K_2Se	12	good
WSe_2	1.4	I_2/KI	10.2	very good

The outlook for electrochemical photovoltaic cells is promising; their efficiencies are already at least as good as those of many solid-state cells, and they still work quite well if the expensive single crystal slices are replaced by polycrystalline materials. The main problem is a lack of stability; many semiconductors are unstable when illuminated in an electrolyte solution, and the subsequent corrosion can seriously limit the performance and lifetime of practical cells. The most stable semiconductors found so far are the compounds that have a layered crystal structure, such as MoS_2 and WSe_2.

4 Photoelectrolysis cells

Free energy and cell electromotive force are related by the expression

$$\Delta G = -nFE$$

where ΔG is the energy change per mole, F is the Faraday, n is the number of electrons transferred in the reaction, and E is the potential difference across the electrochemical cell. Often it is more convenient to consider the energy change per molecule, which means that F is replaced by the magnitude of the electron charge, and the free energy scale is then measured in electronvolts. The standard hydrogen electrode has been chosen as an arbitrary zero point for the scale of electrode potentials, given the symbol E_0. On this scale the oxygen electrode has a potential of $+1.23\,V$, which means that the energy change for the reaction

$$\tfrac{1}{2}O_2 + H_2 \longrightarrow H_2O$$

is $(2 \times -1.23\,eV)$. The reaction can be broken down into two electrode reactions

$$\tfrac{1}{2}O_2 + 2H^+ + 2e \rightleftharpoons H_2O \qquad E_0 = 1.23\ V$$
$$H_2 \rightleftharpoons 2H^+ + 2e \qquad E_0 = 0$$

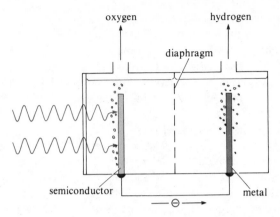

FIGURE 6   A schematic photoelectrolysis cell consisting of an n-type semiconductor and a metal electrode.

The splitting of each molecule of water therefore requires a free energy input of $(2 \times 1.23\,\text{eV})$, and the photoelectrolysis cell aims to get this energy from light.

An idealised photoelectrolysis cell is shown in Figure 6. It consists of an illuminated n-type semiconductor electrode and, short-circuited to it, a second metal electrode. Holes produced by illumination of the semiconductor oxidise water to oxygen, and the electrons in the conduction band flow to the metal electrode, where they reduce water to hydrogen. The principle of the cell is illustrated in Figure 7.

In order for a cell of this type to work, it is essential that the electrons in the

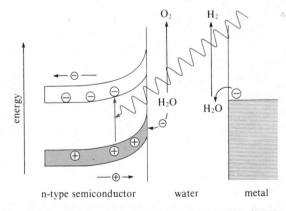

FIGURE 7   Energy diagram for the n-type photoelectrolysis cell. Note the essential difference from Figure 4—the cell is *not* regenerative, but instead produces hydrogen and oxygen.

conduction band should be sufficiently reducing to liberate hydrogen from water. This means that the semiconductor must have a lower electron affinity than the hydrogen ion in solution. Unfortunately, semiconductors with low electron affinities also have large band gaps, so that they absorb only in the ultraviolet region of the solar spectrum. (For example, TiO_2, $SrTiO_3$ and KTa_2O_6, which have been used to split water, all have band gaps greater than 3 eV.) The search for new materials with low electron affinities *and* small band gaps has so far met with no success.

An alternative approach which has much in common with photosynthesis involves using two semiconductor electrodes. An n-type semiconductor is used to carry out the oxidation reaction, and a p-type semiconductor replaces the inert electrode for hydrogen evolution. The principle of the cell is best understood from the energy diagram in Figure 8.

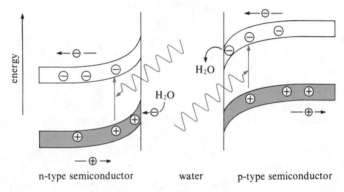

FIGURE 8 Energy diagram for the p–n photoelectrolysis cell. Note that *two* photons are now used to transfer one electron around the external circuit. The photoexcited hole in the n-type semiconductor accepts an electron from a water molecule, whereas the photoexcited electron in the p-type semiconductor is donated to the solution.

The similarity of this p–n photoelectrolysis system to photosystems I and II is made clear in Figure 9, which gives the energy levels for an experimental cell. The n-type semiconductor (TiO_2) has a low-lying ground state (the valence band), so that when an electron is promoted to the excited state (the conduction band), the deep vacancy withdraws an electron from a water molecule. Similarly, the p-type semiconductor has an excited state with low electron affinity, so that an electron can pass to a water molecule.

Practical photoelectrolysis cells are still in their infancy—the best solar conversion efficiencies are still low, around 1%. However, several interesting configurations for photoelectrolysis cells with no external wires have been suggested. For example, the p- and n-semiconductors can be vapour-

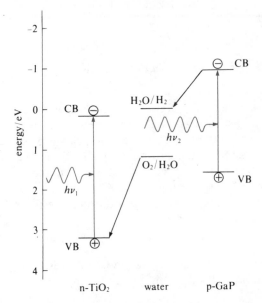

FIGURE 9   Energy level scheme for the n-TiO$_2$/p-GaP photoelectrolysis cell. The diagram shows the similarity with the Z scheme for photosynthesis.

deposited in a polka-dot pattern on a substrate (Figure 10a), or small integrated circuit 'photochemical diodes' can be prepared for use as a powder suspension (Figure 10b).

All these devices have to compete with the alternative of a photovoltaic cell driving a normal electrolysis cell, and there is no doubt that photoelectrolysis cells have a long way to go before they begin to be attractive on the basis of this comparison. Future progress depends on the availability of new stable semiconductor electrodes, and much research effort is therefore being concentrated in this direction.

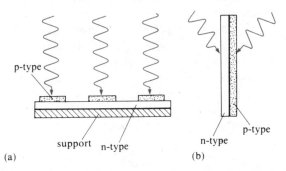

FIGURE 10   Possible integrated electrode configurations for practical p–n photoelectrolysis cells.

Appendix
Using standard redox potentials

A redox reaction is one in which electrons (or electron density) are transferred from one atom or molecule to another. The electron donor is the reducer and is being oxidised, and the electron acceptor is the oxidiser and is being reduced. The concept of standard redox potentials enables the direction in which electrons can be transferred in a redox reaction to be determined, and the energy released in the process to be estimated.

The simplest type of reduction is the addition of electrons to a metal ion to produce a metal atom, for example

$$Cu^{2+} + 2e \longrightarrow Cu \tag{1}$$

The simplest type of oxidation is the reverse process, the loss of electrons from a metal atom to produce an ion, for example

$$Zn \longrightarrow Zn^{2+} + 2e \tag{2}$$

Neither of these processes can occur in isolation, so they are referred to as 'half-reactions.' Electrons have to come from somewhere and they have to go somewhere, oxidising or reducing the species from which they come or to which they go, respectively. The combination of these two half-reactions gives a description of what is observed to occur when metallic zinc makes contact with an aqueous solution of copper ions; zinc dissolves and metallic copper is deposited:

$$Cu^{2+} + Zn \longrightarrow Zn^{2+} + Cu \tag{3}$$

This is a redox process, and it does not occur spontaneously in the opposite direction. Copper cannot be oxidised by a solution of zinc ions.

Standard redox potentials express, in units of volts (V), the reducing 'pressure' of the separate half-reactions of a redox process. For instance, the couple Cu^{2+}/Cu refers to half-reaction (1), and its reduction potential has a value of $+0.34$ V. The couple Zn^{2+}/Zn refers to the *reverse* of half-reaction (2), and has a potential of -0.76 V. The direction of the redox reaction between these two couples, and its potential to release energy, are derived by taking one half-reaction in the (conventional) reducing direction, reversing the other and changing the sign of its potential, and adding the two together:

$$
\begin{array}{lll}
Cu^{2+} + 2e \longrightarrow Cu & & +0.34\,V \\
Zn \longrightarrow Zn^{2+} + 2e & & +0.76\,V \\
\hline
Cu^{2+} + Zn \longrightarrow Zn^{2+} + Cu & & +1.10\,V
\end{array}
$$

The resulting positive sign for the potential tells us the process is thermo-dynamically spontaneous* in the direction written. Had the sign been negative, the reverse process would be spontaneous with a positive potential of the same numerical value.

The free energy change (ΔG) per electron transferred is directly proportional to the electrochemical potential (E), but opposite in sign; that is,

$$\Delta G = -nFE$$

where n is the number of electrons transferred and F is the Faraday.

Standard redox potentials (E_0') can be used in a vertical scale diagram to predict spontaneous electron transfer processes (Figure 1). Conventionally, the scale is arranged with negative potentials (powerfully reducing couples) at the top and positive potentials (powerfully oxidising couples) at the bottom. This means that spontaneous processes will be electron transfers from the reducing part of one couple to the oxidising part of a couple beneath it in the diagram, with a (positive) potential represented by the distance between them on the scale. So, for example, electron transfers (4) and (5) are spontaneous, whereas (6) and (7) are not.

$$\begin{aligned}
\text{H}_2 + 2\text{Fe}^{3+} &\longrightarrow 2\text{Fe}^{2+} + 2\text{H}^+ & (1.19\,\text{V}) && (4)\\
\text{Cu} + \text{Br}_2 &\longrightarrow \text{Cu}^{2+} + 2\text{Br}^- & (0.72\,\text{V}) && (5)\\
\text{H}_2 + \text{Zn}^{2+} &\longrightarrow \text{Zn} + 2\text{H}^+ & (-0.34\,\text{V}) && (6)\\
2\text{H}^+ + 2\text{Br}^- &\longrightarrow \text{H}_2 + \text{Br}_2 & (-1.48\,\text{V}) && (7)
\end{aligned}$$

Electron transfers that produce or eliminate ions are descriptively the most

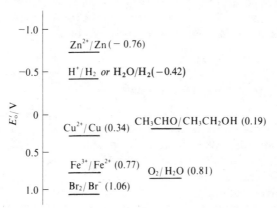

FIGURE 1   Typical display of standard redox potentials in aqueous solution at pH 7 (E_0').

* The process may be too slow to be observed, however; that is, the activation energy may be too high. This is clearly not the case in the copper/zinc reaction, but is so for reaction (8).

straightforward redox reactions. However, many reactions involving changes in covalent bonding are also redox reactions. For example:

$$H_2 + CH_3CHO \longrightarrow CH_3CH_2OH \tag{8}$$

$$2H_2 + O_2 \longrightarrow 2H_2O \tag{9}$$

It is convenient in the present context to consider such reactions as the combination of two half-reactions involving hydrogen ions. For example, we can expand reaction (8) as follows:

$$H_2 \longrightarrow 2H^+ + 2e \qquad (0.42\,V) \tag{10}$$

$$2H^+ + 2e + CH_3CHO \longrightarrow CH_3CH_2OH \qquad (0.19\,V) \tag{11}$$

$$\overline{H_2 + CH_3CHO \longrightarrow CH_3CH_2OH \qquad (0.61\,V)} \tag{8}$$

Similarly, for reaction (9) we can write:

$$2H_2 \longrightarrow 4H^+ + 4e \qquad (0.42\,V) \tag{12}$$

$$4H^+ + 4e + O_2 \longrightarrow 2H_2O \qquad (0.81\,V) \tag{13}$$

$$\overline{2H_2 + O_2 \longrightarrow 2H_2O \qquad (1.23\,V)} \tag{9}$$

Note that half-reaction (12) is the reverse of the process represented by the H^+/H_2 couple which, being effectively the reduction of water, is often designated H_2O/H_2. Similarly, half-reaction (13) represents reduction of oxygen, and its reverse the oxidation of water, so the couple can be designated O_2/H_2O.

Note also that the reduction of water requires the transfer of *two* electrons *to* water per molecule of hydrogen produced, and that the oxidation of water requires the transfer of *four* electrons *from* water per molecule of oxygen produced. Redox potentials are independent of the number of electrons transferred.

Origin of redox potentials

The standard redox potential, E_0, of a couple A_{ox}/A_{red} refers to the potential difference observed when the couple is linked to the H^+/H_2 couple, which is assigned arbitrarily a zero potential. The potential of the A_{ox}/A_{red} couple will be negative if electrons flow towards the H^+/H_2 couple, and positive if the flow is in the other direction. The measurement refers to standardised conditions: pH 0 on both sides, 25 °C, and equal concentrations of A_{ox}/A_{red}. It is frequently more convenient, however, to refer to standard redox potentials at pH 7 (E'_0) and not pH 0 (E_0). This affects only those couples that involve H^+ in their half-reactions. Provided the equation for the half-reaction has equal numbers of protons and electrons on the left-hand side, then

$$E'_0 = (E_0 - 0.42) \text{ volts}$$

Index

Bibliography

The books and articles listed here are optional further reading.

Part 1

Education in Chemistry (1978) pp. 6–30 (issue on Energy).

M. L. Corrin (1978) 'Atmospheric Chemistry' in *Journal of Chemical Education*, vol. 55, p. 210.

Part 2

D. C. O'Shea, W. R. Callen and W. T. Rhodes (1977) *An Introduction to Lasers and their Applications*, Addison-Wesley.

M. Gouterman (1978) 'Optical Spectra and Electronic Structure of Porphyrins and Related Rings', Chapter 1 in *The Porphyrins, Volume III Physical Chemistry Part A* (editor D. Dolphin) Academic Press.

Part 3

J. Griffiths (1976) *Colour and Constitution of Organic Molecules*, Academic Press.

Part 4

N. Wotherspoon, G. K. Oster and G. Oster (1972) 'The determination of fluorescence and phosphorescence', Chapter IV in *Techniques of Chemistry, Volume 1 Physical Methods of Chemistry Part IIIB* (editors A. Weissberger and B. W. Rossiter), Wiley-Interscience.

N. J. Turro (1977) 'Energy Transfer Processes' in *Pure and Applied Chemistry*, vol. 49, p. 405.

'Chlorofluorocarbons and their Effect on Stratospheric Ozone (Second Report)' (1979) Pollution Paper No. 15, Dept. of the Environment, Central Directorate on Environmental Pollution, HMSO, London.

J. N. Pitts Jnr and B. J. Finlayson (1975) 'Mechanisms of photochemical air pollution', *Angewandte Chemie International Edition*, vol. 14, p. 1.

I. M. Campbell (1977) *Energy and the Atmosphere*, Wiley.

Part 5

K. C. Smith (editor) (1977) *The Science of Photobiology*, Plenum Press.

S. S. Labana (1976), *Ultraviolet-light Induced Reactions in Polymers*, The American Chemical Society.

A. Ledwith (1975) 'Photoinitiation, photopolymerisation and photochemical processes in polymers' in *International Reviews of Science, Physical Chemistry Series 2*, vol. 8 (editor C. E. H. Bawn), Butterworth.

G. A. Delzenne (1979) 'Photocrosslinkable polymeric systems and their technical applications', *Makromolecular Chemie*, Supp. 2, p. 169.

M. Fischer (1978) 'Industrial applications of photochemical synthesis', *Angewandte Chemie International Edition*, vol. 17, p. 16.

A. D. Clements (1980) 'Photochemistry in commercial synthesis', *Chemistry in Britain*, vol. 16, p. 464.

A. H. Jubb (1975) in *Basic Organic Chemistry*, Wiley, part 5, p. 187.

J. R. Thirtle and D. M. Zwick (1979) 'Colour Photography', in *Kirk–Othmer Encyclopaedia of Chemical Technology*, Wiley, vol. 6, 3rd edn., p. 617.

R. E. Jacobson (1980) 'Photochemical imaging systems', in *Chemistry in Britain*, vol. 16, p. 468.

K. I. Jacobson and R. E. Jacobson (1976) *Imaging Systems*, Focal Press.

E. Brinckman, G. Delzenne, A. Poot and J. Willens (1978) *Unconventional Imaging Processes*, Focal Press.

Part 6

J. R. Bolton and D. O. Hall (1979) 'Photochemical conversion and storage of solar energy', in *Annual Reviews of Energy*, vol. 4, p. 353.

J. Barber (editor) (1979) *Photosynthesis in Relation to Model Systems*, Elsevier.

Acknowledgements

Grateful acknowledgement is made to the following sources for material used in this book.

Chapter 1.2 *Tables 1, 2 and 4, and Figure 2* from M. J. McEwan and L. F. Phillips (1975) *Chemistry of the Atmosphere*, Edward Arnold.

Chapter 2.1 *Figure 12* from J. A. Giordmaine and M. A. Duguay (1971) in *American Scientist*, vol. 59.

Chapter 2.2 *Figure 2* G. Scheibe (1966) 'Optische Anregung Organischer Systeme 2' in *Internationales Farbensymposium*, Verlag Chemie; *Figures 3, 6 and 7* from J. Griffiths (1976) *Colour and Constitution of Organic Molecules*, copyright by Academic Press Inc. (London) Ltd; *Figure 8* from S. F. Mason, (1970) 'Colour and the electronic states of organic molecules' in *The Chemistry of Organic Dyes*, vol. 3, ed. K. Venkataraman, copyright by Academic Press Inc. (London) Ltd.

Chapter 2.3 *Figures 1, 3, 5 and 6* from M. Gouterman (1961) 'Spectra of porphyrins' in *Journal of Molecular Spectroscopy*, vol. 6, Academic Press Inc.; *Figure 2* from M. Weissbluth (1967) 'The physics of haemoglobin' in *Structure and Bonding*, vol. 2, Springer-Verlag; *Figure 4* from J. C. Goedheer (1966) in L. P. Vernon and G. R. Seely (eds.) *The Chlorophylls (Physical, Chemical and Biological Properties)*, copyright by Academic Press Inc. (London) Ltd.

Chapter 3.1 *Figure 3* from M. V. Orna (1978) 'The chemical origins of colour' in *Journal of Chemical Education*, vol. 55, no. 8 (August), Division of Chemical Education, The American Chemical Society.

Chapter 4.1 *Figure 2* courtesy of Oriel Corporation; *Figure 3* courtesy of Perkin–Elmer; *Figure 5* from D. W. Johnson *et al.* (1977) 'Rapid scanning fluorescence spectroscopy' in *Analytical Chemistry*, vol. 49, no. 8, The American Chemical Society; *Figure 6* from M. A. West (1975) 'Developments in photophysical instrumentation: part I' in *American Laboratory*, vol. 7, no. 11, p. 67, copyright © 1975, International Scientific Communications, Inc.

Chapter 4.2 *Figures 3 and 4* from J. A. Barltrop and J. D. Coyle (1978) '*Principles of Photochemistry*', copyright © 1978 John Wiley and Sons Ltd, reprinted by permission; *Figure 5* from L. Stryer (1968) 'Fluorescence spectroscopy of proteins' in *Science*, vol. 162, November, copyright © 1968 by The American Association for the Advancement of Science.

Chapter 4.3 *Table 2* from R. D. Brown (1979) 'Galactochemistry and the origin of life' in *Chemistry in Britain*, vol. 15, no. 11, The Chemical Society; *Table 3* from M. J. McEwan and L. F. Phillips (1975) *op. cit.*; *Figures 3 and 4* from L. V. Berkner and L. C. Marshall (1964) 'The history of oxygenic concentration in the Earth's atmosphere' in *Discussions of the Faraday Society*, vol. 37.

Chapter 4.4 *Figure 1* (in part) from D. W. O. Heddle and R. W. Ditchburn (1953) *Proceedings of the Royal Society of London (Series A)*, vol. 220, p. 65, The Royal Society; *Figure 1* (in part) from E. C. Y. Inn *et al.* (1953) *Journal of Chemical Physics*, vol. 21, p. 1026; *Figure 2* from J. G. Calvert and J. N. Pitts, Jnr (1966) *Photochemistry*, John Wiley and Sons Inc.; *Figure 3* a private communication from Prof. Julius Chang (1980); *Figures 4 and 5* from B. M. McCormac (1973) *Physics and Chemistry of Upper Atmospheres*, D. Reidel Publishing Co., The Netherlands.

Chapter 4.5 *Table 1* from M. Nicolet (1972) 'Aeronomic chemistry of the strato-sphere' in *Planetary Space Science*, vol. 20, Pergamon Press; *Figures 1, 2 and 3* from M. J. McEwan and L. F. Phillips (1975) *op. cit.*; *Figure 4* from H. Okabe (1978) *Photochemistry of Small Molecules*, Wiley-Interscience; *Figure 5* from P. Crutzen (1974) in *Canadian Journal of Chemistry*, vol. 52, National Research Council of Canada; *Appendix* from H. S. Johnston and J. Podolske (1978) *Reviews of Geophysics and Space Physics*, vol. 16, no. 4, American Geophysical Union.

Chapter 4.6 *Figure 3* from J. Scotto *et al.* (1975) *Measurements of Ultraviolet Radiation in the US, and Comparisons with Skin Cancer Data*, U.S. Department of Health, Education and Welfare.

Chapter 4.7 *Figure 1(a)* data from Los Angeles Air Pollution Control District; *Figures 1(b) and 1(c)* data from P. L. Hanst *et al.* (1975), *A Spectroscopic Study of California Smog*, U.S. Environmental Protection Agency; *Figure 3* from J. N. Pitts, Jnr (1976) in *Mechanisms of Photochemical Reactions in Urban Air–Smog Chamber Studies, Final Report*, vol. II, University of California, Riverside.

Chapter 5.2 *Figure 5* from R. B. Setlow (1961) 'Action spectrum for the reversal of the dimerisation of thymine induced by UV light' in *Biochimica et Biophysica Acta*, vol. 49, Biomedical Press B.V., Elsevier/North Holland.

Chapter 5.3 *Figures 2 and 3* from W. G. Herkstroeter and G. S. Hammond (1966) 'Energy transfer study by kinetic spectrophotometry' in *Journal of the American Chemical Society*, vol. 88, reprinted by permission of The American Chemical Society.

Chapter 5.4 *Figure 2* from M. Gouterman *et al.* (1976) 'Electron transfer from bacteriopheophytin' in *Photochemistry and Photobiology*, vol. 23, Pergamon Press; *Figure 3* from G. Porter and M. R. Topp (1970) 'Nanosecond flash photolysis' in *Proceedings of the Royal Society of London (Series A)*, vol. 315, The Royal Society; *Figure 4* from D. Magde and M. W. Windson (1974) 'Picosecond flash photolysis and spectroscopy apparatus' in *Chemical Physics Letters*, vol. 27, Elsevier/North Holland; *Figure 7* from N. K. Bridge and G. Porter (1958) 'Primary photoprocesses in quinones and dyes. II: Kinetic studies' in *Proceedings of The Royal Society of London (Series A)*, vol. 244, The Royal Society.

Chapter 5.9 *Figure 1* courtesy BASF.

Chapter 5.10 *Figure 1(a)* from W. M. Horspool (1976) *Aspects of Organic Photo-chemistry*, Academic Press, copyright Academic Press Inc. (London) Ltd; *Figure 1(b)* from M. Fischer (1974) 'Application industrielle des synthesis photochimique' in *Actualité Chimique*, Société Chimique de France; *Figure 3* from M. Fischer (1978) 'Industrial applications of photochemical syntheses' in *Angewandte Chemie Inter-national Edition*, vol. 17, Verlag Chemie GmbH.

Chapter 5.11 *Figures 1(a) and (c)–(e)* from A. Schönberg (1968) *Preparative Organic Photochemistry*, Springer-Verlag (N.Y.) Inc.; *Figure 1(b)* from W. M. Horspool (1976) *op. cit.*; *Figure 3* courtesy Applied Photophysics Ltd, London.

Chapter 5.13 *Figure 3* Kodak Limited; *Figure 4* from P. Walker *et al.* (1970) 'Photopolymerisable reproduction systems—Chemistry and applications' in *The Journal of Photographic Science*, vol. 18, The Royal Photographic Society.

Chapter 5.14 *Figures 2, 3 and 4* from V. S. Letokhov and C. Bradley Moore (1977) 'Laser isotope separation' in *Chemical and Biological Applications of Lasers*, Academic Press, New York; *Figure 6* from V. S. Letokhov (1977) 'Photophysics and photochemistry' in *Physics Today*, vol. 30, no. 5, The American Institute of Physics.

Acknowledgements

Chapter 6.1   *Figure 2* from G. Porter and M. Archer (1976) '*In vitro* photosynthesis' in *Interdisciplinary Science Reviews*, vol. 1, no. 2, Heyden and Son Ltd.

Chapter 6.2   *Figure 1* from G. Jones II (1979) 'Energy storage in organic photo-isomers' in *Journal of Photochemistry*, vol. 10, Elsevier Sequoia (UK); *Figure 2* from S. G. Talbert *et al.* (1976) 'Photochemical solar heating and cooling' in *Chemtech*, February, reprinted by permission of The American Chemical Society.

Chapter 6.3   *Figure 2* from R. Govindjee and G. Govindjee (1974) 'The absorption of light in photosystems' in *Scientific American*, vol. 231, no. 6, Scientific American Inc.

Plate 1 Coherent (UK) Ltd, Cambridge; *Plate 2* Scientific Research Staff, Ford Motor Company; *Plate 3* Yorkshire Chemicals Ltd, Leeds; *Plate 7* Heather Angel.